With thanks ...
Martha Deible...
devoted their lives to spreading
the Word.

Gordon Beld

A Novel by Gordon Beld

A GENTLE BREEZE FROM GOSSAMER WINGS

PREP Publishing
Fayetteville, North Carolina

PREP Publishing
1110 1/2 Hay Street
Fayetteville, NC 28305
(910) 483-6611

Copyright © 1999 by Gordon Beld

Book design by Katie Severa
Cover design by David W. Turner

All rights reserved under International and Pan-American Copyright Conventions. No part of this book may be reproduced or copied in any form or by any means— graphic, electronic, or mechanical, including photocopying, taping, or information storage and retrieval systems—without written permission from the publisher, except by a reviewer, who may quote brief passages in a review.

Acknowledgment is made for permission to reprint previously published material: Music Sales Corporation: Excerpt from the lyrics to "Don't You Know?" by Bobby Worth. Copyright © 1958, 1959 (Renewed) by Alexis Music, Inc. and Music Sales Corporation (ASCAP). All Rights Administered Worldwide by Music Sales Corporation (ASCAP). International Copyright Secured. All Rights Reserved. Reprinted by Permission.

Warner Brothers: Excerpts from the lyrics to "And the Angels Sing" by Johnny Mercer, music by Ziggy Elman; and "Let It Snow! Let It Snow! Let It Snow!" by Sammy Cahn, music by Jule Styne. International Copyright Secured. All Rights Reserved.

Library of Congress Cataloging-in-Publication Data
Beld, Gordon, 1927-
    A gentle breeze from gossamer wings : refugees from the Pol Pot era are depicted in fiction / Gordon Beld. — 1st ed.
        p. cm. — (Judeo-Christian ethics series)
    ISBN 1-885288-07-7
        1. Cambodia—History—1975-1979—Fiction.
        2. Cambodian Americans—Fiction. I. Title. II. Series.
PS3552.E4597G46 1999
813'.54—dc21   98-50636
                                                                            CIP

Printed in the United States of America
First Edition

This book is a work of fiction. The events, characters, and plot are products of the author's imagination or are used fictitiously.

FOR

Martha
*whose love and encouragement
provided a glimpse of heaven*

Heng and Kim
who endured Pol Pot's hell

WITH GRATITUDE

To scores of former refugees who have shared their stories and feelings, and who have blessed me with continuing friendship, I am grateful. Except for them, this book wouldn't have been possible. I am indebted also to Carol and Doren Wehrley of Wauwatosa, Wisconsin, who encouraged me to begin writing the story and inspired me to keep at it. Their critique of early drafts of the manuscript helped immensely. In addition, I appreciate the counsel of Gordon Brewer, former coach and athletic director at Hope College in Holland, Michigan, concerning references to inter-collegiate athletics and of Howard Schipper, founder of Freedom Flight Refugee Center in Grand Rapids, Michigan, who read the manuscript to verify its authenticity concerning refugees and service providers. Books, periodicals, and microfilm records at Hope College's Van Wylen Library, Herrick Library in the city of Holland, and Ryerson Library in Grand Rapids yielded essential data. Works by several authors, some of whom experienced the Cambodian holocaust, provided valuable insights. The late Haing Ngor's account of his experiences during the Khmer Rouge era has been particularly helpful. And to three persons who, during the 1940s, opened doors to a lifetime of fulfillment through writing, I am especially grateful:

- Martha Schuitema, 7th and 8th grade teacher at Newhall Public Schools in suburban Grand Rapids, who gave me the essential basics of grammar and composition;
- Ralph Truax, assistant sports editor of *The Grand Rapids Press*, who provided my first real opportunities to write professionally and served as a role model; and
- Kenneth Davis, Wyoming High School principal, who bent attendance rules so that, when I should have been in classes, I could be at the *Press* where lessons were more effective.

— GGB

FOREWORD

Find a need and fill it. Find a hurt and heal it.

That's what *A Gentle Breeze from Gossamer Wings* is all about.

The needy, hurting people in this story are refugees. In the Bible they're called strangers. Jesus was one of them when, as an infant, Mary and Joseph fled with Him to Egypt to escape from Herod.

Later He stressed the importance of kindness to people who fit the description of refugees when He said, "I was *hungry* and you gave Me food; I was *thirsty* and you gave Me drink; I was a *stranger* and you took Me in... Assuredly, I say to you, inasmuch as you did it to one of the least of these, My brethren, you did it to Me." (Matthew 25:35-40)

That seems to make it clear how Christ would have us respond to the plight of these neighbors who don't have the option of going home. But some of us still don't get the picture. One is in this story. Like the priest and the Levite in the Parable of the Good Samaritan, he's content, at first, to pass by on the other side of the road. At home in his placid Indiana college town, he has a hard time imagining he should, or could, do anything about the troubles of millions in far-off Indochina. Sure, something needs to be done. But he's not the one to do it. He has other concerns and responsibilities. The problem's too big. What could he do?

Fortunately, positive attitudes prevail and amazing things take place. That could happen to you, too; and reading this story might start it. Of course, it's dangerous. It could change your life.

ROBERT H. SCHULLER
GARDEN GROVE, CALIFORNIA

PREFACE

Do not forget to entertain strangers, for by so doing some have unwittingly entertained angels.

HEBREWS 13:2

I think I've seen angels. I know I've felt the breeze from their wings.

Some were disguised as a person needing help: hungry, thirsty, a stranger, naked, sick, a prisoner.

Some masqueraded as persons whose only need was to help.

Perhaps some weren't angels at all. They may have been mortals like you and me who were moved by angels, who felt the breeze from their wings.

In this story, angels move about behind the scenes. Maybe you'll see them, maybe not. If you don't, at least you'll meet the people they touched.

Though *A Gentle Breeze from Gossamer Wings* is fiction, its characters confront issues and situations that are real. Residents of the small Indiana college town of Mendon struggle with controversies and frustrations found in many American neighborhoods and workplaces. On the other side of the world, Cambodians deal with social upheaval, slavery, starvation, and impending death. Their horrible existence isn't exaggerated. Millions of them lived through the terror of the Khmer Rouge era. And more than a million didn't.

Some of the story's settings are inventions. You won't find Mendon or Elm Grove on Indiana maps. The village of Millbrook is another imaginary place, but there is a real Millbrook, in Michigan. There were angels there once. Though I never met them, they touched my life. I've felt the breeze from their wings.

There were twelve of them. Perhaps I should say there were twelve special Christians at that tiny village in the rolling countryside of central Michigan. Actually, I don't know how many had angels inside — or behind, tapping them on the shoulder.

The twelve were the entire congregation of Millbrook United Methodist Church. But they didn't question whether a church of twelve members was big enough to respond when a family of refugees from the Cambodian holocaust needed help. They sponsored the family, then persuaded others to sponsor four more.

Their kindness became infectious. Soon, nearly a hundred fugitives from terror were given a new chance for life in nearby communities. And countless Christians, who accepted the challenge to become involved, were enriched. I know. I was one of them.

Now you'll find those twelve people, and however many angels, in *A Gentle Breeze from Gossamer Wings*. They're not the principal characters; they've not even been named. But, in a very real sense, without them there would be no story.

So *A Gentle Breeze from Gossamer Wings* isn't just about seraphs and cherubs in the Indiana boondocks. Oh, you'll find them there if you read carefully. But this story is more than that. It's about what happened in the 1970s and '80s on two sides of the world, about people in Asia and in America and how they came together, how they changed each other's lives.

Some of them, some from Asia and some from America, must have been angels. It's hard to tell. Gossamer wings aren't easy to see, so I think a lot of angels are mistaken for people. And sometimes people are mistaken for angels. But that only happens when they're touched by the breeze of an angel's wings.

— GGB

NOTE

Settings of the chapters in Part I alternate between the United States and Cambodia with action in one locale occurring simultaneously with that in the other. Because of the International Date Line, of course, the date in North America at any given time is one day earlier than in Asia. The events of May 6, 1970, in Indiana (chapter one), for example, occur at the same time as those of May 7, 1970, in Cambodia (chapter two).

The names of Cambodians begin with the surname, followed by given names. Married women keep their original names.

For the meanings of unfamiliar words and phrases the reader is encouraged to consult the Glossary, which can be found at the back of this book. For a list of characters, see Appendix.

CONTENTS

A Break in the Clouds

OCTOBER 29, 1982

Ken MacKenzie didn't like stereotypes. The one about absent-minded professors particularly irked him. Nevertheless, he had to admit his mind was someplace else this morning as his '79 Buick droned westward out of Mendon toward highway 41. He knew about the stop sign there. He'd seen it hundreds of times. But not this morning.

Almost too late, his right foot slammed down on the brake pedal. A screech of rubber grabbing pavement shattered the morning stillness as the car skidded sideways, fishhooked straight, and slid into the northbound lane of the highway. MacKenzie leaned forward, running the back of one hand across his brow as he fumbled at the ignition with the other, trying to restart the engine. The piercing blast of an air horn brought him upright as a semi swerved into the left lane and barreled past.

"I'm sorry," he mumbled in embarrassment. "I should be able to drive and think at the same time. Don't know why I get uptight whenever I have to deal with the government. But that's no excuse."

The woman at his side said nothing. Donna MacKenzie wasn't a critical person. Besides, after nearly 22 years of marriage she knew when to speak and when to keep quiet. Words would accomplish nothing now. The mistake had been made, the apology offered. Ken was a good driver. He'd been negligent. He'd be more careful.

The young woman in the back seat said nothing either. Screeching past a stop sign was nothing to her. She had known real terror, almost constantly, for at least a quarter of her 20 years.

As the engine finally caught, a few scarlet maple leaves drifted down and bounced off the windshield. It was a beautiful morning, at least. With a golden sky behind, frozen dew on roadside weeds, already dried and brown, glistened in the rising sun—a sure sign that ice and snow would soon blanket western Indiana. MacKenzie spun the wheel to the right and started northward on the highway.

It wasn't just the day's business that bothered him. Rain had ruined three of the last four Thursdays and this one, though perfect for outdoor pleasures, wouldn't be spent at one of his favorite haunts. Most could shrug that off. But not MacKenzie. Thursdays were his, and he guarded them jealously. He had no classes on Thursdays, and he avoided scheduling Thursday appointments with his students at Mendon College. They were his days of escape—from the campus, the community, and all their concerns.

Sometimes he'd retreat no farther than the half-acre garden behind his restored Victorian home on Center Street, three blocks from the college. But more often he went off by himself on Thursdays to one of his retreats in the nearby countryside. One was a rippling bend of Honeoye Creek. He could be there five minutes after slipping out the back door at home and tossing his fly rod, waders, and creel into the trunk of the Buick.

Another was Mendon College's Center for Ecological Research, a 120-acre tract of meadow and woodland about 25 minutes southeast of town. Students and staff knew it simply as the Pinery, so labeled because of the towering white pines in its wooded areas. For biologists and geologists the site was ideal for research and study, but Ken treasured its fields and forests for hiking and cross country skiing. Sometimes, though, he'd just sit at the base of a towering tree, lean back against the trunk and lose himself in thought. For working through difficult decisions or pondering the future, there was no place better.

This morning Donna knew what was on her husband's mind. She realized what day it was. And she understood his concern about their afternoon appointment. Reassuringly, she reached across the seat and placed a hand on his shoulder.

"It's a lovely day, Ken. Everything's going to work out all right."

Then she turned to the back seat. "You don't need to worry, Kim Ang."

The Asian girl nodded. "You right, that for sure."

Ken was disappointed that basic sentence elements, such as verbs, still were missing in some of Kim Ang's phrases. But her English had improved greatly during the two years she'd been with the MacKenzies. Her accomplishments in many respects were remarkable, actually.

Bright and charming, she was instantly popular at Mendon High School where she enrolled shortly after moving in with Donna and Ken. Though she hadn't had the benefit of formal education during the previous four years, she adapted quickly to the challenges of study in an unfamiliar language and now was closing in on her first goal, a high school diploma.

Gleaming black hair, bronze skin, and dark, oval-shaped eyes distinguished her from classmates, all of whom were at least three years younger. Education was Kim Ang's top priority and that, too, set her apart from most other students. Because of her passion for learning, teachers adored her.

However, not many of Kim Ang's friends at school, staff or students, were aware of the nightmares she had lived through, or the problems that still plagued her. She told few about her turbulent past, and she was able to conceal her present anxiety from all but Ken and Donna.

For them, the past two years with Kim Ang had been an emotional roller coaster—sinking as she encountered dilemmas and disappointments; rising with her to peaks of accomplishment and joy; then plunging into depths of despair and frustration before zooming again, lifted by her love and gratitude.

Now, as the MacKenzies and Kim Ang motored northward, the pleasant Indiana countryside and the crisp, bright autumn day buoyed their spirits. When they neared Chicago, however, Ken responded to the increasingly heavy traffic with a tightened grip on the steering wheel. By the time they reached the Dan Ryan Expressway south of the Loop, his eyes began to sting as they flitted from the crowded concrete ribbon ahead to tailgaters in the rearview mirror, then to cars and trucks that closed to within inches of his fenders on both sides.

He was still a bit edgy after the close call at the start of their trip. Besides, this was hardly his favorite stretch of road. More wheels whiz past on the Ryan in a few minutes than the main street of Mendon sees all day. But the traffic didn't seem to be bothering the two women.

Donna, fiddling with the radio, had found a station playing the really old oldies and was softly singing along with Della Reese. She'd never forget the lyrics of "Don't You Know." During their courtship she and Ken considered the 1959 hit to be "their song."

"Don't you know," Donna and Della crooned together, " I have fallen in love with you, for the rest of my whole life through?"

She reached over and nudged Ken. He smiled, but his eyes never left the busy road. The duet continued:

> Don't you know, I was yours from the very day
> that you happened to come my way?
> Can't you see, I'm under your spell? By the look in
> my eyes, can't you tell? Can't you tell?
> Now, don't you know every beat of my heart keeps
> crying out ...

Kim Ang was intently following the panorama of south-side Chicago flashing past the window at her left.

But suddenly she gasped—"Oh!"

Donna stopped singing. Ken's foot jerked from the accelerator and hovered over the brake pedal. But he relaxed when the face in the rearview mirror showed no panic. The girl's dark eyes beamed and her arms reached out.

"Oh, America!" The words, little more than a whisper, reverberated like thunder above the roaring motors on the Ryan. She had turned her head and, through the windshield, caught sight of dozens of giant fingers pointing heavenward—Sears Tower, the Prudential Building, and all the others—an impressive sight, even to those who had seen it before.

"Oh, America!" she repeated, louder this time. "I never think I see something so big, so beautiful!"

As a child, she had marveled at the buildings in the city of her birth, Phnom Penh, but the highest of them could only scratch at the ankles of the towering structures now looming before her widened eyes. Phnom Penh, when she last saw it in 1979, was but a shattered ghost of its once glorious past. She was still trying to forget what had happened to it—and to her.

She seemed unperturbed about the problem confronting her today. She'd faced much worse. At least her life wasn't in danger—immediately. Nevertheless, the business at hand was serious. The Buick was heading toward the Chicago office of the Immigration and Naturalization Service where she expected to apply for permanent residency—in a name different from the one she used when she arrived in the country.

She had entered the United States pretending to be someone else. Kim Ang had come to America posing as Tan Chhun Ly, a married woman nine years older than she.

Ken and Donna didn't know whether the girl wasn't concerned, or whether she just didn't show it. They themselves were worried.

When the INS discovers she's not who she said she is, what will happen? Will she be deported?

They had pondered those questions for months, and now they were nearing the moment when they might get the answers—perhaps the ones they dreaded.

But Ken's first problem was getting off the Ryan and through the Loop to the INS office in the Dirksen Federal Office Building. He generally relied on Donna for navigational assistance when they drove through unfamiliar areas. Now he turned to her to confirm their route.

"Is it anywhere near the Madison Street exit?"

"It's supposed to be at 219 South Dearborn. Madison is a couple blocks north. There are other exits you could take."

"I'll take Madison. I've been on that before."

A block from their destination he pulled into the first parking lot without a "full" sign. They stepped from the car and started up the street toward the Dirksen Building. But Kim Ang was hardly aware she was walking. Her eyes were on the towering skyscrapers. Had Donna not taken her arm and guided her along the sidewalk, she'd have had countless collisions.

In front of the building, Ken stopped, placed his hands on Kim Ang's shoulders, and turned her toward him.

"Now, Kim Ang, we have to concentrate on why we're here."

He made sure her eyes were locked on his rather than the fascinations of the bustling city, that she was thinking clearly and understanding the importance of what was about to happen.

"Remember what I said before. When the immigration people ask a question, we will tell the truth." Then even more slowly and emphatically to be sure the words registered, "But we will not answer questions they do not ask. Do not say more than is necessary."

Inside, they discovered the immigration office wasn't a friendly place. As Kim Ang and the MacKenzies waited their turn, shabbily-dressed new immigrants struggled to find the right English words to make themselves understood. Impatient staff members, seeming to resent the intrusions, responded rudely.

However, the few newcomers who were accompanied by well-dressed, seemingly educated, Americans fared better. So Ken, Donna, and Kim Ang were greeted respectfully, if not warmly, by the receptionist and, after a half-hour wait, by Officer Willard Winston.

"Tan Chhun Ly," he called, and then motioned the three into his cluttered office. Papers bulged from cardboard boxes on the floor and from file folders stacked on dented metal cabinets.

"What can I do for you?" he asked, opening a folder labeled *Tan Chhun Ly.*

"This young lady would like to file an application for permanent residency," Ken responded, nodding toward Kim Ang.

"OK," Winston said, reaching into an open desk drawer and pulling out a sheet of paper.

"She needs to fill out this form."

"There's just one problem," Ken said. "The name on the green card should be different than the one in her records."

"What name should it be?"

"Savang Kim Ang," Ken replied.

"Why does the name need to be changed?"

"Because it not be right on my I-94 card when I come to America," Kim Ang said matter-of-factly.

Though Ken tried not to look concerned, he was sure Winston would detect his anxiety. Miraculously, the officer didn't. Nor did he follow up with the obvious next question. He didn't seem to wonder why the wrong name was on the I-94 issued when she was processed for entry.

"Well, you'll have to get your name legally changed in a court of law and then send the appropriate documents back with the application."

"OK, we can do that," Ken asserted quickly, hoping to get out of the office before Winston had a chance to think of the question that could create more problems for Kim Ang. "Thanks very much for your help."

Shoving the blank application into his jacket pocket, he took Kim Ang's hand in one of his, gripped Donna's arm with the other, and guided them toward the door.

Only when they had left the building, retraced their steps to the parking lot, and were safely inside the car did the MacKenzies breathe normally.

"Wow," Ken sighed, "that was a lot easier than I thought it was going to be."

It all happened so quickly that Kim Ang wasn't sure exactly what occurred. But she knew from the expressions on Ken and Donna's faces it was good. The latest of the troubles that always seemed to surround her had evaporated.

The clouds had parted again. But the skies of her life never seemed to be completely clear. She longed for some miracle that would remove all her problems—forever.

Would there ever be a night, she wondered, when the horrors of her past didn't erupt in nightmares that dragged her out of bed, shrieking in anguish? Would there ever be a day when the distress that relentlessly followed her would vanish completely? Somewhere in this great land, could she find a place where she would be secure? Could she ever really feel at home?

PART I
TWO DIFFERENT WORLDS

CHAPTER 1

Putting First Things First

MAY 6, 1970

MENDON, INDIANA

Leaning on the sill of the half-open window, Ken MacKenzie surveyed the placid panorama below his third-floor office in Old Main. Two of his students, each carrying a stack of brightly colored posters, were coming up the walk from Center Street. Otherwise the campus appeared deserted.

Strands of ivy, reaching for the sill at his elbow, swayed in a soothing breeze while early morning sunlight bathed the underlying tableau in a golden glow. A pair of squirrels frolicked on the lawn and spiraled around sycamore trunks in a dizzying game of tag. And somewhere down there a song sparrow seemed determined to assure the world that all was well. Almost monotonously, the same short serenade echoed through the brick-walled canyons of the campus. But despite the persistent songster and the serenity of the setting, Professor MacKenzie wasn't convinced the day would be as carefree as tradition suggested it should be.

For the past 90 years at Mendon the first Wednesday of May had afforded a break from the books. In the spring of 1881, when the college's second academic year was nearing an end, President Alexander Folkert summoned students to a day of spring cleaning and festivities—in that order of priority and occurrence. There had been no break in the academic routine since January, and everyone was eager to suspend the tedium of lectures—even if it meant some physical exertion.

In the morning young women aired draperies, beat carpets, and scrubbed floors in their dormitory while male students attacked campus lawns, gardens, shrubs, and trees with rakes, hoes, clippers, and shovels. Later in the day they were rewarded with an hour of games and an evening meal of all the frankfurters they could eat, served picnic-style in the shade of the campus grove.

At first the annual springtime escape from the classroom was known as "Mendon Pride Day." But soon the young men assigned to eradicate the thousands of yellow-flowered weeds began to call it, with little affection, "Dandelion Day." The name caught on. By the turn of the century no one was aware it had ever been known as anything else.

Through the years time allotted to games and gaiety increased, while the hours devoted to campus cleanup diminished—and eventually disappeared completely. On the agenda now were pushcart races, kite-flying contests, an intramural softball tournament, crowning of the Dandelion Day Queen, and a freshman-sophomore tug-of-war across the Hackmatack River. The evening meal was still in the campus grove, weather permitting, but steaks had replaced frankfurters on the menu.

Next to Christmas, it was Donna MacKenzie's favorite day. She hadn't missed any of the six Dandelion Days since she and Ken moved to Mendon, and she'd always been able to persuade him to accompany her to the festivities.

But Ken was concerned she might be disappointed today. He'd tried to prepare her yesterday when the CBS Evening News pictured confrontations between yelling students and frustrated police while Walter Cronkite described the escalating epidemic of violence and protest on campuses across the country.

Earlier this year the collegians' backlash against the War in Vietnam actually seemed to have cooled. But President Richard Nixon's announcement last week that U. S. troops had entered neutral Cambodia, ostensibly to wipe out North Vietnamese installations there, rekindled the flames of discontent. Then two days ago Ohio National Guardsmen, called out to quell a student protest at Kent State University, shot and killed four students. That tragedy became both the fuse and focus for a new, more violent, outbreak of campus conflict.

"I'm surprised there hasn't been trouble here," Ken had said. "I hope we make it through tomorrow without any."

"Why tomorrow?" Donna asked.

"Well, on Dandelion Day everybody's together in one place at one time. It's an ideal situation for whipping up emotions, if some rabble rouser wants to. Strong feelings and a big crowd can be an explosive combination. I'd hope our kids wouldn't resort to violence to make a point. But with a crowd it could happen."

The televised image of sign-waving, rock-throwing students faded for a commercial. Donna flipped the power switch to off.

"What a shame, Ken. The world's in such a mess. Instead of taking a day to unwind and have fun, kids have to try to do something to fix our problems."

"They don't have to. And they seem to be making more problems than they're fixing."

"Excuse me?"

"Look, I like kids, Donna. If I didn't I wouldn't be teaching. And it's great they're concerned about what's going on. But at their age they don't have all the answers. Even if they did, they're going about it the wrong way. Protesting war by assaulting people in authority is a bit hypocritical at best."

"And is what Nixon's doing right?"

"I don't know. But he's in a better position to know the facts than college kids—and professors, too, for that matter. We elect people to make those decisions, Donna. I think we have to let them do what they're supposed to. I'm not going to get all worked up over things I know nothing about."

She didn't agree. And she hoped he'd realize that what he'd said was rather shallow. She wished sometimes he'd be more concerned about matters of greater consequence. But arguing was against her better judgment. She and Ken had their disagreements, but she rarely let them develop into quarrels. She'd either drop the subject or give in.

"Well, I hope tomorrow will be just like all the other Dandelion Days," she sighed. "If not, I'll be terribly disappointed. Are you going over to your office early?"

"Yeah. I have a stack of themes to grade. Going to try to be there by seven. Come on over when you're ready."

Ken rarely took the car to the college. The campus was just three blocks from home. This morning when he left the house he scooped up the *Mendon Messenger* from the front steps and glanced at the headline on the page-one lead story: "Campuses Erupt in Protest of Widening U. S. Involvement in Southeast Asia." At his office later, after he'd worked his way to the bottom of the pile of sophomore themes, he retrieved the paper from the corner of his desk and scanned the text beneath the head:

> Across the country yesterday college students continued the protests, demonstrations, and strikes that erupted last week when President Nixon sent United States forces across the border into neutral Cambodia to wipe out Vietcong and North Vietnamese installations.
>
> Many of the demonstrators were shocked and angered by the killing of four Kent State University students by Ohio National Guardsmen on Monday.
>
> Students at more than 150 schools across the nation are now on strike. There were fewer confrontations on campuses Tuesday as student leaders met with professors and administrators to plan strikes and demonstrations. However, students at City College in New York burned an ROTC building, and nearly 3,000 University of Wisconsin students battled 250 policemen Tuesday afternoon and evening.
>
> Meanwhile, Boston University administrators closed that institution for the rest of the school term, canceling examinations and giving students 48 hours to vacate the campus. Commencement exercises, at which Sen. Edward Kennedy was to be the speaker, were also canceled.
>
> In Austin, Tex., police fired tear gas to break up a crowd of demonstrators, mostly from the

University of Texas, at the state capitol; and at Ohio
State University 500 protesters skipped and sang
through the ranks of ROTC cadets during a review.
Later in the day National Guardsmen dispersed
disruptive students who blocked entrances to
campus buildings. The day was the fifth in a
student boycott of classes at Ohio State.

On many campuses that had previously
remained calm, protesters occupied buildings and
held sit-ins or in other ways demonstrated their
sympathy for the Kent State victims.

A sidebar of bulletins summarized developments related to the
lead story:

SAIGON, May 6—American forces opened
another front in eastern Cambodia today, moving
across the border at a point 60 miles northwest of
Saigon, according to the U.S. command.

WASHINGTON, May 5—Increasing evidence
indicates that Secretary of State William P. Rogers
and Secretary of Defense Melvin R. Laird seriously
doubted the wisdom of sending American troops
into Cambodia. Reliable sources indicate that
President Nixon's decision to move into Cambodia
was reached in an atmosphere of confusion and
dissension.

WASHINGTON, May 5—President Nixon
moved to quiet increasing criticism from Capitol
Hill today by providing Congressional leaders a "firm
commitment" that American troops would be
withdrawn from Cambodia in three to seven weeks.

"Must be better things to think about," Ken mumbled to himself
as he tossed the paper onto the desk and leaned back in his chair. He
reached to the shelf behind him and switched on the radio, then
whistled along for a few bars as "On the Trail" from Ferde Grofe's
Grand Canyon Suite softly filled the room. He kept the dial set to a
station which offered a steady diet of classical selections and the

15

volume at just the right level to provide a pleasant non-interruptive background for lesson preparation and theme evaluation.

Except for the radio and Ken's sporadic whistling accompaniment, the third floor of Old Main was silent this morning. He loved this old building where he spent nearly as much time as at home. Though his office was tiny and unpretentious, he was glad it was here. The stately yellow-brick edifice was one of Mendon's first two structures.

Originally all of the college's classes met on the upper floors, while the first contained administrative offices and a large assembly room. But now Old Main was home only to the departments of humanities and social sciences.

Sometimes Ken would just sit here and ponder the past. He envisioned someone sitting in this same office 90 years ago, at the time of that first Dandelion Day. He wondered what kind of person that professor might have been, what his interests were, what was most important to him. He pictured in his mind the campus with just two buildings, Old Main and the women's dormitory. In those days male students boarded in private homes near the campus. He wondered whether those young people were as concerned as his students about their government's policies. He thought not.

From the hallway, the sound of familiar footsteps brought him back to the present. Seconds later Donna appeared in the doorway, her lips pursed in a pout and her brow furrowed by a frown. Neither diminished her beauty. If anything, they made her even more alluring—a phenomenon Ken discovered the first time he'd disappointed her. That was shortly after they met eleven years ago. A twenty-year-old college senior then, she had come to Brownsville High School in southwestern Michigan as a teaching intern. Ken was a first-year instructor at the school, and she turned to him as someone near her own age with whom she could share her expectations, apprehensions, frustrations, and accomplishments.

For a few weeks they met only in the faculty lounge and discussed nothing but education. Soon, however, they were meeting off the campus, and academia became less and less a topic of conversation. Their courtship wasn't exactly a whirlwind affair, but Ken gave her a diamond five months after they met, on Valentine's Day 1960. They were married just before Christmas that year.

Then, as now, Ken admired the dense, dark hair that Donna kept closely clipped, almost as short as his own. Her lips were full, her complexion ruddy. Her figure evidenced her passion for tennis and swimming. Though she looked ravishing in anything she wore, she had a knack for selecting just the right attire for any occasion.

But Ken didn't really consider her clothes consciousness a virtue. Donna loved to shop— and to buy. Often she purchased more than an assistant professor's salary could afford. When she looked that good though, and when he felt about her as he did, he found it hard to complain.

For the past nine years her happiness had been his main concern. So now his first impulse was to dispel her dejection.

"Hi," he said cheerfully. "You look great this morning."

The frown didn't disappear.

"You were right, Ken. There *is* going to be some kind of protest today. Kids are putting up signs. They say that when our government is invading neutral countries, napalming innocent kids, and shooting students who object, it's not the time to play games—or something like that."

"Well, I just hope things don't turn violent.

"I'm really disappointed, Ken. I'd looked forward to this day so much."

He got up, took her in his arms and held her, bent slightly and brushed his lips across her forehead. "I'm sorry, Donna. What's happening isn't a surprise though. Remember our conversation during the evening news?"

"Sure, but I sort of hoped things would just go on as usual."

"Well, come on over to the student center. We'll get a cup of coffee and see what's going on."

On the first floor, at the north entrance of Old Main, one of Ken's students was taping a poster onto the outside of the glass.

Ken waited for him to finish, then swung the door open. "Hi, Greg. What's up?"

"We're holding a forum. Hope you'll be there. It's at eleven this morning, west end of the mall. Gotta run now and put the rest of these up."

As he picked up a stack of posters and sprinted up the mall, Ken and Donna paused to read the message on the door. Obviously hand-printed in haste with a felt-tip pen, it read:

STUDENTS OF MENDON SPEAK OUT!
No Dandelions Today
Let's Put First Things First
Express your views and listen to those of
others at a forum on U. S. policy in Southeast Asia:
11 a.m. today at west end of the Mall

A half hour later, after their stop for coffee, Ken and Donna stepped out of the student center onto the central campus mall, a pleasant blend of brick paving, trees, shrubs, groundcover, and benches framed by buildings. The student center, Mendon's newest structure, anchored the east edge of the mall with the administration building and the chapel at the opposite end. Academic buildings lined the other sides.

Donna took Ken's arm as they walked toward the far end of the mall where maintenance workers were installing a microphone and loudspeakers on a portable platform. Ken was pleased the administration apparently was cooperating with students who, so far at least, appeared to have chosen articulation rather than disruption to express themselves.

Students were moving across the mall in greater numbers now, and they were being joined by members of the college staff. Settling onto a bench near the center of activity, Ken and Donna sat back to watch. Within fifteen minutes nearly all of Mendon's 1,326 students and 94 faculty and administrators had assembled at the heart of the campus. Some stood alongside buildings at the edge of the mall, but most sat on cushions and blankets they'd brought.

On the platform, in two chairs a few feet behind the microphone, were Dean of Students James Dunn and president of the Student Congress, Mary Reynolds. Stepping to the mike, Dunn announced that students had asked for an opportunity to exchange viewpoints on their country's activities in Southeast Asia.

"Here at Mendon we believe in a free exchange of ideas," he proclaimed. "That means, of course, we defend the right to express opinions, whether or not we concur." His voice echoed off surrounding buildings. "We agree with John Milton who said three centuries ago: 'Where there is much desire to learn, there of necessity will be much arguing, much writing, many opinions; for opinion in good men is but knowledge in the making.'

"So on this campus today I hope there will be genuine knowledge in the making. But at Mendon we also believe the right of free expression is balanced with a responsibility to respect the views of others. I trust we will maintain that balance today."

Students applauded politely, and Dunn introduced Miss Reynolds as moderator of the exchange of opinions. She outlined the procedures to be followed. Individuals who wished to speak were to come to the platform where their names would be listed by the secretary of the Student Congress. Speakers would be called in the order their names appeared on the list, and their comments would be limited to five minutes. Later, if they wished to respond to remarks of other speakers, they would be permitted to make a single two-minute rebuttal.

For the next two-and-a-half hours students, and a few professors, stepped to the microphone and expressed their views. Most protested American involvement in Vietnam, Laos, and Cambodia. A few defended their government's actions. Cheers erupted on several occasions, but there were no catcalls from those whose opinions differed. Nor were there appeals for disruption or violence.

Ken admired the eloquence and conviction with which several of his students and colleagues presented their views. He himself wasn't tempted to speak. He really didn't feel he knew enough about the issues involved. He still wasn't sure exactly where he stood. He remained convinced the President, if anyone, should know the facts. But he was no longer sure Nixon was using that knowledge to make the best decisions.

Born just before World War II plunged the world into despair, his childhood was clouded by fear of what might happen if the fascists would conquer what was left of the free world. Then, after that war ended, fear of communism supplanted that of fascism. Was it now America's responsibility to protect the world from communism? How far should the red tide be permitted to spread before a stand should be taken? Were the deaths of innocent people in Southeast Asia necessary to stop the communists?

He didn't have the answers. And, frankly, he really didn't want to be bothered. His career and his marriage were what mattered. Let someone else worry about what should or shouldn't be done in Southeast Asia.

CHAPTER 2

More Than Meets The Eye

Savang Siek realized Cambodia was teetering on the brink of destruction. As he saw it, his country was just a tiny island of tranquility in a turbulent sea. War was raging on all sides. Across the border to the south and east, Americans and South Vietnamese were fighting communist forces of North Vietnam and the Viet Cong. To the northeast in Laos, the pro-communist Pathet Lao were battling Laotian government troops.

"I'm afraid the war in Vietnam and Laos is going to spill over into our country," he worried aloud.

As he spoke, Sieng Chhun Sang, the Khmer woman he had married within a year of his arrival in Phnom Penh, listened without comment. She rarely expressed an opinion that didn't concern home life or business.

Siek continued to fret. "I want no part of communism again. The communists made my life miserable once."

His wife nodded, but still didn't speak. Her husband, now a prospering 36-year-old rice wholesaler in Cambodia's capital city, had fled from China ten years ago because of the oppressive communist regime there. She sometimes assisted in the shop but spent most of her time managing their home on the second and third floors of the same building. The Savangs had four children, and Chhun Sang just this morning had told Siek a fifth was on the way.

Their first child, Kim Ang, though only eight years old, contributed to the success of Siek's business. He himself couldn't write in Khmer, and Chhun Sang had kept the records of his rice transactions for the first nine years of their marriage. But this year Kim Ang, whose talent in writing and mathematics amazed her teachers, had relieved her mother of that responsibility.

Each morning, before she left for school, Kim Ang went down among the dusty sacks of rice and carefully wrote out the names of merchants who came to make purchases. Beside each name, she recorded the amount of rice taken and the payment due. At the end of the day, after closing their stalls in the marketplace, the merchants returned to pay Siek. Kim Ang entered the payments, checked the figures against those recorded in the morning, and made sure the purchasers paid for all the rice they had taken.

When the last of the transactions was recorded, Siek and his daughter carefully counted the money and checked the number of *riels* they had deposited in his little wooden box against the figures the child wrote down earlier. Kim Ang didn't mind helping in the first-floor shop. That meant she'd spend less time upstairs looking after her two-year-old sister, Kim Lang, and her brothers, Pheng, 6, and Heng, 4.

Though she was a major player in the adult world of her father's business, Kim Ang wasn't preoccupied with other grownup concerns such as the politics that worried Siek.

But she couldn't help overhearing discussions in the shop. For her elders, these were days of change, of uncertainty, of apprehension. They were alarmed by the battles and the advance of communism in neighboring countries, and they were appalled by corruption in their own. Just two months ago a coup d'etat ended nearly 30 years of rule by Prince Norodom Sihanouk, and rumors persisted that the American Central Intelligence Agency was involved in the overthrow that put Lon Nol in power as prime minister.

None of that worried Kim Ang. She had her mind on other things. After all, she was too young to be bothered about guns and bombs. It was only natural she would be more concerned with dolls and games.

But that wasn't the case either. She rarely took time to play with other children. She had a doll once, but that was long ago. Little Kim

Ang's present passion was, of all things, commerce. When she wasn't in school, or helping her father with his rice sales, she was on the streets selling oranges and sweets. At the age of eight, she had established her own business.

Recordkeeping chores in her father's shop began before six o'clock every morning. But long before that, Kim Ang crept from her sleeping mat and hustled off to the central market where growers from the surrounding countryside brought their produce. After selecting the biggest and best oranges for her day's sales, she would stagger home with huge sacks of fruit and set them aside in a corner of the shop, then record the day's rice transactions.

When the morning's business in Siek's shop was completed, Kim Ang would run up the stairs to straighten her corner of the family's sleeping quarters, change her clothes, comb her hair, and dash off to the private Chinese school where classes began at 7:30. Her studies weren't a concern. Kim Ang was always first in her class to finish assignments. To keep her occupied, teachers often put her to work helping slower learners and checking their papers.

When classes were dismissed at 11:30 for the mid-day break, students who hadn't done well on morning assignments needed to return immediately after lunch. Since that was never a concern for Kim Ang, she would rush home and load a large basket with oranges and sweets. Then she'd hasten to a nearby park and hawk her wares to those who came to visit with friends or to play with their children. By 1:30 she was back in the classroom, but when school ended at 5 o'clock the diminutive huckster was again pushing oranges and sweets in the park and streets near her home.

In the evening, after recording merchants' payments to her father, she again picked up her basket of sweets and took them to a theater, four blocks away, near the central market. The big screen's world of make-believe always attracted a large crowd, and the little peddler did a brisk business as patrons approached the ticket booth.

Kim Ang seemed lighthearted when she was with the theater crowd or at the park, holding her heavy basket of sweets and oranges in one hand and waving a sample of her wares with the other. But she was not a happy child.

She was softspoken and obedient at home and in her father's shop. In her culture that was expected. Family came first and respect for elders, especially one's parents, was taken for granted.

At school she was a model student, an effortless accomplishment due to her innate ability.

On the street she always wore a smile. However, that was a front. It helped sales.

But selling wasn't what really mattered. Kim Ang was at the market buying oranges in the middle of the night, at the park in the heat of the noontime sun, at the theater doorway in the dark of night—not because her greatest desire was to be a kingpin in the world of commerce. Nor was it to satisfy a craving for money. She knew she couldn't buy the one thing that would satisfy her.

What Kim Ang wanted desperately was love. She longed for the attention and affection most other children in her neighborhood accepted as matter of fact. She saw the hugs they received. She envied the words of kindness, the warm smiles, the feeling of belonging, the security of a happy home.

Kim Ang's parents were too busy for that. Her father's business was all that mattered. And her mother didn't seem to understand that Kim Ang, Kim Lang, Pheng, and Heng needed more than a roof over their heads and food in their stomachs.

"If only I can be successful at what is most important to Papa and Mama," Kim Ang told herself, "they will love me. Papa will tell me how good I am. Mama will gently comb my hair before I go to school and hug me."

But it hadn't happened yet.

The Real Story
Stealth Bombers and Illegal Border Crossers

Few in Phnom Penh were aware in 1969 that bombs from American planes were falling on their country. The American aerial assaults began with a secret raid by 48 B-52s on March 17 that year, at the peak of American involvement in Vietnam. And by the time they ended four years later, when Congress ordered a halt to the bombing, the U. S. had dropped more than three times as many explosives onto the neutral country as fell on Japan during all of World War II.

The target of the first 1969 attack was a communist command post in the Cambodian jungles from which the Viet Cong and North Vietnamese were believed to be directing operations against American and South Vietnamese forces. The assault was supposed to deal a crippling blow to the control center. But it didn't, and thousands of additional attacks in Cambodia followed for more than a year.

Of course, Cambodian civilians were among the casualties, and the White House knew they would be. Also, the attacks against neutral Cambodia probably were a violation of international law. And they certainly were a breach of the U. S. Constitution since Congress hadn't approved them and, in fact, hadn't even been informed of them.

Not surprisingly, President Richard M. Nixon did try to conceal what was going on.

Then, when a *New York Times* reporter uncovered the secret bombing and broke the story two months after the raids began, the American public received the news, for the most part, with amazing indifference. Four years later the same information would lead to cries for Nixon's impeachment. But in 1969 there were few protests. Most didn't express approval either. They just didn't seem to care.

It was a different story, however, when American ground forces crossed the Cambodian border in the spring of 1970 to accomplish what the tons of bombs from B-52s had failed to do—destroy the communist sanctuaries.That action, without approval of either the U. S. Congress or the Cambodian government, touched off violent protests on university campuses throughout the United States.

On the other side of the world, the attacks hardly had the outcome the Nixon administration hoped for either. Actually, they cleared the way for the Cambodian communists and the holocaust they were soon to inflict on their own people. As Americans blasted the border region from the air and moved into it on the ground, the North Vietnamese and Viet Cong just moved their bases farther into Cambodia, actually giving them control over more territory. Eventually, these areas were taken over by the Khmer Rouge who, when the Americans finally deserted Cambodia, found victory within their grasp.

For more details, see:

John Barron and Anthony Paul, *Murder of a Gentle Land* (New York, Reader's Digest Press, 1977), page 54

William Beecher, "Raids in Cambodia by U. S. Unprotested," *The New York Times* (May 9, 1969), pages 1, 7

William Shawcross, *Sideshow: Kissinger, Nixon, and the Destruction of Cambodia* (New York, Simon and Schuster, 1979), chapter 1, "The Secret," and chapter 15, "The Bombardiers"

"Raising the Stakes in Indochina" and "Sanitizing the Sanctuaries," *Time* (May 4, 1970), pages 11, 16

CHAPTER 3

A Change In Direction

Ken looked up from the sports page of the *Mendon Messenger* as Donna, humming "Deck the Halls," slid a bowl of hot cereal onto his place mat.

"When it comes to Christmas, Donna, you're still a kid. I'll bet you've been peeking in the closets."

"I am not, and I have not," she countered, feigning a frown as she scooped a pair of spoons from the silverware drawer. "But I'll admit I'm looking forward to today's luncheon."

That was an understatement, and they both knew it. For weeks she'd been experimenting with decorating schemes for her table at the annual United Methodist Women's Christmas party. She and eleven other hostesses would spend most of the morning in the church's Fellowship Hall, each fussily placing six settings of china and silver amid the decorations that would make her table unique.

Donna was using her pale blue dishes, rimmed with a single narrow band of gold, arranging them on a cloth of darker blue amid a simple but striking display of golden ribbons and candles. Her centerpiece would be an exquisite Lladro angel, a souvenir of her summer of study in Madrid fourteen years ago.

After breakfast, as she carefully wrapped and placed the porcelain angel in the box she'd take to church, Ken recalled his *faux pas* after her first holiday luncheon at church. When she ecstatically described the decorations of each hostess, he referred to the event as a competition and asked who won first prize. The careless remark nearly ruined Christmas Eve.

He still thought there were better uses for that much time and effort. But now he knew better than to say so. Last night, when Donna had set out a trial arrangement on the dining room table at home, he'd made appropriate oohs and ahs.

He really wanted the luncheon to be a happy occasion for Donna, and he told her so. She already had one disappointment. Each holiday season since they came to Mendon, she'd persuaded Ken to take her for an after-dark drive through winding streets of the new subdivisions where neighbors tried to outdo one another with dazzling strings of lights outlining houses, filling trees, and spelling holiday sentiments.

But this year there was nothing to look at. With the energy crisis sending gasoline and fuel oil prices higher and higher, President Nixon had urged Americans not to waste electricity on ornamental display lighting.

"Turning off the lights certainly does dim the spirit of the season," was all Donna said. But Ken knew the change was a major disappointment. This morning, however, nothing could dim her spirits. She left for the luncheon, still humming carols.

As soon as she pulled out of the driveway, he tugged on his boots and overcoat and started out toward the college campus. Another four inches of snow overnight complicated walking, concealing patches of ice that lay beneath the new coat of white. Nevertheless, he didn't mind covering the three blocks on foot.

He'd been asked to meet with President William E. Scott at 10 o'clock, and he had no idea why. Ken genuinely admired the affable administrator. There was nothing pretentious about him. When the situation called for it, however, he could effectively use the power of his position.

Scott had come to Mendon in 1958 when the quality of students and staff and the condition of facilities were at all-time lows. A team of consultants, brought in by the Board of Trustees to assess the situation, recommended the struggling institution be put out of its misery. The trustees, however, were determined to save the college and hired Scott to lead the effort.

The new president quickly sent laggard students packing. Ineffective faculty and staff were replaced. Then, as the institution's status stabilized, he directed an ambitious campaign to provide adequate facilities. It worked. Mendon's academic reputation was restored, and nine of its 14 major buildings were constructed during the 15 years of his administration.

In formal situations members of the campus community addressed the prexy as Dr. Scott. But close associates called him Bill while most students and staff, in conversations with one another, referred to him as Scotty. The fact that undergrads never christened him with one of the derogatory appellations they quickly invented for others in high-profile campus positions demonstrated their respect and admiration. They had labeled the prexy's predecessor, Conrad R. Constatius, "Loquacious Constatius" in recognition of his long-winded convocation speeches; and Dean of Students James Dunn, a perfectionist, was generally known as "Overdone."

As he approached the college, Ken saw few footprints in the fresh snow on campus walks. Students had vanished at the start of the holiday recess three days ago, and offices were closed this day before Christmas. One set of tracks, apparently made by the watchman on his latest rounds, wound from building to building. Another led from the president's house toward Weston Administration Center—a one-story building honoring Mendon's best-known alumnus, R. Samuel Weston, newspaper publisher and confidant of United States presidents in early decades of the century. Ken followed the president's footsteps to the east entrance and walked in. The only light visible projected from a doorway at the far end of the corridor.

"Good morning, Ken. Come in."

Scott had seen Ken coming across the mall and called down the hall. They walked through a small outer office and into the president's own spacious quarters.

"I appreciate your coming over on a day like this when you probably have better things to do."

"Glad to. Donna's busy with the ladies at church this morning, and we're quite set for the holidays."

The president guided Ken to one of two chairs beside a large window overlooking the mall and surrounding buildings. He took the other. Ken realized it could be some time before he'd learn why the president had summoned him to the deserted campus. Scott wasn't usually one to plunge right into the business at hand.

"Donna's teaching social studies in the public schools' adult education program, isn't she? How does she like it?" the prexy asked.

Then he recalled 1973's major headlines. "What a year it's been. This Watergate thing's a mess. I'm afraid we haven't seen the worst of it."

He and Ken considered other evidences of corruption in government, particularly the resignation of Vice President Spiro Agnew. Both admired his replacement, Michigan Congressman Gerald Ford.

Then Scott brought up the energy crisis. "Do you think there's really a shortage of fuel? Or are the big oil companies just fabricating this whole thing to run the little outfits out of business and boost their own profits?"

Next he turned to American attitudes about satisfaction with living standards. "What do you think of Gallup's latest findings?"

Ken had read results of the survey. "Well, sir, I found it interesting," he replied, "that we're less happy with the moral climate of the country and more discouraged about the future, even though we seem satisfied with the standard of living."

"Yes, and I think it's encouraging," Scott added, "that more people are realizing it takes something besides material prosperity to provide contentment. That's right in step with what we're trying to do here with liberal arts education. At least, I hope our graduates are aware there's more to education than preparing for a job—and more to life than accumulating possessions."

"I'm sure they are."

"But we really have to do a better job of telling our story," Scott went on. "Too many who should be coming here to study haven't heard what we have to offer. And too many who should be supporting us financially haven't heard why they should."

"That's why I asked you to come here this morning."

Ken wondered what might be coming next. *He's going to ask me how to get more bodies and dollars?*

"I've asked our student recruiting and our fund-raising people to recommend changes that would help them do a better job," the president continued. "They've agreed on one thing. We need to develop a serious program of promotion, of public relations. Up to now we've tried to get by with part-time people who, frankly, haven't really known much about what they're doing. We can't afford to do that any longer.

"I know you have the talent we need. You're familiar with Mendon, and that's important. I'm aware of your journalistic experience, too."

During weekends and summers, as a high school student and early in his teaching career, Ken did reporting and editing for newspapers in his home town and in cities where he'd studied. He had turned down offers of full-time positions with some of them because he wanted to teach.

"I've read nearly everything you've published lately," Scott went on. "You know how to write. That's one of the reasons I think you can get Mendon's story across. Of course, it will take more than that. But I'm sure you can do the job. I'd like you to consider setting up a public relations program for us—and direct it. What do you think?"

Ken was at a loss for words. He'd had no inkling this was what the prexy had in mind to spring on him the day before Christmas. He was happy teaching. He didn't want to be an administrator.

"Well, this is really quite sudden," he said finally. "I do appreciate your kind words, but it will take some thinking."

"Certainly. All I ask is that you consider it. I know you love teaching. And you're good at it. We need you in the classroom. But right now we need your other talents even more."

The president paused, then continued, "If you decide to go along with me, I'd like you to give it at least a two-year try. After that, if you want to return to teaching, your position will be there for you. And, of course, any time later that you'd rather be in the classroom you can go back. We'll write that into your contract.

"We'll want you to be on the job all year long, of course, except for a month of vacation. Oh, yes, there may be some occasional weekend responsibilities. We'll make it worth your while, Ken. We can talk about salary later, but I can assure you of a raise.

"I hope you'll do it. It's very important to the future of the college.

If you accept, I'd like you to start this summer, as soon as the next semester is over and you and Donna have had a chance to get away for a vacation. Give it some thought. Then come back and let's talk some more."

"Thanks for the flattering things you've said. You can be sure I'll give it more than a little thought. I'll get back to you soon."

They shook hands, and Ken left.

Still somewhat dazed by the turn of events, he walked home, lit a fire in the fireplace, and waited for Donna to return.

Two hours later she was halfway through her table-by-table report of the Christmas luncheon when she suddenly remembered Ken's morning appointment.

"I'm sorry, Ken. I didn't even ask about what you've been doing. What did Scotty want?"

"He asked me to quit teaching."

"What do you mean? You can't be serious."

"Well, there's more to it than that. He wants me to do something else."

Donna relaxed slightly, and Ken went on with a complete account of the morning conversation.

"How do you feel about that?" she asked when he'd finished.

"Well, good, since he thinks I can do the job. It involves things I like to do, and it's a challenge. Setting up a PR program for the college, and running it, would be interesting. But I don't want to stop teaching. I don't know. It's not going to be easy to decide. What do you think I should do?"

"Oh no, it's not my decision to make. You know I want you to do what makes you happy, whatever gives you the most satisfaction."

"If it were that simple, I'd stick with teaching for sure. But Scotty laid it on pretty heavy with his 'Mendon-needs-your-talent' approach. One thing, it would put an end to my Thursday adventures. And there'd be weekends I'd be tied up, too. I don't think I'm ready to give up all that."

But he wondered if he was just hoodwinking himself. Could he really say no to Scott? Or were his days in the classroom numbered, whether he liked it or not?

CHAPTER 4

Spur of the Moment Decisions

DECEMBER 25, 1973

PHNOM PENH

The sight of a little girl in ragged clothes, squatting in dirt near the sidewalk food stand, snatching up and chewing on chicken bones tossed aside by customers, wasn't unusual. Ordinarily Kim Ang wouldn't have given her a second glance.

Bedraggled refugees had been pouring into Phnom Penh. Few of them had enough to eat. Bewildered and demoralized, the homeless lined every road leading into the capital. Some plodded alongside ox carts carrying children, older kinfolk, and others too shattered or weary to walk. Jumbled into the quaking carts with them were a few family possessions of sufficient importance and portability to merit space—dishes and pots, kerosene lamps, sleeping mats, crates of chickens.

A few rode bicycles. Most walked. The flow of haggard humanity started as a trickle three years ago, about the time Kim Ang began peddling her oranges and sweets on the city's streets. But this year it became a torrent. The uprooted just kept coming and coming. It seemed to Kim Ang there were two people wherever one had been a year ago.

She worried about what would become of her city and her country. She wondered why so many bad things had been happening. In her short life this was the first Year of the Ox. Were they all going to be like this?

The year started with louder and more frequent thunder from American bombs in the countryside around Phnom Penh. The blasts were close enough to shake the walls at home. For more than half the year the bombings went on. Finally, they stopped. But now there were more explosions. Though not as many, they were closer, right here in the city. Her father said they were from guns and rockets of the Cambodian communists, the Khmer Rouge.

The flood of forlorn people, thousands and thousands of them, began to inundate the city when the heavy American bombing started early in the year. Then, when the bombs stopped falling, the people kept coming, running now from the Khmer Rouge. The homeless were everywhere. Some lived in parks, in freight cars, in doorways. Some had relatives in Phnom Penh who took them into their homes, sometimes cramming in three or four times as many people as before. Many more were in overcrowded camps. Thousands lived in shanties that sprang up along nearly all the city's streets. The more fortunate used sheets of metal. Others fashioned their dwellings from bamboo and palm leaves, or even cardboard.

At age 11, Kim Ang didn't understand what brought all this about. For that matter, neither did most of her elders. She heard some of the refugees tell about fleeing for their lives when American airplanes dropped bombs on their villages. She saw others staggering along the roads, several carrying relatives and friends who had been wounded in the attacks. Lately she met some who said they ran away from their villages when communists tried to force them to join their army or their crews in the rice paddies.

But what made the Americans drop bombs? And why were the Khmer Rouge such harsh taskmasters, taking away all freedom and forcing people to work as slaves?

"The Americans think their bombs will drive out the communists," she'd heard merchants say at her father's shop.

And the communists, according to some who fled from them, boasted they would eliminate the corrupt regime the American imperialists had installed in Cambodia. Then they would build a great new society.

Kim Ang was glad this year soon would end. Perhaps the new Year of the Tiger, the year of her birth, would bring better luck.

Now, though nearly four months had passed since anyone heard the thunder of American bombs, the sound of explosions was starting again. The Khmer Rouge had begun to fire rocket and artillery shells into the crowded city. That frightened Kim Ang even more.

Phnom Penh's people usually knew when American planes were up there. Sometimes they saw a wispy trail of vapor far up in the sky or, if they looked closely, a tiny speck thousands of feet above. And, though the bombs had been close enough to be heard, they never fell on Phnom Penh.

But the deadly new missiles came right into the city! They appeared from nowhere without warning—except sometimes when the cluk-cluk-cluk-cluk sound of the rocket engine could be heard above the street noise. One minute the throngs on the streets would be scurrying about on their business. Then, with a blinding flash and a loud roar, pieces of buildings, and people too, would fly through the air. When the smoke and dust settled, there would be a strange silence, broken only by the sobs of those who lay shattered and bleeding, but still breathing.

That happened yesterday—and the day before. Kim Ang had not been near the blasts, but she had heard about them.

Why are the communists doing this? Why do they shoot their rockets blindly into the city and kill people who aren't doing anything to hurt them? She couldn't help asking herself questions like those, over and over.

Now, as she glanced across the street, the shabby little refugee girl, still squatting near the food stand, flipped a leg bone she'd been gnawing into the air. Arching gracefully toward the white-painted wall behind her, the bone seemed to be hanging in space when the cluk-cluk-cluk-cluk sound drove Kim Ang instinctively to the ground.

But the waif just sat there until, suddenly, a large hole opened in the wall just three meters above her head. There was no flash of light, no ear-splitting roar—only the crack of the rocket crashing into the building and the clatter of debris falling to the street. The charge in the missile had failed to explode! Kim Ang glanced up to see the panic-stricken girl running toward her. Their eyes met and their arms reached out.

They stood, holding each other, shaking, too terrified to speak. Finally, Kim Ang started to pull away, somewhat embarrassed. She didn't want to be seen by someone she knew, clinging to this grimy girl. But the mystic magnetism that had drawn them together stopped her. She took the girl's hand and led her down the street to a shaded park. There Kim Ang first heard, from someone her own age, what it means to be a refugee.

As they went through the preliminaries of "What's your name?" and "How old are you?" Kim Ang studied the features of her new friend. She marveled that, beneath the layers of mud and dust, the waif was someone very much like herself.

Wash her up and change her clothes, Kim Ang thought, *and I might be looking in the mirror.*

The child's name was Heng Ay Leng. She had been born just a month after Kim Ang, and she came to Phnom Penh from Neak Luong, a town on the east bank of the Mekong River about 60 kilometers southeast of the capital.

Kim Ang had heard of Neak Luong. It was the place where Americans dropped bombs by mistake last summer, killing more than a hundred people and hurting hundreds more.

"When did you come to Phnom Penh?" Kim Ang asked, wondering if the bombs had anything to do with the girl being here.

"Last summer," Ay Leng responded. "In August."

"Was it because of what the Americans did?"

"Yes. They killed my father—and my brothers and sisters. Mother and I weren't in the house. We had gone to the river at dawn to see if we could buy some fish. My brothers and sisters were still sleeping. My father was a soldier. He was on a patrol most of the night, so he was sleeping, too. Mother and I were gone for only about 10 minutes. Then it happened.

"The sound was terrible. It seemed to go on and on, but it was really just a minute or two. We saw pieces of buildings and trucks, all kinds of things, flying through the air. The ground was shaking. Big clouds of smoke began to fill the sky. Then it became very quiet— but not for long. We heard people crying and screaming."

The urchin continued her recitation of terror matter-of-factly.

"Mother ran back to our street, and I was right behind her. When we got to the top of a little hill at the end of the street, smoke and dust made it hard to see. Some things we could see, and some we couldn't. We could see where our house was, but we couldn't see our house. It was gone. So were all our neighbors' houses.

"My mother fell on the ground. She shouted, but I couldn't hear what she was saying. It was just noises. She hit the ground with her fists, like she wanted to hurt it. She just kept doing that. I got down next to her and put my arms around her. But it was a long time before she stopped. Then she just lay there and cried.

"Finally, I helped her get up. We started again toward where our house used to be. We walked a few steps, and then we started to run. I held on to Mother's hand all the time. When we came close, about thirty meters away, Mother stopped. She couldn't go closer. She was squeezing my hand really hard and looking at a splintered tree in front of our neighbor's house. Hanging from one of the branches was a shredded piece of cloth, mostly covered with blood. But part of the pattern still showed. I knew it was my sister's dress—my littlest sister, Ay Ving. She was three years old. I had another sister, too. And three brothers. All my brothers and sisters were younger than me."

Ay Leng recited the tale of horror with no sign of emotion. The tragedy had made a shambles of her life, had killed six of the seven people who were closest to her, had vaporized her home, and forced her to struggle for survival on the crowded streets of a big, strange city. It seemed to have drained all her tears and her feelings.

She continued her story. "We didn't stand there long before some men came. They took us to a part of the town where the bombs didn't hit. Some women there tried to make us feel better. But we didn't. The next morning Mother said we had to leave Neak Luong. There was nothing there for us anymore. That's when we came to Phnom Penh. There's not much for us here either. But this place doesn't have as many bad memories."

"Where do you live now?" Kim Ang asked.

"In the hotel," Ay Leng responded.

Not likely, Kim Ang thought. *This girl dressed in rags and chewing on garbage doesn't live in any hotel.*

"It's called the Cambodiana," Ay Leng continued. "The builders didn't finish it, and now they made some places in it for people who don't have houses. It's like a camp. Each family has a little room. Well, not a room exactly. It's more like a bed, about two meters long and one meter wide. Mother and I are lucky because there are just two of us, and we didn't have anything to bring with us when we came from Neak Luong.

"Some families have lots of people, and they all have to take turns sleeping in that little place. If they brought things with them, they have to keep all that there, too. It's not a very nice place. It's dark in there, just a few dim light bulbs to help you see. There are too many people. And some people have chickens and pigs."

Kim Ang continued her questioning. "What does your Mom do? Does she work to get money to buy food?"

"She can't find any work," Ay Leng replied. "She goes every day to the lines of people who wait for food from the Americans. Sometimes she comes with me here to see what is thrown away near the food stands. Sometimes we go to the markets to see if something was thrown away there."

"I'm going to work now. You can help me," Kim Ang suggested, remembering she might already have missed some of her regular customers for oranges and sweets at the park near her house. Tugging Ay Leng along, she walked briskly toward home, wondering as she went whether this had been a good idea. Being seen with this ragged girl might not be good for business, or her reputation.

At her house, she had Ay Leng stand on the street while she ran upstairs to get her basket of merchandise. Her Mother certainly would scold her for keeping company with someone who looked like that.

As she grabbed her basket of fruit and sweets and started down the stairs, she had another idea. She stopped, spun around, and went to the cabinet where she kept her dresses. Pulling one out, she folded it up and hid it in the bottom of the basket of oranges. She had bought the dress last year with her own money, but she knew her Mother would be very angry if she discovered she was giving it away.

Here I am, she thought, *deciding to do something else without thinking it through, something else that really might not be a good idea.*

She wasn't sure just why she was doing this. Was it because business would be better if her assistant looked cleaner, neater, better dressed? Or was it because she felt sorry for someone who, in some ways, was so much like herself—but whose life, in most ways, was so different?

The Real Story
An Impersonal War

In 1973 as controversy regarding America's bombing of Cambodia escalated, Congress ordered that the attacks stop on August 15. With the deadline nearing, pilots of the giant droop-winged B-52s that carried out the raids, in interviews with journalists at their base in Thailand, described the deadly assignments as impersonal and boring.

Flying more than five miles above their targets and pressing buttons to send their deadly cargoes plummeting onto the Cambodian countryside, the B-52 crewmen themselves were in little danger—hardly greater than that of their commercial counterparts at the controls of passenger jets back home. Nobody below was shooting, at least with anything capable of hitting them.

"I don't think about what the targets are," one American airman said. "We just fly the missions."

"It's difficult for me to worry about Phnom Penh," another told a reporter. "I think the end of the bombing means going home. Everybody's tired of being here. It's been a long drawn-out affair, and I think everybody's ready to go home to their families."

One pilot, at least, did eventually think about what the targets were and did worry about Phnom Penh. On June 19, 1973, Capt. Donald Dawson, guilt-ridden about deaths he might have caused, refused to fly and court-martial proceedings against him were begun. Just weeks before the Supreme Court was to hear the case in 1974, the government averted further embarrassment by halting the proceedings and granting Dawson conscientious objector status.

Meanwhile, during the final weeks of bombing, a series of errors resulted in attacks on friendly targets in heavily-populated areas—the most devastating at Neak Luong, 38 miles southeast of Phnom Penh, on August 8.

U. S. officials tried to put the best possible face on the disaster, but newsmen on the scene readily saw through the subterfuge. Although casualties totaled at least 145 killed and twice that many wounded, a government spokesman described the damage as "minimal" and "no great disaster."

Back home, television newsman Hughes Rudd observed, "There is no such thing as minor damage from a B-52. If you look at a B-52 strike from half a mile away, it looks like the end of the world. If you're under it, it is."

Subsequently, the U. S. government offered the Cambodians compensation of $100 per casualty and fined the navigator of the plane $700.

For more details, see:

Peter R. Kann, "U. S. Crews in Thailand See Cambodia Bombing as Impersonal Task," *The Wall Street Journal* (Aug. 6, 1973), pages 1, 12

Sidney Schanberg, "Bomb Error Leaves Havoc in Neak Luong," *The New York Times* (Aug. 9, 1973), pages 1, 4

William Shawcross, *Sideshow: Kissinger, Nixon, and the Destruction of Cambodia* (New York, Simon and Schuster, 1979), chapter 19, "The Bombing"

Joseph B. Treaster, "Bombing Crews Just Want to Go Home," *The New York Times* (Aug. 5, 1973), pages 1, 5

"When the Bombs Fall by Mistake," *Newsweek* (Aug. 20, 1973), pages 34-35

CHAPTER 5

Delight and Despair

APRIL 16, 1975
WESTERN INDIANA

The friendliness of small towns was the clincher that brought the MacKenzies to Indiana eleven years ago when Ken was considering job offers from Mendon College as well as Nazareth College in Kalamazoo, Michigan, a city with ten times as many people.

Though Donna hadn't experienced small-town life until she went away to college, Ken always lived in rather tiny communities, except for his few years as a graduate student at the University of Michigan.

Hoping to impress Donna, he spoke often when they first met about experiences in what he called "the big university city"—until she commented that Ann Arbor usually wasn't printed in large letters on the maps. She had been raised in Milwaukee and didn't even consider that to be especially big.

By the time she'd completed her teaching internship at Brownsville, where she and Ken met, Donna was as much at home in small towns as he. Neither liked the prospect of battling big-city traffic every day to get to work, or enduring a lifetime of congestion on subways or busses. Both realized the advantages of larger cities: the cultural attractions, the variety of goods and services, the excitement. But it wasn't for them. They preferred tree-lined streets that became silent by 9 p.m., shopping in stores where clerks smiled and called you by name, and walking on sidewalks where people greeted you in passing—even if they'd never seen you before.

They'd lived in Mendon long enough now to be able to shrug off the ridicule of out-of-town friends who couldn't understand why they'd stay in a place as dull as this. Donna and Ken never thought of

Mendon as dull, though they conceded they weren't likely to see themselves, or anyone they knew, on the evening news. Events the world regards as exciting, or even interesting, seldom happened in Mendon. And, if they did, likelihood of the word getting out was diminished by the fact that the closest television station and large-circulation newspaper were more than sixty miles away.

Ken had learned to appreciate that reality in his new role as the college's public relations director. Since it was now his responsibility to promote a favorable image of the college, he was grateful that occasional student and staff transgressions, spicy news possibilities if the college were located in a larger city, usually escaped the notice of the press.

The PR advantages of Mendon's remoteness first became apparent to him last fall when county sheriff's deputies arrested the new college chaplain, Raymond Stanowski, for drunk driving after he'd maneuvered his car through several rows of corn in a field north of town. The *Mendon Messenger* didn't even report the incident. But the *Benton County Chronicle*, a weekly published in nearby Itasca, carried a brief account at the bottom of page two. Told about it by a friend, Ken planned to pick up a copy at the corner drugstore on his way home, but the *Chronicle* rack was empty. Two other stores he checked were also out of the paper. Then he went to the Main Street News Center.

"Do you have this week's *Benton County Chronicle*?" Ken asked the proprietor.

"I did yesterday," he replied, "but then one of those new guys at the college came in and bought all I had left, 23 of them."

"That's interesting," was all Ken said. But to himself as he walked out he mumbled, "Well, that's one way of managing the news."

Many in Mendon would learn of the chaplain's problem anyway, but he was grateful the college wasn't in South Bend, Gary, Fort Wayne, or Indianapolis. Reporters there were prone to be more aggressive and less sympathetic. A story about the chaplain of a Christian college getting pinched for drunk driving would certainly get good play, and he'd be spending a lot of time on damage control.

This spring, ten months after moving from the classroom to an administrative office, Ken found himself thinking more and more about ways he could hasten a return to teaching. His new job had started out well enough. The assignment was challenging as well as interesting. But circumstances of the past few months had been discouraging.

He was more troubled, in fact, than he'd been that Christmas Eve of '73 after President Scott asked him to accept the PR assignment. When he'd finally faced reality that night, admitting to himself he really didn't have a choice, he was at first angry and then despondent. He admired Scott, but he didn't like what was happening. He was being forced out of the classroom, actually. And further, he didn't appreciate the president's timing. Christmas that year had been much less merry.

Then, with his days as a teacher nearing an end, he'd become more accepting—even eager to make the change. And the first several months on the job went smoothly. Ken always enjoyed writing, and the new assignment gave him a chance to do more of it. News releases about college activities were easy to crank out; news writing skills were second nature to him by then. Producing text for college publications, however, was something new, though a challenge he liked. And recognition of his efforts, especially by the president, was rewarding. Scott was a master motivator and brought out the best in his staff by lavishing praise. As each of Ken's publications came off the press, the president greeted it with enthusiasm.

Scott seemed to take a special interest in his new PR man. He kept an open door to his office, and often when he'd see Ken walking past he'd summon him inside.

"How about a cup of coffee, Ken?" he'd call out. "Come in here and tell me what's going on. What's that charming wife of yours been up to lately?" Then, with an impish grin, "What in the world did someone as gorgeous as she see in you anyway?"

They'd spend a half hour talking, rarely about college business. They'd cover gardening, fishing, philosophy, local politics, investment tips. It was always Ken who would check his watch and call the session to an end.

"Time for me to get out of here," he'd say. "I've got to protect my own image. If I'm seen in here too long, people will think I've really screwed things up."

Ken's acceptance of his new assignment had paralleled his increasing admiration for Scott. The anger and discontent evaporated. Then, just before the start of the academic year last September, the bad news broke. The president hadn't been seen on the campus for several weeks, and the general assumption was that he'd merely extended his vacation time in the West to make some calls on potential benefactors. Actually, he'd been at the Mayo Clinic in Minnesota where tests revealed an inoperable brain tumor.

After Dr. Scott's death in December, the Board of Trustees picked one of its own to serve as interim president until a search committee could find a successor. James Kirchener, retired CEO of a Fort Wayne appliance manufacturing company and chairman of the college's Board until three years ago, was highly respected among Indiana industrialists. In retirement he'd developed a management consulting business.

"I am willing," he said, "to cut back on those activities to give full attention to the affairs of the college."

In January he and his wife moved into the president's home alongside the towering oaks of the campus grove, and he took over the president's office.

Right from the start Ken felt bad vibes. In a matter of days it was clear that Kirchener's *modus operandi* was a far cry from Scott's. He may have been a management expert in the estimation of some, but his style wasn't what Mendon expected, or needed. At least that's the way Ken saw it. At his first staff meeting, Kirchener made it clear he would call the shots:

"When I want advice, I'll ask for it," he said bluntly.

His years of service on the Board, he felt, gave him a good perspective of Mendon's strengths and weaknesses.

"I'm not coming in as a stranger," he claimed. "I have served this college for several years and I can lead it through these recuperative days."

Ken resented the inference that Dr. Scott's administration had left the college in some kind of sickened condition.

Then, within a month of taking over, Kirchener advised Ken he believed changes were necessary in Mendon's public relations program.

"What we need to do, Dr. MacKenzie," he stated, "is bring in a consulting firm to study the college's public relations setup and then suggest improvements. I envision this relationship with the consultants lasting indefinitely.

"The firm I have in mind will help us tremendously," he went on. "They have experts in many fields: research, program development, media relations, publication design and production. They have the big picture. They can help us get national visibility. That's what we need."

Ken knew that to disagree would be useless. Kirchener had made up his mind. That was all that mattered. He realized, too, that he was no longer in charge of the college's PR program. Kirchener was. He could only hope the search for a permanent president would go smoothly and quickly and that the new prexy would have some of Scott's characteristics and none of Kirchener's—or better yet, that he himself could get out of the administration building and back into Old Main.

In the months that followed, Ken avoided Kirchener as much as possible and went about his work as before. But his enthusiasm had died. In two weeks the public relations consultants would be on the campus for preliminary discussions. Despondent again, he told Donna he needed to get away. So he arranged to take a week of vacation early and made reservations for a cabin at Turkey Run State Park.

They had spent a springtime weekend there a few months after their wedding and had fallen in love with its rugged terrain, towering trees, and gurgling streams. Turkey Run was only an hour's drive south of Mendon, but that was far enough. Without the campus in sight, Ken hoped he'd be able to forget what was happening there.

After arriving at Turkey Run four days ago, Ken had started to unwind. They had the park almost to themselves the first couple days, a Saturday and Sunday, and Donna coaxed him out onto the hiking trails each morning. Hand in hand, they descended into rocky canyons and climbed wooded hills, marveling at the forest floor dappled with white, yellow, and lavender patches of trillium, buttercups, and violets and pausing occasionally to identify soloists in a symphony of songbirds headed northward after a winter in the South.

One afternoon they drove along back roads of the surrounding countryside, hunting covered bridges. Donna loved the old wooden spans and had been eager to return to Parke County where more than thirty still stood. Before dusk they explored five, pausing longest at Leatherwood Creek where Donna's favorite, Sim Smith Bridge, stood in the shadows of towering sycamores. Ken had carved their heart-encircled initials on one of its supporting timbers 14 years ago. They were still there.

Most afternoons, however, they enjoyed a separate togetherness in their cabin with books they'd brought along—sitting alongside one another on the couch but carried off in different directions by the imagery of the printed pages. Evenings restored a complete oneness as they'd snuggle at the edge of a crackling campfire, enjoying the warmth of one another's presence.

Here at Turkey Run, released from the schedules and constraints of everyday routines, from the interruptions of doorbells and telephones, from committee meetings and concerns of coworkers and neighbors, they were able to focus completely on one another. Though trying to boost his own spirits, Ken made sure he said and did things to please Donna. And she, recognizing the problems that had torpedoed his spirits, was determined the week would refresh and renew him.

The mutual selflessness wasn't something new, merely put on for a special week. From the start, their marriage had been a good one. They couldn't imagine life without one another.

At midafternoon of the day before their departure, however, realization of the imminent end of their glorious holiday brought a touch of melancholy. They'd been reading, or pretending to, for nearly an hour when Ken broke the silence, voicing what had been on both their minds.

"Donna, why does this week have to end?"

He pulled his hands from the pages he'd been reading, slipped an arm around her shoulders, and eased her head gently to his chest. The book tumbled from his lap, bounced off the edge of the couch, and fell to the floor. As she pondered whether she really needed to respond to the question, he bent and brushed his lips across the back of her neck. If an answer was necessary, she decided, it could wait. She twisted slowly in his arms, turning her body and lifting her head until their lips met.

They'd kissed thousands of times, and she still marvelled that his lips could evoke such feelings of tenderness, devotion, ecstasy. Slowly their heads parted. Neither spoke. Silently, however, Ken prayed.

Dear God, thank you for this wonderful woman. She is more than I deserve. She comforts me. She cares for me. She thrills me.

Prayer and lovemaking seemed not to be incongruous. He was amazed only that he didn't remember having combined them before. He and Donna always considered the physical expression of their love to be a gift from God—and a gift they gave one another. They were grateful it was theirs alone, that neither had ever shared it with any other.

The sensation of Donna's body pressing closer to his, shifting slightly, fanned smoldering desire. She lifted her head, ran her fingers through his hair, pressed her lips again to his. Their intimacy was unhurried, purposely. They relished the slowly unfolding passion, then basked in an amorous afterglow.

Ken sat on the floor, his back against the couch. Donna, lying with her head against his chest, studied the tousled hair and face she'd first seen in the doorway of room 201 at Brownsville High School. Flecks of gray were now visible amid the dark strands at his temples. Wrinkles at the corners of his eyes were more pronounced. But the matured Ken MacKenzie was still a handsome man.

She reached up and stroked the back of his head. The movement wiped out a dreamy, distant look in his eyes. He gazed down into hers. They were dark, almost black, expressive. He'd always been able to read her feelings in them.

As a child she'd sometimes used them to convey displeasure or defiance, but Ken had known them to speak mostly of love. They had a smoldering warmth that buoyed his spirits and, when necessary, melted any reticence. Now they reassured him of her affection and her concern. And to be sure he understood, she responded to the question he'd asked an hour earlier.

"Our week is ending, Ken. But our happiness isn't. I'm sorry Kirchener's attitude has made your job such a chore. Things will get better. I know they will."

"I'd never make it without you, Donna." He pulled her closer and held her tightly. But, head pressed against his chest, she couldn't see the evidence of discouragement reappear on his face.

Yes, without Donna the past few months would have been much more difficult. His prayer of gratitude had been sincere. Nevertheless, even Donna's love couldn't completely dispel his gloom. Her words of encouragement, the magic of her eyes, even the afternoon's ecstatic reassurance of their love had been unable to do that.

He missed teaching. He missed Thursdays at Honeoye Creek and the Pinery. He missed Scotty. He wasn't looking forward to returning to his office on Monday morning, and he was far from enthused about the scheduled arrival of the outside PR consultants a week later.

He knew many had far greater problems. But that didn't seem to help. Despite the pleasure of the week and the passion of the afternoon, he was still dejected.

CHAPTER 6

Peace at Last

APRIL 17, 1975

PHNOM PENH

Things could only get better. At least that's what Kim Ang thought as she stirred restlessly on the sleeping mat in a hallway at her grandparents' house. Seventeen persons spent last night in the tiny dwelling, a building which had seemed crowded with only its five customary inhabitants: grandfather Sieng Sy, grandmother Chen Yi, and Kim Ang's three unmarried uncles, Hong, Tong and Teng.

Yesterday, as the sounds of war grew louder and rumors of the impending fall of the city to the communists swept through the streets, Sieng Sy and Chen Yi's married children and their families congregated here where Kim Ang's mother, Sieng Chhun Sang, had spent her childhood. Now 33, Chhun Sang was the oldest of the six children of Sieng Sy and Chen Yi, the only grandparents Kim Ang had ever known. Her father's parents died before he fled from China, several years before she was born.

Nearly two years ago, when the Khmer Rouge began showering Phnom Penh with artillery shells and rockets, Sieng Sy and his children agreed that if the situation became critical they would gather here to face the uncertainties of the future together. Since then they had become accustomed to the blasts which rocked the city at all hours of the day and night. They knew death could come at any moment—even before the sound of incoming rockets and shells would give a warning.

By yesterday there was no doubt the situation had become critical. The time had come to assemble at the family home. Uncle

Phim Kim Eng—the husband of Chhun Sang's sister, Sieng Lang, and a lieutenant in the Cambodian Army—had sent word the Khmer Rouge were advancing on the city from all sides.

Kim Ang arrived at her grandparents' home shortly after noon with her parents, brothers, and sisters. Two hours later they greeted uncle Sieng Nheng and his wife, Thay Chhun Phing, who was pregnant with their second child.

"You look so weary," Grandfather Sieng gasped as his son entered the house. "I think you're working too hard."

"I've seen too much blood," Nheng sighed. "I'm a doctor, and the sight of broken bodies shouldn't upset me. But there are too many—and a lot of them are children."

A steady flow of wounded had kept him at Prea Ket Mealea Hospital through the night. Exhausted, he left at noon only to drive Chhun Phing and their two-year-old son, Dao Siv, to his parents' home. Before retracing his steps to the black Citroen, left idling at the gate, he paused in the doorway to be sure Chhun Phing and Dao Siv were comfortably settled. Then he sped off again toward the hospital. Earlier there had been far more victims of rocket and artillery shells than beds to accommodate them. Now there would be more.

Chhun Phing, usually outgoing and talkative, said little. Her mind was elsewhere as she spread a mat on the hallway floor and nestled Dao Siv into a corner for a nap.

Hours later a pall of smoke hung over the city, obscuring the setting sun, as Kim Ang sat in the doorway studying the procession beyond the gate. Most were refugees searching for food and shelter. One figure emerged from the crowd and grew larger. As it stumbled closer, Kim Ang realized it actually was three persons—a woman carrying a child while another, slightly larger, clung tightly to her sampot. When they neared the gate, Kim Ang recognized them, jumped up, and ran inside to tell the others Aunt Lang was coming.

Sieng Lang, the only sister of Kim Ang's mother, was a favorite of her thirteen-year-old niece. Sensing Kim Ang's unfulfilled need for love, Lang lavished special attention and affection upon her, sometimes as much as she gave her own two-year-old son, Meng Ty, and daughter Chhun Phon, who was four.

Uncle Kim Eng wasn't with them. In the current crisis a leave was out of the question. Kim Ang helped her aunt settle the children onto unfamiliar beds before spreading out her own mat in the hallway.

For what seemed like hours she listened to the thump of distant explosions and pondered what the dawn might bring. Inside the house the silence was eerie. The others apparently were sleeping. Outside, however, the continuous thunder of rockets and artillery shells, mostly in the distance but some nearby, mingled with the din of cars, squeaking bullock carts, and people shuffling along the street. Finally weariness prevailed, and slumber wiped away her worries.

Now, with the light of a new day filtering in through the window above her, Kim Ang rolled over and slowly opened her eyes. As the fog of sleep slipped away, she realized the explosions had stopped. She jumped up and peered out the window. People were in the streets, but they didn't seem afraid.

"Perhaps peace has finally come," she told herself.

Last night she had listened as her father and uncles considered what was happening to their country.

"I don't like communists," her father had said. "Cambodian communists, Vietnamese communists, Chinese communists—they are all the same!"

"But the officials of our government are corrupt," Uncle Hong argued. "The communists can't be any worse. At least, if they win the war tomorrow, the shooting will stop. If it doesn't, we'll all be killed anyway."

None was optimistic, but all knew the five years of fighting between the Khmer Rouge and soldiers of the Lon Nol government was nearly over. Lon Nol had fled from the country on the first of April. The Americans had pulled out four days ago. The city was surrounded by the Khmer Rouge. There could be no more fighting.

What will it be like if there is peace? Kim Ang wondered. *Surely, it will be wonderful. We won't have to be afraid of getting killed. Everybody will have enough to eat. The refugees can go home, and the city will not be so crowded. We can all go back to our own houses. The suffering will end.*

The floor creaked behind her and she turned to see Lang.

"Aunt Lang, the guns have stopped shooting. Is there peace now?"

The woman came to the window, put her arm around her niece, and looked down at the street below.

"I don't know, but I surely hope so."

Lang leaned closer to the glass, staring down the street at an approaching man who stayed in the shadows of the buildings.

"There is Uncle Kim Eng!" she gasped, running to the stairway. She dashed to the door and threw it open. By the time her soldier husband slipped through the gate and walked briskly to the house, the entire family was at the doorway.

"What has happened?" Grandfather Sieng asked.

"The Khmer Rouge are in the city. The government can't survive," the officer stammered, hardly able to catch his breath. "Now please excuse me. I have to get out of this uniform. The Khmer Rouge are coming. Lang, do you have my other clothes?"

She took his hand and they quickly ascended the stairs.

The others, edging cautiously through the door, looked up the street in the direction of a commotion a block away. A military truck, white flag flying from its antenna and carrying men dressed in black, was moving closer. People were running around it and shouting. The cries grew louder:

"The war is over! We are free! Peace at last!"

A man ran down the street, perhaps a hundred meters ahead of the soldiers, shouting. As he came near, Kim Ang could make out the words:

"Put up a white banner. Show the communists you want peace!"

A large white sheet had already been unfurled from a window farther up the block, and soon similar pieces of fabric fluttered from balconies and peaks of many nearby buildings. People were hanging out whatever they could find that was white: shirts, shawls, towels, sheets.

Now the truck was close enough for Kim Ang to hear as the driver raced the engine, depressing the accelerator with his right foot while riding the clutch with the left. She stared at the soldiers on the truck and trudging along behind it. They wore black pants and black jackets, with dirty checkered kramas wrapped around their

Mao caps or covering their shoulders. On their feet were Ho Chi Minh sandals made of rubber tires.

As they moved nearer, Kim Ang was astounded. Were these really the Khmer Rouge? They were just kids actually, most hardly older than she. The driver had a hard time seeing over the dashboard of the truck, and most of those walking behind seemed dwarfed by their weapons. Curiously, they were unimpressed by the cheering crowds. Ignoring the adulation, they looked straight ahead. Those walking weren't in step or in neat lines, and their movements and expressions reflected a sinister determination. They didn't speak. They didn't smile.

Kim Ang glanced at her uncles, standing between her and the procession of Khmer Rouge. They didn't seem bothered by the stern appearance of the child warriors. Uncle Tong, in fact, was grinning, apparently amused by the sight of soldiers hardly taller than their guns. But Kim Ang began to worry again. She didn't like the contemptuous looks of the gunmen in the street. If this was peace, maybe it wouldn't be so wonderful after all.

Aunt Lang, who had stayed inside with her husband, appeared in the doorway and beckoned Kim Ang.

"Don't shout or move quickly," Lang told her, "but go quietly to the others and tell them to come inside—a few at a time, not all at once so they attract attention."

When all were in the house, Uncle Kim Eng explained why he'd asked his wife to summon the family.

"Some of you may think peace has finally come and now everything is going to be better," the Khmer Army veteran began. "But officers in our intelligence section have interrogated refugees from villages taken over by the Khmer Rouge. I know how those people were treated. The communist soldiers are brutal. They demand their orders be obeyed instantly. Refusal means death. It won't be different here. There's rejoicing in the streets now. But trouble is coming. It's best, for now at least, to stay in the house. Let the others run on the streets and welcome the Khmer Rouge.

"And one other thing. Please don't give any hint that I've been a FANK officer. We don't know what the Khmer Rouge will do to government soldiers. Until we do, it won't be wise for me to admit my occupation."

Tong, the family jokester and a perennial optimist, tried to relieve the tension that followed his brother-in-law's admonitions.

"Surely, we don't have to be afraid of those little upstarts. They can hardly carry a gun, let alone aim one."

"The Khmer Rouge overran the country," Kim Eng reminded him. "They have the guns now. Why do you think so many people ran away from them? Where do you think the thousands of refugees in Phnom Penh came from?"

Embarrassed by the reprimand, Tong steered the conversation to an analysis of what might happen during the next few hours and days.

The answer wasn't long in coming. From the street, above the din of the crowd, came the sound of shooting and of excited voices shouting through hand-held loudspeakers. Suddenly, two grimy, dust-covered soldiers with grenades hanging from their belts, one carrying a speaker and the other waving a pistol, burst into the house.

"You must leave!" the one with the handgun shouted. "You have to get out of the city so we can purify it. There has been too much corruption here. You must go now. The Americans are going to bomb us very soon! You don't need to take anything with you. You will only be gone for two or three days. Go now!"

"If you have any weapons," the other yelled, "lay them in the street! You will be punished if you take any guns with you, or if they are found in your house. All weapons now belong to Angka Loeu. They will be collected by Angka."

As quickly as they had come they were gone. The door, standing wide open behind them, framed the spectacle of a miserable multitude stumbling slowly along the crowded street. So many people were crammed into the thoroughfare they could scarcely move.

Looking at one another in astonishment, the members of Sieng Sy's family blurted out questions that defied answers.

"Who is Angka?"

"What is happening?"

"Why would the Americans bomb us?"

"We've been living with explosions for a long time. Why go away now? And why do we need to go for only two or three days?"

"Where are we going?"

"What will happen if we don't go?"

As preposterous as the evacuation order was, thousands and thousands of Phnom Penh's citizens were obeying it. And despite the admonition of the Khmer Rouge that they need not take anything along, the people were struggling beneath burdens of rice, pots and pans, cackling chickens, blankets, prized possessions, clothing. Some were able to balance the loads on their heads, their shoulders, or their hips. Others had heaped everything onto bicycles and motorbikes or into carts and cars they pushed along. Moving faster than a walk was impossible, so those who had cars made no effort to start the engines. Better to save the fuel for later.

Several carried children or relatives too aged or ill to walk. Some children clung to their parents' clothes. Many were crying. All were terrified.

Even Kim Eng had been unable to offer a sensible answer to the questions of his relatives. The whole situation made no sense. His intelligence contacts had provided no clue the Khmer Rouge would try to do something as ridiculous as to empty an entire city of millions of people. He needed more information. It would be risky but he decided to go outside and see if he could learn more. Surely, among the thousands passing by would be someone he knew, someone who had seen or heard what was going on in other parts of the city.

Kim Eng stood just inside the doorway, peering into the mob that trudged past toward the outskirts of the city. For nearly an hour he watched the procession, his anxiety heightened by the occasional sound of gunfire. Finally, he found a familiar face in the crowd—Heng Vann, a sergeant in his unit. Kim Eng dashed to the middle of the road, grabbed his arm, and tugged him back to the house.

"Where are you going?" Kim Eng asked as they stepped inside the door.

"To my brother's house. Fortunately, it's the same direction the Khmer Rouge told us to go."

They continued down the hallway to an unoccupied room and closed the door. Kim Eng thought he might hear things that should, for now at least, be kept from the women and children.

"What's going on out there?" He pointed toward the street. "Where are all these people coming from?"

"I assume the Khmer Rouge have been here and ordered everyone to leave," Sergeant Heng responded. "They've said everybody has to get out of the city. But a lot of people are still in their houses, hoping the order will be rescinded. Some were told to leave tomorrow, some in a few hours. Most were ordered out right away. Obviously, there's some confusion, but everyone has been told to get out of the city."

"I've heard shooting. There certainly can't be any resistance to the Khmer Rouge any more. Who's doing the firing?"

"The Khmer Rouge," the sergeant replied, matter-of-factly. "Sometimes they're shooting in the air to move people along. Sometimes they're shooting people who don't obey fast enough. A few minutes ago I saw an old friend from my school days. He said he was passing a house when a communist soldier—just a kid, probably 14 years old or less—ordered everybody to keep moving. A young guy, maybe about 20, turned around and started back to his house. He called over his shoulder that he needed to get his sandals. He was about three meters from the door when the KR kid shot him in the back.

"And they're shooting us if they find out who we are. We have to be careful. An hour ago I passed a corpse lying at the side of the street. It was Sreap Meng Leng—you know, the corporal in our supply section. The KR caught him before he was able to get out of his uniform."

"I'm worried about my brother-in-law, Dr. Sieng Nheng," Kim Eng said, searching the sergeant's face for a sign of recognition. "Do you know him?"

"No. I know he's a doctor at Prea Ket Mealea Hospital, but I've never met him. I don't know what he looks like."

"I was hoping you could tell me if he's all right. But I know that's hardly possible in all this confusion."

"I do know something about Prea Ket Mealea. It's the first place the Khmer Rouge went. One of my neighbors is a nurse there. She was ordered out by the communists. So were the doctors, the few who were still there. Most left when they heard the Khmer Rouge were coming. When they got there, the KR ordered everybody out, the patients too—even the ones who couldn't walk. A few lucky ones had friends who pushed their beds while others held their IV bottles.

"My neighbor saw two patients in one bed. They were pushing it down the street with crutches, like fishermen punting a boat in the shallows of the Mekong.

"She told me one man was carrying his son, a boy of about eight. He'd been hit by shrapnel. Doctors had just amputated the child's leg, and he was still on the operating table when the Khmer Rouge came in. They wouldn't even let the doctors bandage the wound. The father carried the boy out into the street. Blood was all over him and the pavement. This nurse has seen much pain and suffering in her work. But she couldn't talk about these things without crying."

Kim Eng had hoped for better news. When Heng Vann left, he went back inside. But he didn't tell the others everything he'd learned. They'd already seen and heard enough to disturb them.

"That man was a sergeant in my unit," Kim Eng reported to the circle of relatives. "He's going to his brother's house. He says some people are staying in their houses, hoping the order to leave will be changed. I think we can stay here, at least tonight. But we should be ready to leave. We need to put the things we can carry into bundles.

"The sergeant's neighbor is a nurse at Prea Ket Mealea. She told him Nheng probably is on his way here." She hadn't said that, but he needed to hold out some hope. He wouldn't tell them now what happened at the hospital.

"Streets are crowded all over the city. It's not possible to drive on them. So Nheng will have to walk. It will take a long time. If we can stay here tonight, maybe Nheng will arrive by morning."

That was all Kim Eng thought they should hear. Peace, it seemed, had come—and gone, all in a matter of hours.

The Real Story
A Cause for Celebration

At Phnom Penh, the 17th day of April in 1975 dawned with a promise of peace. That, coupled with the traditional mid-April beginning of the Cambodian new year, assured this would truly be a day to remember. After five years of war, the Khmer Rouge were victorious, and Phnom Penh was eager to welcome the new leaders who would march into the city at any moment.

Word spread that the populace should demonstrate its desire for peace by flying white flags. Sheets, shirts, and towels quickly were hung from windows and balconies. White ribbons adorned arms, girls' hair, and bicycle handlebars.

At 7 a.m. the first of the communist soldiers appeared, waving cheerfully to exuberant welcomers lining the streets, then stopping to embrace them. But these, it was discovered, weren't really Khmer Rouge. They were Phnom Penh students who thought they would take control of the city and then hand it over to the guerrillas.

Within two hours the real Khmer Rouge arrived, and the exhilaration vanished. Most of the Cambodian communists were young, some only 13 or 14 years old. They were solemn, silent, dirty, mean-looking. Their uniforms were black pajama-like garments accented with checkered scarves, Mao caps, and Ho Chi Minh sandals made from rubber tires. Most carried Chinese AK-47 or American M-16 rifles. Some toted pistols, grenades, and rockets.

This day, they proclaimed, would indeed start a new year—the Year Zero. This would be a new beginning. Phnom Penh and Cambodia would never be the same.

Almost immediately came an incredulous order. The city must be evacuated. All of its 2.5 million inhabitants had to leave. There were to be no exceptions—even for the wounded and sick. As a matter of fact, they were the first to go.

Starting at Preah Ket Melea Hospital, the city's largest, the Khmer Rouge ordered everyone out. Hundreds walked, limped, and crawled through the exits. Beds of those unable to move by themselves were pushed into the streets. At other hospitals it was the same.

Then Phnom Penh's 2.5 million other residents were forced to join the miserable procession. Loudspeakers blared the astonishing order, and gun-waving soldiers enforced it, sometimes explaining that the Americans were going to bomb the city or that it was still corrupt and they had to empty it before cleaning it up.

For more details see:

John Barron and Anthony Paul, *Murder of a Gentle Land* (New York, Reader's Digest Press, 1977), chapter 1, "Peace Dawns"

Arnold R. Isaacs, Gordon Hardy, MacAlister Brown, *Pawns of War* (Boston, Boston Publishing Company, 1987), pages 111-112

Haing Ngor with Roger Warner, *A Cambodian Odyssey* (New York, Macmillan Publishing Company, 1987), chapter 6, "The Fall," and chapter 7, "The Wheel of History"

Russell R. Ross, ed., *Cambodia: A Country Study*, Area Handbook Series (Washington, D. C., United States Government as represented by the Secretary of the Army, 1990), pages 48-51

William Shawcross, *Sideshow: Kissinger, Nixon, and the Destruction of Cambodia* (New York, Simon and Schuster, 1979), chapter 24, "The Beginning"

Pin Yathay with John Man, *Stay Alive, My Son* (New York, The Free Press, a division of Macmillan, Inc., 1987), chapter 2, "Evacuation"

CHAPTER 7

No More Tears

APRIL 19, 1975

PHNOM PENH

Kim Ang was sleeping, though not soundly, when Uncle Nheng arrived at Grandfather Sieng's house before sunrise yesterday, just as Uncle Kim Eng had said he would. The sound of voices downstairs awoke her, and she moved to the top of the steps to listen in the darkness.

Her uncles had been taking turns keeping watch through the night, and Hong was waiting in the murkiness of the unlit house when the doctor approached the doorway. Aunt Chhun Phing, unable to sleep, spent the entire night at the window overlooking the front gate. When the dim silhouette of her husband appeared on the path, she dashed past Hong to the door and threw her arms around him.

At first startled, then overcome with joy at finding his wife safe, Nheng was unable to speak. His arms pressed her swollen body against his. She sobbed uncontrollably, managing only to gasp her feelings as they embraced:

"I'm so glad you're here. I love you so much."

After several minutes Nheng turned her slightly, putting a hand on her belly and feeling the tiny arms and legs moving beneath his palm.

"Is our little one all right?"

"I think so. But I'm so afraid. Our world is falling apart. What's going to happen to this child?"

Nheng didn't know what to say. Should he protect her with lies? Or should she know what had been happening?

Hong interrupted before his brother could answer.

"If you know anything, you must tell us. What happened at the hospital? What's it like on the streets out there? We've been ordered to leave. Where can we go? We need to make some decisions. We need information."

Nheng, still holding Chhun Phing's hand, led her into the front room. Hong followed.

Kim Eng had heard the voices below. He stepped around Kim Ang at the top of the stairs and descended to join his in-laws.

"I know a little about what happened at the hospital," he said, "but I haven't told the others. I didn't want to alarm them before it was necessary. But Hong is right. Now we all need to know what's going on. We need to be able to make the best decisions."

Nheng still wasn't sure Chhun Phing should hear more that would upset her. But he knew that soon, perhaps any moment, she might witness the insanity of the Khmer Rouge herself. Perhaps it's better she hear about it before she experiences it, he decided.

"Well, the situation isn't good," Nheng began. "I won't go into all the details. But what I saw at the hospital and on the streets coming here leaves no doubt the Khmer Rouge aren't our saviors. They're ferocious maniacs.

"The things they're doing make no sense. They tell everyone to get out of the city for two or three days because the Americans are going to drop bombs. Why would the Americans bomb us now when the war is over? And why would they do it for just two or three days? Then they say they need to purify the city. What does that mean? They keep talking about Angka. Who, or what, is that?"

He didn't expect answers, and he didn't pause for them.

"At the hospital they barged in and ordered everybody out. Instantly. Everybody. Doctors, nurses, patients—even the ones who couldn't walk. We had patients everywhere—in the hallways, storage rooms. I was bending over a wounded man in the corridor when a KR kid grabbed my arm and pulled me away. He screamed that I had to get out. 'Angka will take care of that now,' he yelled. He had a pistol in my face. I had no choice. I'd die if I didn't go."

Chhun Phing winced, and her expression revealed concern and fear, but she seemed to be all right.

"When I left the hospital, I knew driving with all the people in the streets would be impossible. But I thought at night, when the crowds thinned, maybe I could. As I stood there wondering what to do, a KR soldier came up, pointed his rifle at me, and demanded that I *lend* the car to Angka Loeu. I've learned not to argue with men who have guns. He drove off, blowing the horn and scattering people in all directions. And I started out walking."

He looked at Chhun Phing again.

"On the way I saw many corpses lying in the streets. No, the Khmer Rouge aren't our friends. We need to be very careful. And for me, it's better if nobody knows I'm a doctor."

Kim Eng nodded in agreement. "For me, too. They're killing officers of the Army of the Republic."

"What can we do? Where can we go?" Chhun Phing pleaded.

There weren't any easy answers. The darkness, their weariness, the complexities of the situation closed in on them.

"It will soon be dawn," Hong reminded them. "We'll need all the rest we can get. Who knows what the morning will bring? We'll talk to the others then. Now let's try to rest."

None would be able to sleep. But all knew they needed to conserve their strength.

Kim Ang, hearing her uncles and aunt ascending the stairs, went back to her mat. Lying in the darkness, she pondered what the dawn might bring. Though she had never really been afraid of the dark, she thought it strange to be more apprehensive about the approaching light than the present blackness.

At daybreak Chhun Phing's questions were still unanswered, and they now confronted all of Sieng Sy's extended family. Grandfather called the adults into the front room.

"Kim Ang, you are to supervise the children upstairs," he told her.

She had hoped she'd be able to listen to the grownups' deliberations. Uncle Teng was only a year older than she, and he was there. However, she knew she was the logical choice for looking after the seven younger children. She was a girl and the oldest grandchild.

She'd hardly gotten them to the second floor when she heard the front door burst open. Strange voices began shouting. Khmer Rouge!

She looked down the stairs and saw four of them. Grandfather was in the doorway of the front room at the far end of the hall.

"You have to go now," one of the soldiers ordered. "The American planes are coming. And we have to clean up the city. Don't bother to take anything with you. You must go now! Leave immediately or we will shoot all of you!"

From a window of the room directly above the front entrance, Kim Ang saw the four soldiers run into the street, then turn up the path to the next house. More Khmer Rouge were in the streets, yelling orders to keep moving, waving their guns in the air, and occasionally firing shots above the crowd.

Her parents and her uncles and aunts now crowded into the hallway between the front room and the entranceway. Grandfather stood closest to the door.

"We must obey now," he said. "We will leave, but we will take the things we have packed. Get the children and your bundles. And hurry. We must stay together!"

A half hour later the nineteen family members went out the gate and into the street. Kim Ang glanced back over her shoulder at the old house where she had spent many happy childhood hours. She wondered if she'd ever see it again.

Though the sun was still low in the sky, the heat was already oppressive. And the air was filled with dust kicked up by the thousands who trudged along. April, near the end of the dry season, is the hottest month of the year in Cambodia. Kim Ang immediately sensed the desperation of the multitude that swarmed about her, moving steadily, slowly, sullenly toward the outskirts of the city. The typical Khmer joviality had vanished.

She hadn't gone a block before she understood why. A squad of communist soldiers came out of an alley and forced its way through the crowd. In their path were a father and mother and their three children who became separated, the parents on one side of the soldiers and the children on the other. When the father shouted at the Khmer Rouge and tried to break through to the children, the leader of the squad pulled out his pistol and shot both the parents. Soldiers standing nearest the bodies pushed the helpless children back into the tide of humanity that continued to flow along the street.

"Do not cry," one of them called out to the panic-stricken children. "Angka does not allow crying. Angka will be your father now."

Kim Ang was trembling.

How could anyone do something like that? she thought. *No wonder the people are so afraid and just keep moving along, blindly following the orders of the Khmer Rouge, walking on and on without even knowing where they're going.*

The three orphans were swallowed up in the slowly moving mass. Kim Ang edged nearer the cluster of her relatives. She certainly didn't want to become separated now. Though she had never minded being by herself, she dreaded the possibility of being all alone among these thousands of somber strangers, with the savage soldiers pointing guns and giving orders from Angka.

On the street today no one was waving flags or shouting greetings to the Khmer Rouge. Those who two days ago were overjoyed at the prospect of peace, now plodded hopelessly along the dusty street with all the rest, heads down, hoping not to offend or attract attention of the dirty, black-clad youngsters with the guns.

"We're not free people anymore," Kim Ang mumbled to herself. "We can't even decide where we're going. Maybe we can never go home again. We're just refugees."

The words, not really intended for anyone to hear, were lost amid other mutterings and shuffling feet. But the thought stayed with her: *I'm just a refugee.*

Then a new, louder, sound reverberated above the street. Loudspeakers were blaring monotonous messages, broadcasts of the government radio station taken over by the Khmer Rouge.

"Long live Cambodia and the revolution!" said a male voice.

"Long live our peaceful, independent, democratic country!" shrieked a woman.

The harangue continued, the voices alternating:

"Our people have won a great victory, freeing the beautiful city of Phnom Penh and our wonderful Cambodia!

"We must maintain the greatest vigilance to keep our nation and our people always free!

"Now there are no rich people or poor people. Everybody is the same. We will all go to work in the countryside and we will build an even greater Cambodia. We will defeat our enemies with an army of workers, armed with tools to build canals and dams and dikes. We must all sacrifice for Angka to make our country more powerful!"

Kim Ang tried to ignore the diatribe but couldn't.

"What was that he said?" She nudged Aunt Chhun Phing who was walking at her side.

"I didn't understand," her aunt responded.

"The man said something about going to work in the country, about building canals. Are we going to have to work in the country?"

"No, I don't think so. That's hardly possible. City people don't know anything about work in the country. We're just going out of the city for a few days—in case the Americans drop bombs, and so the Khmer Rouge can clean things up. I don't think …"

Chhun Phing's voice trailed off and she slumped to the ground. Nheng, who had been carrying Dao Siv, quickly handed the infant to Kim Ang and bent over his wife. The relatives huddled around them, unwilling to move on and break up the family group.

"She may be going into labor prematurely," Nheng called out to those around him. He fumbled in his backpack and pulled out a stethoscope. Chhun Phing regained consciousness as soon as the instrument touched her abdomen.

"I'm all right," she said. "Just became dizzy for a minute. I'm all right now."

Nheng eased her slowly to her feet. They couldn't stand here long. They would attract attention of the Khmer Rouge. He shoved the stethoscope back into the pack and took Dao Siv from Kim Ang.

But it was too late. A scowling young soldier charged into the circle.

"What did you put in the bag?" he snarled at Nheng.

"Nothing, really. Just a thing I found on the street. I don't know what it is."

"You lie. You are a doctor. I saw one of those things in the hospital, around a doctor's neck."

"No, comrade. I am not a doctor. I am only a taxicab driver," Nheng pleaded. "I found the thing on the street."

"Do not tell me lies. You must come with me. Angka wants to talk to you."

He pushed Nheng, still holding Dao Siv, out of the circle with the barrel of his rifle.

"You. You, too." He motioned to Chhun Phing. "Angka wishes to meet you."

"Please, comrade," Grandfather Sieng interrupted. "He is my son …"

"Do not beg," the boy with the gun growled. "Be quiet! And move on! Else I will kill all of you right now!"

Kim Ang was devastated. What would they do to her aunt and uncle and her little cousin? They disappeared up an alley with the Khmer Rouge pointing guns at their backs.

Neither she nor the others could do anything to help. They couldn't even cry. It was forbidden by Angka.

CHAPTER 8

God's In His Heaven

JUNE 7, 1975
MENDON

"Ken, your toast is getting cold."

Donna had neglected him for a moment as she followed the antics of three squirrels, zig-zagging wildly through groundcover in a woodsy corner of the yard just beyond the dinette windows.

She loved this tiny room with its expanse of glass on three sides and came here often to read or sew, sometimes to write letters or just sit and think.

From her chair at the table, she enjoyed the view of two pleasant, contrasting landscapes. At a corner of the yard to the left were native trees and shrubs in a setting similar to those of Ken's favorite countryside haunts, places he enjoyed less frequently now since moving from the classroom to the public relations office at the college. A green carpet of periwinkle flowed around tree trunks. Here and there wildflowers poked up and swayed in the gentle morning breeze. Behind them a six-foot board fence, weathered to silvery gray, formed a solid backdrop which blotted out city sights beyond the MacKenzies' property line.

Through the panes to her right, behind Ken's chair, was a more formal and showy area, the rear approach to the house with expanses of brick paving and multicolored annuals in raised beds and containers. Between it and the driveway, a short stretch of picket fence with an inviting wooden gate, both painted a gleaming white, extended back to the garage.

The third wall of windows, behind Donna, overlooked a neatly trimmed lawn and, beyond a low fence of stacked split rails, the large garden which provided berries and vegetables for the kitchen as well as an escape from workaday concerns.

With Donna's focus on the frolicking squirrels, Ken's mind wandered. Turning back to him, she caught the dreamy look in his eyes.

"I know you've got a lot on your mind today, Ken."

With commencement activities at the college scheduled to begin in a few hours, this would be one of his busiest days.

"But what are you thinking? A penny for your thoughts," she prodded.

"The year's at the spring," he responded, slowly. "And day's at the morn; morning's at seven…"

"Oh, come on. What's all that?" She thought he was teasing.

"You don't recognize it?" Then he continued, "The hillsides dew-pearled; the lark's on the wing; the snail's on the thorn: God's in his heaven—all's right with the world."

"Oh sure, Browning isn't it?"

"Right. From *Pippa Passes*. You remember the story?"

She thought for a moment. "No, not really. But don't tell me. I'm going to find it in the bookcase this morning. I'll read it before I go over to the campus for the ceremony. Those lines are beautiful—and really appropriate now. I'm glad all's right with your world again."

The seven weeks since their Turkey Run getaway had brought a surprising turnaround in Ken's situation—and his disposition. He'd been apprehensive, to say the least, of meeting the representatives of Bradley & Noland, the Indianapolis public relations firm Kirchener was bringing in. The session had been scheduled for 10 a.m. on a Wednesday, a week and a half after the return from Turkey Run.

"I'd rather have a couple teeth pulled than go to work this morning," he had muttered in the doorway that day.

Donna pressed her lips to his with more passion than customary for a routine farewell, held the kiss a little longer than usual, and caressed his cheek with her fingers.

"It's all going to be OK, Ken," she whispered. "Trust me."

But he didn't. Every step of his three-block walk to the campus he theorized possible criticisms he expected from Kirchener and the new consultants, then formulated the responses he'd make.

Two hours later, ready for battle, he walked toward the office where, a year and a half earlier, President Scott had changed the course of his life. He could still see Scotty sitting there, skillfully maneuvering him out of Old Main and into the college's administration building.

If only I'd found a way to say no. Or if Scotty hadn't died. The words were just thoughts, but Ken wondered for a moment if he'd actually said them and quickly turned to look back and see if anyone might have overheard.

As he stepped into the small office between the hallway and the president's quarters, Mary Swenson greeted him.

"Right on time, Ken. Dr. Kirchener's expecting you."

Mary had been President Scott's secretary for twelve years. Ken had never known anyone to say an unkind word about her. Kirchener, however, felt she lacked assertiveness and would have replaced her with someone who smiled less and threatened more, but he knew he'd be in trouble with some members of the Board if he did. Several trustees regarded Mary as a personal friend. As she pushed the buzzer to announce his arrival, Ken heard voices in the next room and realized the Indianapolis consultants were already there.

The door opened and Kirchener waved Ken in. With him were two men who stood to be introduced. The taller, wearing a gray pinstripe business suit, seemed about 10 years older than Ken and had the fit-and-trim build of a serious jogger. The other appeared to be just a few years out of college, was a tad overweight, and wore a navy blazer with tan trousers that could have used a pressing.

"Dr. MacKenzie, I'd like you to meet Joseph Waterford and Scott Delaney from Bradley and Noland. Joe is a vice president of the firm, and Scott will be our principal contact person."

Waterford was the jogger type, Ken noted, and Delaney the one with the baggy pants.

"I hope I'll have frequent contact with you, too," Waterford responded, extending his right hand. His smile seemed genuine.

Ken felt a pang of guilt for having prejudged him. Waterford certainly didn't seem to match the threatening-outsider image Ken's mind had concocted.

"I've seen some of the things you've done here, Dr. MacKenzie, and I'm impressed. I know our firm can help Mendon, but it's apparent the college's public relations program is already in good hands."

Astonished by the unexpected compliment, Ken managed a "Thank you" and an "I'm pleased to meet you," then glanced toward Kirchener whose scowl evidenced displeasure with Waterford's comments.

"Hi, I'm really glad to have an opportunity to work with you," Delaney chimed in. "I've been looking over the new admissions viewbook you produced, Dr. MacKenzie. I really like your approach."

Ken knew Kirchener was even more irritated by the second compliment, though he said nothing. Just a few weeks earlier he'd called Ken on the carpet, along with Admissions Director Steve Fowler, telling them the publication was the worst of its kind he'd ever seen.

"Kids won't respond to that saccharine stuff," he had thundered. "From now on, I want to see the layout and copy for every piece of admissions literature before it goes to a printer."

Ken had proposed the viewbook concept to Fowler at the start of the academic year. After an enthusiastic response, he gave the project top priority for several months. His idea was to use quotes from Mendon undergraduates in the text for the publication and to include those same students in the photographs illustrating college programs and activities.

Fowler identified twelve photogenic students who could express themselves well. Ken interviewed each, eliciting their thoughts about why prospective students should consider Mendon, why they themselves came to the college, what they liked about Mendon's programs and professors. Then he followed the twelve with a camera for several weeks, accumulating scores of photos to illustrate various aspects of campus life.

Graphic designers and printers who worked with him in the

final stages of the project were enthusiastic about the concept and content. And, after the presses had cranked out the finished product, so were all on the campus—except Kirchener.

"The quotes and pictures of those students certainly made your text credible," Delaney continued. "It should be a great sales piece. I wish I'd thought of the idea."

That was about as much as Kirchener could take. "Well, gentlemen, we'd better get down to business and discuss what needs to happen to fix Mendon's public relations program."

"As I said a few moments ago," Waterford responded. "Mendon's PR doesn't really need fixing. Perhaps fine tuning would be a better appellation for what Bradley and Noland might help you bring about."

Ken realized Waterford's contradiction of Kirchener was an unusual and bold stance for the consultant to take at such an early stage of relationship with a client. He felt assured he'd be able to count on the new acquaintance as a square shooter, a man who spoke his convictions even if doing so might not be best for business.

During the two-hour session that followed, the consultants had even more plaudits for Ken. Kirchener responded to each with silence or a "Well, but ..." Ken decided he could endure him, though, especially with the renewed self-assurance he'd picked up from Waterford and Delaney.

Waterford, in outlining what Bradley and Noland could do for Mendon, agreed with Ken that, even with intensive promotional effort, the college's name wasn't likely to become widely known beyond Indiana and Illinois—unless significant innovative academic programs could be implemented.

"But with our firm's national media contacts," he added, "we should be able to secure some recognition of Mendon in publications and newscasts that have large national audiences. I'd suggest that, as a first step in fine tuning your PR program, we undertake an extensive survey of the college's publics: alumni, students, their parents, citizens of the community, Methodist clergy, church leaders. PR is a two-way business. We have to be aware of what your publics know and think about you if we're going to relate to them properly."

Ken agreed. When he left Kirchener's office, he was confident he'd be able to work with these men.

That afternoon, reflecting on the unexpected course the conference in Kirchener's office had taken, Ken recalled Donna's farewell. Anxious then to tell her what happened, he misdialed, caught the mistake before the ring, and tried again.

"Hello."

He loved her melodious voice.

"How did you know?" was all he said.

"Ken? How did I know what?"

"That everything was going to be OK. Remember saying that? Or did our goodbye kiss erase everything from your mind?"

"Well, yes. But it's coming back to me now. I think I also said, 'Trust me.' Did you?"

"Actually, no," he confessed. "But everything's OK." And then he gave her the details of his morning meeting.

That had been more than five weeks ago, but his renewed confidence hadn't diminished. He was feeling as good about himself as when he'd been teaching. It had been a great spring, and now today's commencement was an appropriate culmination. He'd have preferred to be a participant in the program, as he'd been while teaching, rather than a recorder of events with camera and notepad. But it still was a great day.

Donna wouldn't think of missing a Mendon graduation. She loved the ceremony's pageantry, the camaraderie of graduates, the pride of parents, the range of feelings. Her spine tingled when grads and professors marched into the auditorium while the college band played *Pomp and Circumstance.* Her eyes became misty when she'd hug a departing student who'd been particularly close to Ken and herself.

This afternoon, shadows were lengthening by the time Ken put away his notes and cameras at the office and met Donna on the administration building steps. The crowd had vanished, and the campus was quiet as they walked slowly, hand in hand, toward home.

"All is right with the world, Ken." Donna squeezed his hand and looked up at his face, grateful it no longer was clouded by doubt and despair.

"And I know the story of *Pippa Passes* now. I found it on the shelf in your den. It's marvelous how many lives she changed in one day, just singing as she passed by. Imagine, working in that terrible silk mill for 364 days every year, only getting New Year's Day off. Aren't you glad we're living at a time when people don't make little girls work like that—and in such terrible places?"

"Yes, I'm glad." He smiled down at her. "If little girls were forced to work long hours in dangerous, dirty places for hardly any pay, you'd get all uptight about it. And I wouldn't get any peace."

He was kidding—sort of. Donna did have a propensity for rising to the causes of the disadvantaged and mistreated. Ken was outspoken only when it was necessary to protect himself, or Donna. But she wasn't hesitant about coming to the defense of anyone, if she thought she could help.

Vindicating the victimized wasn't on her mind today, however. This perfect day was the culmination of a beautiful season, not only a springtime of new life in the world that surrounded Ken and herself but a time of wondrous renewal for their spirits as well. She was determined the evening would be as enchanting as the day had been delightful. She had planned it carefully—dinner by candlelight with Ken's favorite, Chateaubriand, while London Symphony recordings softly serenaded them with love themes by Mascagni, Puccini, and Elgar.

It was indeed an unforgettable day, and evening. There could be no doubt: God was in His heaven and everything was all right.

CHAPTER 9

Another Day In Hell

JUNE 8, 1975

ANCHHANG ROUNG, CAMBODIA

Food and sleep. They were constantly on Kim Ang's mind. She couldn't get enough of either. And she couldn't think of anything else—except the killings. Would the soldiers come and take her away, like they had so many others who were never seen again? That possibility obsessed her.

In this jungle clearing where the eyes of Khmer Rouge taskmasters never closed, fear followed her like a shadow—always silent, always present. She was afraid she would do something, say something, to displease Angka.

Just a few days ago, when she and her family arrived at this new village, she hoped the chaos in their lives might be ending. Nothing could be worse, she thought, than the weeks of wandering after the evacuation of Phnom Penh. As bad as that time had been, however, it was better than this.

During the wearying weeks of walking after leaving her grandparents' home, each of the adults and older children had struggled with bundles and suitcases. Inside were prized family possessions and things considered essential for the few days they expected to be away from the city. Though not heavy, Kim Ang's load had been awkward to carry. Besides a large electric fan Grandmother had insisted on taking along, she had the account book for her father's business and her own clothing, rolled up and tied with rope.

What good will this fan do outside the city where there probably isn't any electricity? she thought.

But the wishes of her elders were never to be questioned.

Another burden—concern about what the Khmer Rouge may have done to Nheng, Chhun Phing, and little Dao Siv—weighed heavily on the remaining sixteen as they continued their trek. Exhausted by the physical exertion needed to carry themselves and their loads, nauseated and terrified by the sight of bodies lying along the roadside, confused by the lack of sense in all that was happening, they plodded on and on.

Once beyond the outskirts of the city, they wandered aimlessly, knowing they had to keep moving to avoid the wrath of the Khmer Rouge. But where were they supposed to go?

Finally, after several days, soldiers ordered the millions they forced from the cities to go to their native villages. Grandfather Sieng had relatives in a town near Kompong Cham, to the northeast, so he decided the family should go there. They followed Highway 5 northward to its junction with Highway 6, then walked along that route to the east. Slowed by the children and the tiring grandparents, the group often proceeded less than 10 kilometers a day. They had covered only half the distance to their destination when soldiers stopped them at a checkpoint.

"This road is closed," a black-clad youth with an AK-47 snarled.

"But my native village is that direction, near Kompong Cham," Grandfather Sieng told him, stretching the truth a bit. It wouldn't be wise to tell them he came from China. Many of the pure Khmer didn't like the ethnic Chinese, and he knew he would be high on the Khmer Rouge list of those to be eliminated.

"Too many people already went that way. The road is now closed. You cannot take that road. You must go someplace else."

"Where shall we go?" Grandfather was puzzled by the contradictory orders.

"You can go north toward Kompong Thom," the unconcerned soldier replied, "or you can go back toward Highway 5."

Since no one in the group was familiar with the area to the north, they decided to retrace their steps to Highway 5.

"This is crazy," Uncle Tong grumbled when far enough away so the Khmer Rouge at the checkpoint couldn't overhear. "They don't have any plan. They're just forcing people to keep moving. First, they don't know where we're supposed to go. Then we have to go to our native villages. But many of us don't have native villages to go to. Now, if we say we have a native village, they tell us we can't go there anyway."

As slowly as they had proceeded east, Kim Ang and her relatives trudged back westward along Highway 6. With the wet season beginning, they sought shelter at night in deserted pagodas or houses, whatever they could find. Sometimes they found nothing and could only huddle beneath a makeshift canopy, fashioned from sticks broken off nearby trees and a plastic sheet from Uncle Hong's bundle.

Each day the bag of rice carried by Kim Ang's father became less and less a burden. Finally it was empty. Sometimes they were able to buy small amounts of the grain from others who had pilfered it from unguarded warehouses. However, money was worthless and rice itself had become the basis of exchange. Grandfather had traded gold for some and was lucky to get it. Those who had rice usually refused to sell.

Hunger was increasing. People were beginning to eat leaves and bark from trees along the roadside. Inadequate nourishment began to exact a toll, compounded by the weariness of endless walking and the psychological impact of uncertainty and fear. During early days of the evacuation, most of the dead along the road were FANK soldiers. But here in the countryside, far from Phnom Penh, the rotting, maggoty flesh of some of the oldest and youngest of the wanderers now lay in roadside dust, covered only by tears of relatives and friends too weak and weary to bury them.

Moving slower and slower, Kim Ang wondered how long they could go on. Grandmother had to rest more often, and Grandfather developed a noticeable limp. When they again reached the junction of Highways 5 and 6 they found, as expected, that the route to the south toward Phnom Penh was closed. They turned northward and, nearly seven weeks after they'd left Phnom Penh, stumbled into the outskirts of Kompong Chhang. There they were halted at another checkpoint.

"You must go to Chhnok Trou," shouted a grimy Khmer Rouge,

pointing to a dirt road leading off to the west. Kim Ang felt too weary to take another step, and she knew most of the others were even more tired than she. But she turned and was about to leave when a shrill voice froze her.

"Stop! What is that book you are carrying?"

The black-clothed youth stared icily at Kim Ang from behind his automatic rifle.

"The records of my father's business. He sold rice in …"

She realized she was saying too much and stopped abruptly. The soldier, little older than Kim Ang, snatched the book from her hand and threw it into a fire at his side, almost upsetting a pot of rice intended for his platoon's next meal.

"Books are forbidden. Only imperialists have books. And we do not need anyone to sell rice. Now you will grow rice. Go to Chhnok Trou."

He raised his weapon with one hand and pointed again with the other. Kim Ang scurried to the far side of her family, putting as many of them as possible between herself and the belligerent boy with the gun.

When they reached Chhnok Trou, their reception was even more chilling. Blocking the path were five soldiers, two of them girls no older than Kim Ang. In the weeks since the Khmer Rouge had come to power she had seen many *mit neary*, but none as young as these filthy, gun-waving girls.

"We will take you to your new home," one of them growled. "Walk down that trail. We will follow. Move quickly."

Kim Ang was already terrified, but her fear increased with each step as they were forced deeper and deeper into the jungle. With the soldiers shouting curses and firing guns over their heads to hurry them along, they staggered on for three days before they were turned over to the chief of the village of Anchhang Roung.

As one of the Old People, who had submitted to communist rule while the war was still going on, he ranked lower than the Khmer Rouge but higher than the New People—those such as Kim Ang and her family who had been driven out of cities after the communist victory.

Though dressed in black like the Khmer Rouge, the chief was older than any of the soldiers Kim Ang had seen. She guessed he was in his forties, maybe fifties. His hostile demeanor foretold trouble.

"Don't even think of trying to escape," the village leader greeted them. "If you do, you will be shot immediately. You have three days to build your houses. Then you will work for Angka. I will give work orders later. Your first day for building a house will soon be over, so start now. You can find material in the cuttings at the edge of the forest."

In the distance Kim Ang could see some of the villagers. A few swung machetes, but most used crude axes made from sticks and stones to slash at trees and undergrowth as they tried to extend the clearing into the thick vegetation. Nearby were perhaps a hundred flimsy huts. She saw none she'd call a house. She knew theirs would be no better. Her father and her uncles had never built anything like that. Even if they had been skilled carpenters, there were no suitable materials here for building a decent house.

However, none of the family would complain. They'd learned during the evacuation and the exhausting journey to this place that complaining was sufficient cause for execution. None wanted an invitation to go into the jungle to meet Angka.

Their first rule for staying alive was: *Be silent.*

They saw and heard what happened when people complained or asked the wrong questions. They learned never to protest, always to ignore injustice and suffering.

While the family group was all together, before starting out to collect materials to begin building their huts, Grandfather Sieng gave them a second precept:

Never do anything first.

"My father once told me," he said quietly to his family, "only a fool tests the depth of the water with both feet. Before we do something or ask for a privilege, we must see what happens when others do so. We might miss opportunities. But we also will avoid fatal mistakes."

During their first days at Anchhang Roung they learned advice from their new neighbors, as well as one another, could prevent serious errors, perhaps even preserve their lives.

While carrying poles from the edge of the jungle to his building site, Uncle Tong saw another newcomer struggling to level one corner of his hut. It was obvious the man's previous employment had nothing to do with physical labor.

"That will be much easier, friend, if you use a lever," Tong said, trying to be helpful. "Here, put this short, thick piece of wood near the hut like this. Now lay this longer pole across the top and put one end under the floor. Then we just push down on the other end."

The man was amazed as they, almost effortlessly, raised the entire corner of the hut, then slid a rock under the structure to keep it at the right level.

"Thank you," he said, looking around to see if they had been watched. "Now let me give you some advice. I am grateful for your help, but others here may not be. It's best never to appear to have education or to know something others don't know. It's safest to blend in with the crowd. Always try not to be noticed."

Don't be different became rule number three.

Then, on the second evening in the village, when the meager servings of rice gruel were ladled out, an old man ahead of Kim Ang stumbled and his cup fell to the ground. The entire contents spilled into the mud at his feet. He found only a few small grains which he quickly plucked from the dirt and pushed into his mouth. After Kim Ang followed him to his hut and discreetly gave him half her serving, she returned to face the anger of her mother.

"You must be concerned only about your own family. Don't ever do that again, Kim Ang."

Generosity had never been one of her mother's virtues, but Kim Ang knew this time she was right. If they were to survive, they would have to be careful about what they gave to strangers.

Selfishness is OK was added to the list.

Darkness came early that night. Swirling storm clouds swept in, unleashing a torrent of rain as Kim Ang and her parents huddled beneath the partially thatched roof of their unfinished hut. Rumbling thunder added to the eeriness. Kim Ang's brothers and sisters were already asleep in a corner kept somewhat dry by a piece of plastic slung above them. She crouched in another corner, peering through uprights of the uncompleted walls of the hut. In a flash of lightning, she saw a figure.

"Father, someone is coming."

By the time Savang Siek moved to the edge of the hut, the man was there.

"Excuse me," he said. "I don't mean to alarm you. I just came here today. This afternoon I saw you at work on your house. I believe you were in a group just ahead of me on the street in Phnom Penh several weeks ago. A woman in that group—she was pregnant—fainted. And a man, perhaps her husband, tried to help her. Then the Khmer Rouge came and took the man and the woman and a child away."

Siek searched the man's face. *Was this stranger bringing good news?*

"The man is my wife's brother. The woman is his wife, and the child is their two-year-old son. Do you know where they are?"

The man looked down. "Yes, but..." He hesitated. "I believe they are dead."

Kim Ang shrieked, and her mother began to sob. Siek grabbed his daughter and clasped a hand over her mouth, then slipped his other arm around his wife.

"We cannot cry. The Khmer Rouge will hear. The punishment will be severe. To them, crying is criticism of what they're doing. We must bear our sorrow silently."

Then, to the stranger, "Please, if you know more, tell us what happened."

"I didn't see it myself. I only saw the Khmer Rouge take them up the alley. But my brother, who was on his way to meet me, told me what he saw. From his description of the people I am sure they are the same ones." He paused.

"Go on, please."

"My brother was about 25 meters away when one of the Khmer Rouge pointed a pistol at the man. The soldiers were yelling at the man and woman, something about doctors being higher than the rest of the people.

"The soldier with the pistol told the man, 'If you think you are so high, climb that tree.' When the man started to climb, the soldier shot just below his feet. He kept shouting, 'Higher, higher.'

"The man kept climbing. Finally, the branches couldn't hold him and he fell to the ground. To be sure he was dead, the soldier shot him in the head."

Kim Ang and her mother, trying to remain silent, were both shaking violently.

"And the woman?" Siek asked.

The man glanced at the distraught mother and daughter. He said nothing.

"They will learn eventually," Siek said softly. "It might as well be now."

"For her, it was much worse," the stranger continued. "One of the Khmer Rouge took a knife and slashed open her belly. He pulled out the baby and slammed it against the tree. Another took the little child, their son, and grabbed him by the legs. He smashed his head against the tree, too. Then they walked away, laughing."

The storm continued through the night, drowning out the muffled sobs of Kim Ang and her mother.

In the morning Siek quietly conveyed the ghastly news to his in-laws and emphasized the need to conceal their sorrow. They would have to go about their work as usual, completing the construction of their huts. They must not appear unhappy in the eyes of the Khmer Rouge.

After their meal of thin rice gruel that evening, Kim Ang and her relatives were summoned before the village chief to receive work assignments.

"Angka has given you fine houses to live in," he began. "Angka also gives you food to eat. In the morning you may begin to show your gratitude for all this. You will go to work for Angka."

Studying the expressionless faces lined up before him, he turned to Grandfather Sieng. "Old man, you will report to work with group 28. Your job will be to weave baskets.

"Your wife will also stay in the village. She will care for the children who are less than six years old.

"You five men," he continued, pointing at Kim Ang's father and Uncles Hong, Tong, Teng, and Kim Eng, "You will help to clear the forest. Your work group is number 23."

He turned to Kim Ang's mother and Aunt Lang. "You two women, your work group is number 18. You also will clear the forest.

"Which children are less than six years?"

Aunt Lang pointed to four-year-old Chhun Phon and her two-year-old brother, Meng Ty. Kim Ang's four-year-old sister, Kim Leang, was identified by her mother.

"They may stay with their grandmother. How old are you?" He stared at Kim Ang's sister Kim Lang.

"I'm six."

"You will be in work group 29. You will gather reeds for making baskets.

"Those two boys are assigned to work with the dam builders." He pointed to Kim Ang's brothers Pheng, who was eleven, and nine-year-old Heng. "In the morning soldiers will take you to another camp."

He pointed at Kim Ang.

"You will dig canals. You, too, will go to a new camp in the morning.

"All must report to their assigned groups in the morning. You may go now."

Kim Ang was devastated. Her world was disintegrating. Forced from her home and all that had been familiar, stunned by the murders of her aunt and uncle and little cousin, malnourished and exhausted by weeks of walking, terrorized and enslaved by gun-wielding soldiers, she now was to be separated from her parents and siblings—from everyone she knew.

The Real Story
A New Society

Evacuation of the cities in April 1975 signalled the beginning of a drastic and devastating upheaval of Cambodian society. To meet their basic goal of making the country self-reliant, Khmer Rouge leaders determined to increase rice production. Dams had to be constructed, canals dug, reservoirs built, rice harvested and planted. And for that to happen, they reasoned, Cambodia's city dwellers must become slave laborers in the countryside.

Evacuation of the cities, however, was just one evidence of the Khmer Rouge destruction of Cambodian culture. Buddhist monks, revered by Cambodians since the thirteenth century, were killed or enslaved with the rest of the population. Doctors, as well as others who were educated or wealthy, were executed. There was no money, no mail, no contact with the outside world.

Worst of all for Cambodians was the calculated assault on traditional family relationships. Even among Asians, Cambodian attachment to families is exceptional. And now every act of the Khmer Rouge seemed determined to eliminate families. New societal categories were established, ignoring families and eliminating them as meaningful units.

In the new Khmer Rouge scheme of things, the basic categories were those of Old People and New People. The Old People were primarily lower-middle-class peasants who, rather than fleeing when the Khmer Rouge came, had stayed in their rural villages and supported the revolution. The New People were those evacuated from the cities when the Khmer Rouge took over in April 1975 and were new to the revolution.

The Old People, who had endured a bleak existence for years, regarded the New as wealthy, useless, and corrupt. The former city residents, on the other hand, believed they were superior to the ignorant villagers. But the New People were, at best, slaves. They lived in constant fear, knowing they could be executed for disobeying orders. Death might be the penalty, too, for crimes such as supplementing their inadequate diets by foraging, speaking foreign languages, or wearing glasses.

There were new villages as well, with flimsy huts built by former city residents with no carpentry skills. Sometimes they were erected right next to old villages with empty houses that could have been used. The new masters obviously were determined nothing from the past would be used in the new society.

For more details, see:

John Barron and Anthony Paul, *Murder of a Gentle Land* (New York, Reader's Digest Press, 1977), pages 130-131, 136-137

Elizabeth Becker, *When the War Was Over* (New York, Touchstone Book, Simon & Schuster, Inc., 1986), pages 214-216, 237-253, 264-270

Russell R. Ross, ed., *Cambodia: A Country Study*, Area Handbook Series (Washington, D. C., United States Government as represented by the Secretary of the Army, 1990), pages 51-59

CHAPTER 10

Let It Snow

JANUARY 29, 1977

MENDON

"It's the picture tube, Ken." Duane Landon frowned as he turned from the innards of the TV set he'd disassembled on the MacKenzies' family room floor. "I don't know if you could find a replacement for it. I know I don't have one."

"Darn!"

Ken pounded a fist on his knee and leaned back in his chair. He'd been watching the repairman's dissection with little knowledge of the procedure, but high hopes for its success.

"I can't complain about getting my money's worth out of that old set. But it could have died at a better time."

"Well, if you're looking for entertainment you won't find much else the next few days," Landon observed. "The storm shut down just about everything here. You can't get out of town either."

Still benumbed by the icy blast that swept through western Indiana and much of the Midwest yesterday, Mendon was a quiet, cold place this Saturday. A blizzard with winds up to 60 miles an hour had whipped snow into huge drifts, and all but a few streets in town were still clogged. Though hardly anyone had ventured out today, a few Main Street merchants opened their stores, and when the phone rang at Duane's TV Sales and Service, Landon was there.

"I'll just close up the shop," he told Ken. "I've been here two hours and haven't seen a customer yet. Came in on the snowmobile, so I can make it up to your place in a few minutes without any trouble."

Duane probably wouldn't have made a house call in this weather for just anybody. But he and Ken, who met while on the Trustee

Committee at the Methodist church, had become fishing buddies and close friends. Ken had been watching a special weather report on an Indianapolis channel this morning when the screen suddenly went blank, right after a segment showing snowmobilers from Renssalaer, to the north of Mendon, rescuing 400 travelers stranded on Interstate 65.

Television really wasn't a necessity for Ken and Donna. Most days it wasn't turned on except to check the news and weather. But they did enjoy some of the Saturday night programs. During stormy winter weekends, Ken liked nothing better than to get a good fire going in the fireplace and relax, often reading but occasionally watching TV.

He'd been looking forward to an evening like that—popping some corn, turning down the lights, then snuggling up with Donna on the sofa to watch Mary Tyler Moore, Bob Newhart, and *All in the Family*. Usually they took in *The Carol Burnett Show*, too, but at ten tonight they'd hoped to see another installment of the eight-part series *Roots*, a televised version of Alex Haley's best seller that they, and most in the country, had been watching all week.

"Now what?" Ken looked at the tubes and tools spread around on the floor next to the television cabinet, then at Duane.

"Well, I guess you could curl up with a good book."

"That's what I do most nights. But Donna's looking forward to *The Mary Tyler Moore Show* tonight. It's her favorite, and she says they're discontinuing it soon. Like everybody else, we've been watching *Roots,* too, and we don't want to miss that."

"Uh, well, you could buy a new set, though I do hate to take advantage of a man in a predicament."

"I'll bet. What have you got?"

"Closest thing to what you've had would be a 19-inch Magnavox Videomatic Color model. It's $479. That's 70 less than list."

Ken had never spent that much without doing a lot of comparison shopping and thinking, or without consulting Donna. He knew he wouldn't have a chance to do any comparing today. And Donna wasn't home. But he'd like to buy the set from his friend. And he'd like to have it now.

"Well, Duane, I think you've got me where you want me—snowbound on a weekend with the final installments of *Roots* coming up. But how do we get the thing here?"

"I've got a sled that attaches to the back of the snowmobile. Give me an hour to go home and get it. From there I'll run back to the shop and pick up the box. Should have you back in business in no time."

Donna was among the few in Mendon who braved today's frigid weather. After breakfast she clamped on her cross country skis and headed out across streets still impassable to wheeled conveyances. She'd been gone nearly three hours when she swished through a drift in the street, two houses from home, just as Landon was zooming away on his snowmobile with the empty sled behind.

In the back hallway, brushing snow off her jacket and shaking it out of her hair, she shamed Ken for not coming along.

"You really missed it. The town's beautiful. So's the countryside—cold, but beautiful. And it's nice and quiet. No cars or trucks making a lot of noise. Just a few snowmobiles." Then, remembering Landon, "What was Duane doing here, Ken?"

"Well, about as soon as you left the television went kaput."

"Did Duane fix it?"

"Nope. Picture tube died. He doesn't have one like it, and there's no hope of finding one anyplace today."

Donna's face clouded with disappointment, and Ken figured his hasty expenditure wouldn't be challenged. So he started his explanation.

"I knew you were looking forward to tonight's programs. There really didn't seem to be any alternative to buying a new set. The old one was hardly worth fixing, even if we could get a new pic-…"

"How much?" she cut in.

"Just four hundred seventy-nine."

She didn't say anything right away. He could read her eyes though and knew he might not be completely out of trouble. She walked into the family room and looked at the replacement.

"It's nice, Ken. Good picture. But we really can't afford that now."

"Sure we can. We put three thousand dollars into savings last year. Remember?"

Donna hesitated again, took his hand, and led him to the sofa.

"Ken, I've been hoping, with that money, I could persuade you we can afford to adopt a child."

The last thing he wanted was an argument about that today. Donna longed to be a mother. When they'd learned years ago they'd never be able to have children of their own, she'd started talking about adoption. Ken liked kids, but he balked at the idea of adopting.

"If God wanted us to have children," he'd said, "He'd have made it possible."

Donna, better at logic than one-liners, convincingly argued that adoption would bring them satisfaction.

"Besides," she'd say, "think what it will do for a child who desperately needs the love of a caring family."

She'd presented her case several times, but Ken always protested.

"This isn't the time to take a big step like that," he'd say.

Invariably he had a reason why adoption would have to wait. It had been two years since Donna last brought it up. He'd hoped the subject had been put aside forever. Knowing, however, that she was unlikely to let go of an aspiration so important to her, he wasn't surprised he was hearing it again.

Ken took both her hands in his.

"I want you to be happy, Donna. Really. I know how much you want a child. Just give me a little more time before we consider something as important as this. Things are rough at the college right now. I need to focus my attention on what's happening there, on whether I'm going to be able to keep working there. I need your support."

"How long is it going to be this time, Ken?"

He picked up on the hint of sarcasm.

"I don't really know. Maybe a few months. Maybe a year or two. It all depends on the new administration, on whether things improve or not."

Donna fought back tears. She realized Ken needed to know she was concerned about his latest frustrations at work. She squeezed his hands, then released them and wrapped her arms around his waist, leaning forward and dropping her head to his chest. She wouldn't press the issue now. The going really had been tough for Ken during the past several months.

A year ago he was encouraged when the college's Board of Trustees selected a new president. That guaranteed interim President James Kirchener would be gone by July. And the new man, Edgar M. Edwards, came to the Mendon presidency with good credentials. At one time a Methodist clergyman, he also had taught religion at Penn State, then held a series of administrative positions at Southern Methodist and Ball State universities. He was a dean at Ball State when he applied for the Mendon presidency.

At first, Ken believed the trustees' choice would strengthen the college's ever-loosening ties with the Methodist church and restore the cooperative spirit that prevailed on the campus during President Scott's administration.

At the fall meeting of the Board of Trustees, just a month after his inauguration, Edwards proposed appointment of a committee to develop what he called "a new covenant relationship with the Methodist Church." Ken hoped this might be a move to close the gap between the college and the church that established it.

Thirteen years ago his only concern about joining Mendon's staff was the college's already-apparent inclination to separate itself from its founding principles. A red flag had gone up when, during an interview with the academic dean, Ken referred to Mendon as a "Christian" college and was advised the correct descriptor was "church-affiliated."

Though it was no consolation for him, the situation was the same at hundreds of other denominational colleges. After conforming closely to tenets of founding churches during early decades of their existence, the institutions declared their independence to varying degrees. In most cases, the relationships began to crack when financial support from churches dwindled. To survive, the colleges turned more and more to corporations, foundations, and individuals. Then, to accommodate these new friends and keep the dollars flowing, the schools changed policies the churches had dictated. When that happened, church support declined even further. The downward spiral gained momentum. The rifts widened. Some colleges declared themselves completely independent.

Now Mendon considered itself "Methodist-affiliated" but was virtually free from church control. Three Methodist pastors were members of the Board, and some prominent businessmen who happened to be Methodists also were trustees. But faculty members no longer needed to support the principles of the Methodist Church—or any church for that matter. Ken once hoped at least the college's Religion Department would support a strong link with the church. However, the newest appointment to the faculty in that discipline didn't consider himself Christian, let alone Methodist.

At the trustee meeting, when Edwards began to elaborate on his proposal, Ken's optimism faded.

"As I see it," the president said, "this new relationship should recognize both the commonness and the diversity of the college and the church. It should encourage cooperation in fulfilling the goals of both while recognizing the right of each to exist without interference of the other.

"I believe that in this new covenant the college should express its gratitude to the denomination which gave it birth and nourished it through its formative years. The church, while relinquishing both its obligation to support and its right to control, should pledge to encourage individual Methodists to share with the institution their talent and their treasure. The Mendon College Board, I believe, should be self-perpetuating without regard for membership in a church or any other group."

What Edwards had in mind, as Ken interpreted his comments, was that the church as an institution would give less direct financial support to the college and would have even less influence concerning what happened on the campus. The college, however, would have greater access to individual Methodists as providers of financial support and prospective students. The crevice between the two institutions would widen still further, and the college would consider its church relationship nothing more than a source of dollars and bodies.

"Sometimes I wonder," he told Donna after the meeting, "why I'm not working for a state institution. The only difference between Mendon and a university like Indiana or Purdue is the size of the place. The hypocrisy of promoting a'church-affiliated' college where there is so little regard for the church does bother my conscience."

Ken knew that months, perhaps years, might pass before trustees would agree on a proposal to be submitted to the church for approval. However, he was already considering what his response should be if and when Edwards would ask him to assist in drafting a final version. How could he, as an advocate of closer college-church ties and greater Christian emphasis on the campus, contribute to an agreement that would widen the breach between Mendon and the Methodist Church?

While still struggling with that eventuality a month ago, he was called to the president's office and asked by Edwards to begin writing text for a publication to be used in an upcoming fund drive.

"This campaign is very important," the president began, "to the institution and to me personally. It must succeed, Dr. MacKenzie. Our goal is significant, a sum larger than any the college has attempted before. We'll tie it in with the centennial we're celebrating in '79. I want a very persuasive publication, and I'm hoping you'll be able to write it for us."

Edwards outlined purposes of the campaign—increasing the college's endowment fund, providing more financial aid for students, hiring additional faculty, renovating three campus buildings, and constructing a new physical education facility.

"Our goal will be twelve million dollars."

Edwards paused to let the number sink in. Ken merely nodded.

"When we announce the Centennial Campaign," the president continued, "we'll show we've already made considerable progress toward the goal. We already have half the total."

Now Ken was impressed.

"That's fantastic. You've certainly had some successes in your first months on the job."

"Thank you. It's not been easy, but two of our trustees have promised they or their foundations will provide a million."

"That's two million," Ken noted. "Who's giving the other four?"

"That's the Foster Foundation grant of last April. It hasn't been designated for a specific purpose, so we'll do that as part of this campaign."

Ken couldn't believe what he was hearing. Edwards was planning to inflate the record of his fund-raising accomplishments by giving the impression that money raised in an earlier effort came in under his leadership. The subterfuge wasn't even smart. Most people would realize where the four million came from.

"But, but those funds were received in an earlier campaign," Ken stammered. "We announced that grant last spring. We can't count that money twice."

"This isn't counting it twice," Edwards defended himself. "Now we're just saying what we're using it for."

"It seems to me," Ken tried again, "we told people at the end of the last campaign that we received four million dollars from the Foster Foundation. Now we'll be giving them the impression we have another four million."

"We won't specifically say it's a new four million. We'll just ignore the announcement made before I became president."

"Well, sir, I don't think that's ethical. I won't write something as misleading as that."

Edwards stared at Ken, his eyes narrowing, teeth clenching.

"I don't see what's unethical about it. We got a grant last spring. I came here last summer. Now we're going to say what the four million will be used for. And we'll announce we're going to raise eight more."

"Pardon me, sir," Ken responded. "I didn't ask to be Mendon's director of public relations. President Scott pressured me to take the position and, reluctantly, I did. Since then, in all I've done, I've tried to be open and honest with Mendon's publics. We can't afford to be other than that now.

"If you want to say clearly that four million dollars of the funds for this new campaign comes from money raised during the '74-76 drive, I can write that with a clear conscience." Ken hesitated, then added, "But I don't think it would be very smart."

"Very well, Dr. MacKenzie. That's what we'll do. Write it that way. I want a first draft in two weeks. You can go now."

Ken walked out, wondering what Edwards would do with the draft when he received it. He was sure the text, as he would write it, would never get into print. Nobody could be so stupid as to start a campaign saying two-thirds of the money already received also was counted in an earlier fund drive. But the bigger question was whether Edwards would stick with his original plan and include the money, or whether he would think better of it and reduce the goal by four million dollars.

That had been a month ago and he still didn't have the answers. He'd submitted his draft to Edwards two weeks ago and there had been no response. That, as far as he was concerned, was good. He'd done what he was supposed to do. The next move was up to Edwards. He wasn't going to worry about it.

Now, as the wind picked up and swirled snow outside the family room windows into new drifts, Donna's embrace tightened.

"I'm sorry, Ken. The new TV looks great."

Her face was still buried in his sweater and she spoke softly, but he heard.

"I shouldn't have given you a bad time about buying it. I'd have been more disappointed than you if we didn't have it tonight."

She paused, lifted her head. Their eyes met.

"And I shouldn't have rocked the boat now by bringing up my dream. But you haven't heard the end of it. We can make a difference in some kid's life. I want to be a mother, and I know you'll be a darn good father. I won't say more about it today, Ken. But I'm not giving up."

Her eyes were sparkling with determination—and warmth.

"You're some special woman, Donna. I don't deserve you."

"Well, no," she joshed, "but you've got me."

Leaning forward, she pressed her lips firmly to his. Then, as he responded with predictable eagerness, she pulled back teasingly and stood up.

"Now, Kenneth, enough of that! We need to get our money's worth out of this television set. I'll go into the kitchen and fix something special for supper. We can eat out here. You round up some logs and see if you can make that fireplace look a little more cheery."

"OK, I guess heaven can wait. But I'm not giving up either."

Pulling himself to his feet, he took a couple of logs and some kindling from the woodbox at the end of the hearth and arranged them on the grate.

In the kitchen, Donna was singing:

> *Oh, the weather outside is frightful,*
> *But the fire is so delightful,*
> *And since we've no place to go,*
> *Let it snow, let it snow, let it snow....*

CHAPTER 11

Liberty or Death

Kim Ang snatched the tiny lizard from the edge of the ditch and snapped its neck, then plunged it into the pocket of her filthy black pants. The lightning quick motion hadn't been detected. She'd have a special treat after tonight's ration of watery rice soup.

There were risks involved in ventures such as this, to be sure. Punishment was severe for anyone caught supplementing the inadequate diet provided by Khmer Rouge taskmasters. They would tolerate no such expression of dissatisfaction.

Still separated from her parents and all who had been friends during her first fifteen years, Kim Ang battled weariness, pain, depression, and loneliness as she struggled to exist under the brutal new regime of Pol Pot, the Khmer Rouge leader. Now her only constant companions were hunger and death.

A year and a half ago, soon after she'd been taken from her family and assigned to the canal digging crew, hunger drove her to make her first kill. That was a rat she'd cornered in a storage shed. She'd not yet learned the secrets of stealth, and the noise of clubbing the animal nearly gave her away.

Then she'd been taken to another camp to work in the rice paddies where potential dietary supplements were more abundant. Five months here had made her a better hunter, too. She became adept at capturing frogs, snakes, snails, fish, worms, insects, crabs, lizards—anything that moved and could be eaten.

She also was better at disguising her actions with plausible ruses in case anyone was watching. Today, she pretended to stumble, falling so her hand enclosed the lizard as she hit the ground. She'd learned, too, how to cook the forbidden prey surreptitiously. New People were permitted to build small open fires for brewing tea made from roots. Kim Ang would slip the protein-rich victims of her hunting into the kettle of tea, then replace the lid so they wouldn't be seen.

She worried less now about being discovered, but she wasn't careless. She still had enough fear to make her cautious. But it was counterbalanced by the thrill of the deadly game she played with her oppressors. Winning satiated her hunger, yes, but restored her self-respect, too.

Nevertheless, the stakes were high. She learned that, during her first month at the canal-digging camp, from a friend who lost. The girl, just a year older than Kim Ang, had been assigned to the kitchen crew. At an opportune moment she slipped some rice, a couple handfuls, into her sarong. That night, as she was cooking it, a suspicious Khmer Rouge overseer investigated and uncovered the crime. She began beating the girl. A second Mekong, hearing the commotion, stormed into the hut. The two tied the girl's hands behind her back.

"So you want more rice!" the first screamed, forcing a glob of the partially cooked grain into the girl's mouth.

"Eat! Eat!"

She pushed more rice in and the girl began to choke, then vomited. Beating her with bamboo rods, the two women shoved her outside and led her away. She was never seen again.

Under the new regime, stealing was but one of many crimes punishable by death. Having too much education was another. Teachers, students, doctors, lawyers, business leaders, engineers were hunted down and disposed of. So were their wives and children. People who wore eyeglasses soon learned to get along without them. To the Khmer Rouge, they were evidence of education and wealth.

Nostalgia was a serious offense, too. Kim Ang had known persons invited to "go to work on the mountain" after they'd been overheard talking about the good old days in the city. Others had merely sung a song they'd learned before the revolution. People who went to work on the mountain never came back. Their bodies littered the jungle. The sight of rotting corpses and body parts wasn't unusual. Some were buried in shallow graves, and protruding bones sometimes tripped persons who strayed into the killing grounds.

Before her transfer to the rice fields Kim Ang often walked near the river which provided water for the canals she was forced to dig, and many mornings there were corpses floating downstream in the current.

A month after she began work in the paddies, six soldiers came to the camp and ordered one of the girls to go with them. A week later one Yotear, drunk and boasting carelessly, was heard to say he and the other five had raped the girl again and again until she died. If Angka learned that, the soldiers would be executed. But who would dare report them?

When will it be my turn to die? Kim Ang wondered as death became more and more matter-of-fact. The sight of an approaching soldier would trigger terror, send her heartbeat racing, her head reeling. Then the fear of death would ebb away, forced out by a new tide of longing that it would quickly take her.

It must be better to be dead than always hungry, always afraid, she'd tell herself.

And then, two months ago, death restored her desire to live.

After a particularly distressing day, sleep was about to cast a comforting cloak over her aches and depression. Perhaps, she hoped, it would be accompanied by dreams of better times. Nights often brought a measure of reassurance. Days meant oppression and trouble. In darkness there might be an escape from daytime nightmares.

Suddenly, a sound at the entrance of her hut startled her.

"Kim Ang," a voice whispered.

She dared not respond.

"Kim Ang, it's Uncle Hong."

He'd been here before, but not for months. Her camp near the rice paddies was just four kilometers from Anchhang Roung where most of her relatives had remained. Occasionally one of her uncles would slip through the jungle at night to bring news or to inquire about her welfare.

"Yes, Uncle Hong. I'm here. Come in."

"Are you feeling strong enough to travel?" he asked abruptly.

"Grandfather isn't well. He's been too weak to work, and the Mekong won't give food to anyone who doesn't work. We've tried to give him some of ours, but he refuses. He accepts leaves and roots that we bring, but they aren't enough. He's failing, and I don't know how long he can live. He longs to see you."

"Can I get to your village and back before dawn?" Kim Ang asked.

"Time won't be a problem," Hong assured her. "But we'll need to be very careful we're not seen. I'll go first and wait for you by that leaning tree at the edge of the forest."

An hour later they crept across a clearing between the jungle and the crude dwellings at the edge of Anchhang Roung. Kim Ang slipped into the hut, and Hong crawled beneath it to keep watch. Moonlight brightened the floor near the doorway where Grandfather Sieng was lying on a mat. He was little more than a skeleton. As her eyes adjusted to the darkness, she realized her mother and father were there as well. Grandmother sat behind them, leaning against the wall. Kim Ang's mother embraced her oldest child and sobbed softly, but the parents deferred to the feeble patriarch to speak the first words. He twisted slowly on the mat and struggled to lift himself to a sitting position. Kim Ang pulled away from her mother and threw her arms around Grandfather Sieng.

"Child, I am sorry these times have brought you so much trouble," he sighed.

She hugged him and tilted her head to rest against his.

"I am well, Grandfather. It is for you we should feel sadness. You are a good man and you have been very kind to everyone. You do not deserve this burden of pain and grief."

"Thank you, Kim Ang. But do not be sad for me. I will soon leave this terrible place. I needed to see you one more time before I go. My first grandchild is very special. Now I am happy. You must not give up hope, Kim Ang. These are dreadful days, but you must fight to live and to have a better life."

The effort to speak was tiring. He paused to catch his breath.

"There may be a time," he continued haltingly, "when you can escape to a better place, perhaps even America. Promise me that, if you reach freedom, you will work hard to get an education. When you have knowledge in your head, you have something no one can take away."

"I will, Grandfather. I promise."

Talking had exhausted him. He couldn't say more. Kim Ang continued holding him for a moment, then slowly lowered him to the mat. When his eyes closed, she moved back to her parents. Their life, she learned, had been as hard as hers. Kim Ang never felt a special closeness to her mother and father, not the kind she shared with Grandfather Sieng or Aunt Lang. But they were her parents. She missed them. She hated the Khmer Rouge for keeping them apart, for making life so miserable for all of them. She wanted to tell them she loved them, but the words wouldn't come out. They had never talked of love. Even now they were able to speak only of the troubles of the present, the happiness of the past, the uncertainty of the future.

A rustle at the doorway interrupted them. Kim Ang had forgotten Uncle Hong.

"Kim Ang, we must go now. There's just time to get back to your camp and then for me to return here before daybreak."

They spoke little during the hurried, melancholy walk back through the jungle. Kim Ang knew she'd never see her Grandfather again. Fortunately, they encountered no patrols of Pol Pot's soldiers, and Kim Ang's absence from the camp hadn't been detected. An hour after her return she was up and facing another depressing day in the paddies, weary with lack of sleep but buoyed by the hope Grandfather had instilled.

Now, two months later, she thought of his words while she sat through another of the boring political education sessions the Khmer Rouge required everyone to attend two or three evenings a week. She had heard it all before—many times. Every speaker intoned the same thing, over and over and over.

"You must forget about the old days," the leader shouted. "Forget about fancy clothes and automobiles. What good is an automobile now? We don't need the things the imperialists gave you. We don't need schools anymore. All we have to know is how to dig canals and how to grow rice. We do not have to go to school to learn that. You are lucky Angka watches over you. Now that you do not have anything, you look to Angka for everything you need. Angka is generous and gives you food and shelter. You do not even have to pay taxes. Angka is merciful. You were wicked in the past, but Angka has forgiven you. To show your appreciation, you must purify yourselves. Do not try to hide anything from Angka. Angka's eyes and ears are everywhere."

On and on the harangue went. And then it was time for the *kosangs*. Kim Ang dreaded these ritualistic warnings of transgressions against Angka, and she breathed more easily when they ended. The hours of monotonous pronouncements, however, left her as weary as if she had spent the time in the paddies. When the meeting finally ended, she trudged slowly back toward her hut. Nearly there, she heard a voice calling softly from the darkness behind her:

"Kim Ang, is that you?"

She turned and squinted at the approaching girl.

"Ay Leng!" she exclaimed, though scarcely louder than a whisper.

The two who had met amid dust raised by a crashing dud rocket in Phnom Penh three years ago hadn't seen one another for nearly two years. They threw themselves into one another's arms, much as they had in their terror-filled first meeting, and clung to one another in the shadows.

"When did you get here?" Kim Ang asked, finally.

"Just this afternoon. I had been near Battambang, but our group was sent to Anchhang Roung. Then I was taken here today with ..."

"I'm so glad," Kim Ang cut in. "I haven't been with any of my friends or relatives since the day I was sent away from Anchhang Roung a year and a half ago."

"But I bring sad news," Ay Leng continued. "At Anchhang Roung I saw your Uncle Hong. He told me your grandfather died two months ago. He said you had been with him the night he died."

"Yes, I expected he would die soon. He was very weak. I am sad, but at the same time I am happy. My grandfather deserved a better end to his life, but now his suffering is over." She brushed a tear from her cheek.

Ay Leng reached out, took her friend's hand and led her to a grassy spot at the base of a tree.

"Please sit down here. I have more bad news."

Kim Ang said nothing. She dared not ask who or what?

"It is your family—your father, your mother, your sisters."

"What do you mean?"

"They are dead."

"No!"

Ay Leng, afraid the cry would lead a Mekong or Yotear to them, clapped a hand over Kim Ang's mouth and drew the other arm around her trembling, sobbing friend. Several minutes later, hugging Kim Ang and stroking her hair, she continued:

"Your uncle said someone, probably a merchant who envied your father or didn't like him, told the Khmer Rouge he was a wealthy businessman from Phnom Penh. He and your mother and your two sisters were taken away last week. Yesterday a friend of your uncle told him he'd seen their bodies in the forest."

Kim Ang cried more loudly, and Ay Leng pulled her closer, pressing the tear-streaked face against her own chest to muffle the sobs. Moments later, she spoke again:

"Kim Ang, your uncle believes the Pol Pot soldiers are looking for your brothers and for you. They know you are in this area, but they don't know exactly where. He said if I saw any of you, I should tell you to try to escape to Vietnam or Thailand. I'll go with you, if you want me to."

"How could you go without your mother?"

"I've been without my mother for more than a year. She became sick when she was bitten by a snake. It happened in a rice paddy near Battambang. She died two days later. I'm the only one of my family left now. Maybe you are, too, unless your brothers learn what has happened to your family and are able to get away. Your uncle said he'd try to get word to them, but he didn't know exactly where they are."

"Where can we go? When shall we go?" Kim Ang, stunned by this new tragedy, was incapable of making such life-and-death decisions.

"The Pol Pot soldiers would probably expect us to go toward Thailand," Ay Leng observed. "It's closer. So I think we should go south, to Vietnam."

"When?"

"We can't wait. We don't know what tomorrow will bring. The Pol Pot soldiers might learn by then that you're here. They may be on the way now. I don't think we have a choice. We must leave tonight."

"All right. Give me fifteen minutes, and then meet me where the trail goes into the forest at the east side of the camp."

Kim Ang hurried to her hut and gathered up the few possessions she'd take. Thrusting them into a sack, she slipped out and cautiously made her way around the edge of the camp to the rendezvous. She was sure the quarter hour had passed, but no one came.

Finally, a shadowy figure moved along the fringe of the forest and approached. She dared not call out. It might be a soldier. She slipped back into the brush. Not until the dark form was just ten meters away was she sure it was Ay Leng.

She called, keeping her voice low, "Ay Leng."

"Yes. Are you ready? We must go quickly, quietly."

They started down the trail, Ay Leng leading the way. They didn't speak. They stepped softly. They listened carefully for sounds that might be soldiers.

Are we headed for freedom, Kim Ang wondered, *or death*?

The Real Story
Evening Entertainment

For Cambodia's New People, the usual reward for long and tiring days of hard labor was required attendance at an evening political education session that was humdrum one minute, horrifying the next. Unless bright moonlight enabled a return to work, all villagers were required to assemble in the communal dining hall or a nearby field for three, sometimes four, hours of boring speeches, revolutionary songs, and chanted slogans.

But what villagers dreaded most were the *kosangs*, accusations of transgressions against Angka, which often preceded the brainwashing lectures. During the time for *kosangs*, anyone might accuse anyone else of a wrongdoing. Sometimes the charges were based on fact, sometimes on envy or vengeance. Protestations of innocence were unheard of. The accused was expected to confess and promise to do better. Minor misdeeds might result in a penalty of less food or more work. Major trespassers could be sentenced to "be reeducated," "visit Angka," or "go to work on the mountain." All knew those expressions were synonymous with "execution."

At the evening sessions, all sang the songs and chanted the slogans with enthusiasm. Everyone fought drowsiness during the boring claims of the glories of Angka and the ridiculous declarations of the good fortune of all who now lived in this place where everyone was equal and happy. Those were the healthy things to do.

But keeping eyes open and heads from nodding wasn't easy. The lecture lines were always the same: "You must forget about the old days... We don't need technology... We don't need schools... We don't need doctors... You can produce more... You must give yourself to Angka... You have everything you need... Angka is merciful... Angka made you free."

To anyone with any intelligence, the statements were absurd. It seems incredulous that even the speakers could believe what they were saying. But villagers learned the thing to do was to echo and applaud the preposterous phrases. Any sign of disrespect for Angka would surely lead to an invitation to work on the mountain.

For more details, see:

John Barron and Anthony Paul, *Murder of a Gentle Land* (New York, Reader's Digest Press, 1977), pages 132-134

Joan D. Criddle and Teeda Butt Mam, *To Destroy You Is No Loss* (New York, The Atlantic Monthly Press, 1987), page 92

Haing Ngor with Roger Warner, *A Cambodian Odyssey* (New York, Macmillan Publishing Company, 1987), pages 3-5, 132-134, 138-141, 211-213

Pin Yathay with John Man, *Stay Alive, My Son* (New York, The Free Press, a division of Macmillan, Inc., 1987), pages 45, 148

CHAPTER 12

Storm After The Calm

APRIL 9, 1979

MENDON

Though it had lasted nearly two years, the truce was an uneasy one. Ken tried his best to avoid crossing swords with President Edwards. He'd have preferred to keep their paths from crossing, too, but he knew that was impossible. Being a key subordinate on the president's staff, and having an office in the same small building, assured he'd see more of Edwards than he wanted.

The two had avoided further major confrontations, but their disagreement about the ethics of counting four million dollars in two different fund drives wouldn't soon be forgotten by either. Ken had won that battle. Edwards backed down, agreed not to include the four million in the Centennial Campaign, and reduced the goal accordingly. But Ken sensed Edwards wasn't the type to accept reproof from an underling appreciatively. He doubted his victory would be without cost.

He was amazed that, so far, relations with Edwards hadn't been more strained. There was no warmth between them, to be sure. They distrusted one another. They were uneasy in one another's presence. Nevertheless, they were able to work together effectively. Perhaps that was because both realized a fracture in their fragile relationship now could be devastating for the institution.

This, after all, was Mendon's centennial year. The college had celebrated the hundredth anniversary of its founding two months ago with a special convocation, and a series of centennial lectures, concerts, and other special events was continuing through the remainder of the school year. At any other time an open conflict between them, though unfortunate, might be tolerable. But Edwards couldn't afford to lose Ken now. His knowledge of the institution and his relationships with others on the campus made him indispensable in handling centennial arrangements.

Other staff members assisted with some of the details, but Ken was responsible for choreographing the entire centennial observance and producing a host of special centennial publications. The last of them, and the biggest project of all, was a history of the college. He was relieved it was completed. Six thousand copies had been delivered to the campus on Friday, and Ken took one home that afternoon to show Donna.

The format of the book, presenting the college's story topically rather than in conventional chronological order, had been proposed by Edwards. The president also recommended that several staff members contribute chapters rather than burden one person with writing the complete history. The suggestions, Ken had to admit, were good ones.

He himself wrote an account of the college's interrelationships with individuals and organizations in the Mendon community through the years. Other administrators and professors contributed chapters on the college-church relationship, Mendon's presidents, the faculty, curriculum changes, campus development, athletics, and other student activities. Ken edited the drafts and handled arrangements for design and printing.

"Are you pleased with the way it turned out?" Donna asked as he handed her the book.

"Yeah, I really am. Lots of people worked hard to bring it off."

"How about Stan Bruder's chapter on church relations? You had some concerns about that, didn't you?"

Ken had wondered whether Bruder, a member of the Religion Department faculty, would present an accurate account of what happened to Mendon's church connection through the years.

"Yes, at first. But it's OK. Actually, Bruder did a good job of summarizing the changing relations between the church and the college. My problem isn't with what was written in 1978-79. I'm bothered by what happened since 1878-79. Reading now about those hundred-year-old dreams of Mendon's founders and their sacrifices to establish and sustain a Christian college reminds me how far we've slipped."

Donna left her chair on the other side of the family room, slid onto the sofa next to Ken, and leaned her head on his shoulder.

"I know. You've said that before. Do you still feel you might as well be working at a state university?"

"Sometimes. But I realize I wouldn't be happy in a big impersonal place. I like being on a small campus. And we've been at Mendon so long I have sort of a family feeling about the place."

Donna squeezed his hand and scrunched closer.

"I hoped you'd say that. I don't ever want to leave here."

"Well, you shouldn't have gotten me going on that, though. You could get me all worked up, and then I'd spoil your whole weekend."

As it turned out, the weekend couldn't have been better. Balmy temperatures rode in on a gentle southern breeze, fashioning two perfect days to enjoy their favorite springtime activities. Saturday was devoted to the yard—tilling the garden, raking leaves that escaped last fall's cleanup, pruning trees and shrubs. That evening Ken reread several chapters of the college history, more for his own enjoyment than any practical purpose, while Donna concentrated on a stack of magazines she hadn't had a chance to read.

"Have you seen the latest *Newsweek*?" she asked Ken when he'd finished his reading.

He could tell the conversation was going to be heavy. Her eyes had that troubled look. She was concerned about something. She's probably still upset about the nuclear plant accident in Pennsylvania. Can't be the article about the possibility of Britain having its first woman prime minister. Those were the only two he remembered.

"Yes, I read it a couple days ago," he responded cautiously. "Scanned it, I should say. I didn't read it cover-to-cover. That accident at Three Mile Island makes you wonder about nuclear power."

"Did you read about Cambodia?"

"No, can't say I did. Must have missed it. What about Cambodia?"

"There's still a lot of trouble there. The Vietnamese haven't been able to wipe out the Khmer Rouge. They control the cities, but in the countryside the Khmer Rouge come back as soon as the Vietnamese have passed through a place, and the things they do are terrible."

"Like what?"

"Like killing people for no good reason. They kill people just for something like accepting food from the Vietnamese. In one place they captured a bunch of villagers who had gone to a nearby city and were coming home to harvest their rice. They killed them with axes. More and more Cambodians are trying to escape to Thailand. Here's what one of the refugees said."

She ran her finger down the page to find the quote, then read:

"'At some places along the road there were piles of dead civilians with their throats slit. At other places there were dead Vietnamese and Khmer Rouge. I was never far from the sights, the sounds and the smells of killing.'"

She looked up and studied Ken's face for reaction.

"People who work with the refugees in Thailand say the new arrivals are in worse shape than the earlier ones," she continued. "They're so dazed by what they've gone through they can hardly function. They can't even build their own shelters in the camps. They just sit around like zombies."

She put the magazine down.

"What can we do?"

"I don't think we can do anything, darling. After all, Cambodia is on the other side of the world. It isn't our problem. The fighting there is between Vietnamese communists and Cambodian communists."

He wasn't surprised she was disturbed about trouble thousands of miles away. This was just like her. She couldn't stand the thought of anyone suffering or being mistreated. If there was any kind of problem, she wanted to know how she could help.

Her worried expression changed to one of disappointment, though she had known Ken wasn't likely to share her concern. He shielded himself from other people's problems, telling himself he had enough of his own. He might be concerned if friends or acquaintances were having problems. But he wasn't going to go begging trouble halfway around the world. Besides, there was always going to be something wrong someplace. There were just too many problems. One or two people couldn't make a difference.

"It's none of our business," he continued. "We didn't cause the problem, and it's not our responsibility to fix it. It won't do any good to trouble yourself with all the world's problems, Donna."

"I'm not so sure we didn't cause it. I don't know a lot about what's been happening in that part of the world. I do know we fought a war against the Vietnamese, and I know Cambodia was somehow involved. We dropped bombs on Cambodians when we weren't even at war with them. But placing blame isn't what matters now. The important thing is people are suffering and dying, and nobody's doing anything about it."

"But, honey, there's just nothing you or I can do." There was just a hint of frustration in his voice.

"Maybe not. But we can't keep ignoring things like that. We ignored Hitler when he was killing millions of Jews. Then thirty years later the Khmer Rouge kill millions of their own people and nobody does anything about that, except the Vietnamese. And even their invasion hasn't stopped it. They're still killing. We can't keep sticking our heads in the sand, Ken."

They didn't reach an agreement. Neither expected one. Disagreements like this had nothing to do with their love for one another. They could disagree without disrespect.

Ken often kidded Donna about her concerns, argued with her about them sometimes. But her compassion was one of the things he most admired about her. And Donna, though wishing the plight of people such as the Cambodians would be more disquieting for Ken, appreciated his steadiness. Only problems affecting them personally seemed to bother him.

"Well, I guess we didn't solve that," Donna said finally, smiling and tossing a friendly jab at Ken's chest.

He intercepted her arm, grabbed it, and pulled her to him.

"That's what I like about you, Donna. Most women would kiss and make up after an argument. You follow your nasty words with fists."

"Did I say I'm not ready to kiss and make up? Try me."

The troubles of Cambodia were put out of mind.

By Sunday morning, Ken had forgotten the discussion and Donna didn't mention it. After church, she packed a picnic lunch and they drove out to the Pinery for an afternoon of bird watching, wildflower hunting, and just being together. They lost track of time, and the sun had slipped behind darkening clouds in the west when a clap of thunder alerted them to an approaching storm. Their dash to the car wasn't quite in time. Caught in the downpour and drenched by the time Ken opened the door, they slid onto the front seat.

Donna leaned her head against his shoulder as he started the engine.

"Thanks for a lovely day. I'm thoroughly dampened—on the outside—but my spirits are soaring."

"No need to thank me. You made the lunch. And my weekend. It's been great."

By this morning, Ken felt renewed, relaxed, ready for whatever challenges the week might present. But a ringing telephone greeted him at the office, and the events that followed were more than he counted on.

"MacKenzie, this is Dr. Edwards," the voice on the other end said. "I need to talk to you. Would you come down to my office?"

"Sure. Be right there."

He wondered what this was all about. Edwards sounded disturbed.

Well, I'll find out soon enough, he told himself as he headed down the hall.

"Go right in, Ken," Mary greeted him, then added in little more than a whisper as he passed her desk, "but be careful. He's not happy this morning."

Mary had survived Kirchener and, so far, Edwards. Ken marveled that, with her talent, she was willing to work with men who made her life difficult.

She must really love this college, he thought. *It can't be the people she works with.*

He tapped on the door and swung it open without waiting for a response.

"Have a seat, MacKenzie," the president said. "We have a problem."

Ken didn't respond.

"I had a call from the commissioner of the Double-I-Double-A."

Ken felt a bit relieved. Reference to the Indiana Intercollegiate Athletic Association meant the problem had to do with sports. Mendon was one of the association's seven members. He assumed that, if it's sports, it can't be too big a deal.

"The commissioner says a complaint was filed against us, alleging two of our football players benefitted from unauthorized assistance. He says there'll be an investigation. If that's the case, word is bound to get to the press. We've got to be ready for that."

Edwards paused, waiting for Ken to comment.

"Well, is the allegation based on fact?"

"Yes, I'm afraid it is."

"Then the thing to do is be open with the press."

Edwards's jaw dropped and he stared at Ken.

"You can't be serious! You call yourself a PR man and you want to admit publicly that we've violated Double-I-Double-A and NCAA regulations!"

"Yes, sir. If that's what we've done, I'd suggest we admit it."

"Well, we're not going to—not to the Double-I-Double-A, or the NCAA, or the press. So far, there's just a complaint. Somebody's probably just heard some rumor. We're not going to forfeit last fall's championship season, wreck our athletic program, and disgrace this institution in the midst of its centennial."

"If those things happen," Ken responded, "it won't be because of openness with the press. It will be because some of our students, and perhaps some of our staff, made mistakes."

"We're not going to admit those mistakes, MacKenzie. You'll tell any inquiring reporters that the allegation is unsubstantiated, that no Mendon athletes have received any kind of assistance not permitted by Double-I-Double-A and NCAA regulations."

"I'd like to do that, Dr. Edwards. And I could, if it were true. But you just told me the allegation is based on fact. I will not lie to the press."

"Are you refusing to do what I order?" Edwards shouted.

"Yes, sir, if you're ordering me to lie. Since you haven't given me the details of what prompted the complaint to the Double-I-Double-A, I'll respond to questions by saying I'm unable to provide any information concerning the allegations. Then I'll refer the questioners to you, or to someone else if you wish.

"Meanwhile, I'll be in my office writing a letter of resignation from the position of public relations director. It will be on your desk by noon. I expect that, as agreed when I accepted this administrative appointment five years ago, I will rejoin the teaching faculty at the start of the next term in September. I'll fulfill responsibilities of the public relations office through the month of June. Then I'll devote my time to preparation for classes I'll teach in the fall."

The president's mouth was open, but no words came out. Ken spun and walked out, smiling and winking at Mary as he passed her desk.

"This is as good as the weekend," he said aloud to himself as he burst into the hallway, barely missing a passing student who dodged quickly to avoid a collision. She stared at him quizzically.

"Pardon me," he called back over his shoulder. "Best Monday morning I've had in a long time."

CHAPTER 13

Exodus

Out of reach of the Khmer Rouge, Kim Ang had nursed her debilitated body and spirit back to a modicum of health during two years as a fugitive in Vietnam. Then, nearly two months ago, after invading Vietnamese troops freed Cambodia from the sadistic oppressors who had turned it into a preview of hell and a gigantic burial ground, she returned to her homeland. But now she had to flee again.

Memories of her first escape from Cambodia still haunted her, and she dreaded the thought of having to go through such an ordeal again. That first time the risk balanced the reward. No price would have been too high for freedom from Khmer Rouge tyranny and terror.

But this was different. Things had changed. After all, the Vietnamese had befriended her. They had taken her in and made her welcome when the authorities in her own country wanted to kill her. Now that the Vietnamese had driven out the Khmer Rouge, she couldn't understand why Grandmother and her uncles insisted on escaping to Thailand.

She'd had no rest since returning to Cambodia. Still weary after the long journey from Vietnam to Phnom Penh, she had taken to the road again, walking northwest all the way to the Thai border region. And now she faced again the perils of a wilderness no-man's land along the frontier—just like two years ago when she crept out of the Khmer Rouge camp in the cover of darkness with Ay Leng.

Then, during an exhausting three-week trek along rugged trails leading southward toward Vietnam, the two girls often hid in undergrowth to avoid Khmer Rouge patrols and robbers. But the worst perils were the land mines and booby traps lying silently on the forest floor, especially near the frontier. Curiosity or a misstep, they knew, could trigger a blinding explosion and bring sudden death. And there were the poison-tipped punji stakes that killed as surely, but more slowly and painfully. Bodies along the trail in varying stages of decomposition confirmed that death lurked in the shadows, ready to grasp the unwary.

Near the border every step had been taken with caution. Even so, Kim Ang's bid for liberty nearly ended within site of her goal. She stumbled, and when her right foot came down just off the trail she knew instantly it had struck something unnatural—a hard, flat object. And from it a spearlike piece of metal protruded above the edge of her sandal.

She had barely missed one of a dozen poisoned points protruding from a concealed board. Had her foot landed a couple centimeters to the right, or a trifle farther ahead or behind, a spear would have sliced her sandal and gone through her foot.

She was grateful she lived to tell about the incident, as she did a week ago when she finally found her surviving relatives in Sisophon, more than three hundred kilometers northwest of Phnom Penh. They wanted to know everything that had happened during the two years since she last saw Grandmother and Uncle Hong on the night Grandfather died.

Of the nineteen who left her grandparents' home in April of 1975, when the Khmer Rouge ordered Phnom Penh evacuated, only nine had survived. In the cluster of relatives at Sisophon now, Grandmother sat at Kim Ang's left and Uncle Hong to the right. On the other side of Uncle Hong were his two brothers, Uncles Tong and Teng. To Grandmother's left were Aunt Lang and Uncle Kim Eng with their children—Chhun Phon, now eight years old, and Meng Ty, six. None in the group knew whether Kim Ang's brothers, Pheng and Heng, were still alive.

Also with them now was Ay Leng, who had come back to Cambodia with Kim Ang in the wake of the invading Vietnamese. The orphan girl was Kim Ang's closest friend, and they vowed to stay together.

After recounting the close call with the barbed spike two years ago, Kim Ang told of her life in Vietnam.

"The Vietnamese treated us well," she assured, looking to Ay Leng who nodded affirmation. "After we crossed the border, soldiers took us to the police station. We had to stay in the jail for a month, until they were sure we were not Pol Pot people. But they gave us food, and they were kind to us."

"When we said we wanted to help in a hospital, they let us work with the nurses."

"Other people helped us, too," Ay Leng cut in. "They found a place for us to live and gave us money to go to school. Later, we tried to pay them back. But they wouldn't take it."

"We were happy there," Kim Ang affirmed. "The work wasn't hard. We weren't afraid someone would take us away and kill us. It was peaceful. I'm sorry you weren't there. I feel guilty I didn't come to Anchhang Roung and ask you to go with us."

"That would have been impossible, Kim Ang," Uncle Hong said matter-of-factly. "You had to run for your life. If you had come to Anchhang Roung, you might have been discovered by the soldiers there. We couldn't have gone with you anyway. Grandmother was too weak. You did the best thing."

"Thanks for saying that, Uncle Hong. But I'm sad you had to suffer with the Khmer Rouge for two more years."

She studied the faces in the circle. Exhaustion, malnutrition, and constant fear had left their marks. Then, as tears clouded her vision, she thought of those no longer among them—Grandfather, starved because he'd been too old and weak to work; her parents, two sisters, and maybe two brothers, murdered because her father was a wealthy merchant; Uncle Nheng, slain because he was a doctor; Aunt Chhun Phing and little Dao Siv, killed because they were his wife and son.

Hong noticed the tears. "At least, we're together again now," he consoled and then, to divert her attention from the missing faces, asked, "How did you get back to Cambodia and find us here?"

"Coming back to Cambodia was easy after the Vietnamese chased Pol Pot's soldiers into the jungles," she explained. "About the middle of January, people in Vietnam told us Pol Pot and his army were gone. They said Cambodian people could go back to where they lived before. So we decided to go to Phnom Penh. We went back to our old house, and to yours, too, Grandmother. But they were just ruins. Everything was broken. They were filthy, and there were rats running around."

"Yes, I know," Hong interjected. "We were there, too."

"Oh, of course. You told Grandmother's neighbor you were coming here to Sisophon. That's how we knew where to look for you. Ay Leng came here with me because she is sure none of her relatives are still alive."

The two girls completed their account of life in Vietnam and their journeys to Phnom Penh and Sisophon, then asked about experiences of others in the circle during the past two years. None cared to dwell long on that misery, however.

"My own family is very fortunate," Uncle Kim Eng observed. "Lang and our son and I would not be alive now if the Khmer Rouge had discovered I was an officer in the Army of the Republic."

"What happened after the Pol Pot soldiers were chased away by the Vietnamese?" Kim Ang asked.

"We didn't know what to think at first," Uncle Hong replied. "We assumed Vietnamese communists would be the same as Cambodian communists. But they didn't kill people, unless they were Pol Pot soldiers. And they said we didn't have to stay where we were and work in the rice paddies any more. We could go to look for our families. We could go home.

"First, we tried to find your brothers, Kim Ang. We went to the camp where they were sent after we arrived at Anchhang Roung. But it was empty. We asked everywhere we went, but no one knew anything about them.

"In the ruins of the camp we found a cart that we fixed so Grandmother wouldn't have to walk. We took turns pulling it, two at a time, and started out toward Phnom Penh. For nearly two weeks we traveled. When we arrived we discovered, like you did, that our houses were in ruins. Everything seemed dirty. We couldn't stand the smell of decaying bodies. And there wasn't enough food.

"Grandmother thought some of her relatives in Sisophon might still be alive, so we decided to come here. You made the same journey, so you know it's a long, difficult one."

"Did you find any of Grandmother's relatives?" Kim Ang asked.

"Yes, one of my cousins is here," Grandmother replied. "Her name is Nuom Yong. She has a husband and three sons and three daughters who are still alive. Two daughters and the children of one already escaped to Thailand. The others are with her. One of the sons has a wife and a little boy. Like us, they have nothing and they are discouraged."

"We talked to many people during our travels," Uncle Kim Eng added. "We heard things are very bad all over the country. Pol Pot's soldiers destroyed nearly everything—houses, temples, bridges. And they are still causing trouble in many villages. The Vietnamese control the cities and the highways, but the Khmer Rouge are still a threat. The biggest problem, though, is food. There isn't enough. The rice supply is very low. The Vietnamese are using some to feed their soldiers, and they are sending some to Vietnam."

"We've decided we have to escape to Thailand," Uncle Hong broke in. "Many are going to starve here. We must go soon, before the Vietnamese decide to stop us, before the rainy season makes traveling even more difficult. Grandmother's cousin and her family will go with us."

Kim Ang didn't agree. She didn't believe the Vietnamese would send rice to Vietnam and let Cambodians starve. She had lived with Vietnamese people for two years. They hadn't treated her that way. But arguing with elders was unthinkable. She'd have to do as Grandmother and her uncles said. The decision had been made. She'd have to go along with it.

Nevertheless, as she and the others plodded toward the Thai border during the past week, Kim Ang searched her mind almost constantly for a way to avoid going through another hazardous no-man's land and into an uncertain future.

Then last night she was awakened by a haunting noise, probably an animal or bird in a nearby tree. In the darkness, Grandfather's face appeared. And she remembered his last words to her: "There may be a time when you can escape, perhaps even to America." She couldn't recall the exact words, but she knew he'd urged her to get an education because that was something no one could take away.

"Grandfather wants me to go," she assured herself. "I'll do it, and I'll get an education."

This morning Uncle Hong reluctantly hired a guide to lead them across the hazardous final stretch of terrain to the border. The fee was high, an ounce of gold for each of the ten persons in his group. The husband of Grandmother's cousin paid the guide eight ounces for his family. They dared not proceed without the help of someone familiar with the mountain jungles and their hidden dangers— mines, bandits, Khmer Rouge guerrillas. But they were aware many of the guides were outlaws, too.

"Anyone who takes our money to lead us to Thailand could also take it from the Khmer Rouge to lead us to them," Uncle Kim Eng warned.

They feared being turned over to the Khmer Rouge, or taken to a place in the jungle where they'd be robbed, but they dreaded even more the possibility of being lost in this wilderness. That would be certain death.

So, soon after sunrise, they placed their faith in the stranger and followed his footsteps through the undergrowth. Before the sun went down again they'd know whether they would be rewarded with freedom, or failure—or worse.

The Real Story
The Refugee Flow Becomes a Flood

Though Cambodia and Vietnam were both controlled by communist regimes during the latter half of the decade of the '70s, relations between the countries were far from cordial. But the animosity was nothing new; the Khmer and Vietnamese had been at odds for hundreds of years.

Within a month of their victory over Cambodian government forces in April 1975, the Khmer Rouge were involved in skirmishes with the Vietnamese. Although tensions lessened in 1976, trouble escalated again the following year with the Khmer Rouge instigating a number of border clashes. Their raids into Vietnam continued and in September 1977 Pol Pot's soldiers killed hundreds of Vietnamese civilians.

Vietnam responded with an incursion into Cambodia, then withdrew with the assumption the Cambodians had been punished. But Pol Pot claimed victory and continued his belligerence. In 1978 Khmer Rouge massacres of ethnic Vietnamese in Cambodia intensified. Finally, Vietnam's leaders opted for an all-out military response and sent an invasion force of 120,000 across the border on December 25, 1978.

The invaders reached the eastern banks of the Mekong River by January 5 and two days later entered Phnom Penh with virtually no resistance. There they installed a puppet government headed by two former Khmer Rouge officers who had defected to Vietnam, Heng Samrin and Hun Sen. The Khmer Rouge retreated to the west, forcing civilians to accompany them, and took refuge in mountainous jungles at the border with Thailand where they regrouped and operated as a guerrilla force as they had prior to 1975.

The Vietnamese, who controlled most of the country, encouraged the displaced thousands to return to their original homes and permitted greater freedom of movement. But the new freedom didn't go much beyond that. Cambodians were still denied many basic rights and, the way they saw it, those in charge were still communists. An even more ominous problem was the specter of starvation. Confiscation of rice by the Vietnamese and destruction of it by the retreating Khmer Rouge had resulted in a severe food shortage.

Consequently, the flow of refugees toward Thailand became a flood after the December 1978 invasion, and by summer of 1979 nearly 100,000 Cambodians were at the Thai border.

For more details, see:

J. Patrick Hamilton, *Cambodian Refugees in Thailand: The Limits of Asylum* (New York, U. S. Committee for Refugees, 1982), pages 1-6

Virginia Hamilton, ed., *Cambodians in Thailand: People on the Edge* (New York, U. S. Committee for Refugees, 1985), pages 4-8

Arnold R. Isaacs, Gordon Hardy, MacAlister Brown, *Pawns of War* (Boston, Boston Publishing Company, 1987), pages 160-167

Haing Ngor with Roger Warner, *A Cambodian Odyssey* (New York, Macmillan Publishing Company, 1987), pages 405-406

Russell R. Ross, ed., *Cambodia: A Country Study*, Area Handbook Series (Washington, D. C., United States Government as represented by the Secretary of the Army, 1990), pages 66-70, 262-267

CHAPTER 14

Decision Time Again

JUNE 9, 1979
MENDON

Ken knew it would happen. In late April, less than three weeks after his confrontation with President Edwards, the NCAA's Division Three Infractions Committee advised the college it had begun an investigation concerning allegations that two football players received unauthorized assistance.

As Ken expected, the attempted press cover-up by Edwards backfired. When confronted with questions about a possible Indiana Intercollegiate Athletic Association investigation, he first denied there was a problem.

"They're just rumors," he told reporters. "Nothing to them. We have always abided by all Double-I-Double-A regulations."

Then, a few days later, with skepticism persisting, he said if there were to be an IIAA investigation Mendon would certainly be cleared of any charges. A week after that, the bomb exploded. In a joint announcement, the IIAA commissioner and the chairman of the NCAA Division Three Infractions Committee spelled out the charges against Mendon: At least two players on the college's 1978 football team, in violation of both IIAA and NCAA regulations, allegedly received financial assistance from a Mendon alumnus. The assistance was provided on the basis of athletic rather than academic ability. Arrangements for the assistance were made with the knowledge of at least one member of the Mendon staff.

The investigation would be conducted by the NCAA with full cooperation of the IIAA, according to the announcement. And none of those alleged to be involved would be named, nor would any other information concerning the allegations be provided, until the NCAA completed the inquiry and determined what sanctions, if any, were to be imposed.

Though the charges remained to be proved, Mendon's image was doubly tarnished, first by the apparent violations and then the effort to hide the facts. Newspapers and broadcast stations throughout Indiana were having a field day with the story. And it was all happening smack-dab in the middle of the college's long-awaited centennial observance.

The jubilation of 1978's undefeated football season, which brought the college's second consecutive IIAA trophy, was forgotten. But at the end of the season last fall, President Edwards had spoken of the back-to-back championships as if they had been the greatest accomplishment at Mendon in years.

"Our football team is but a reflection of our college," he boasted to alumni groups and gatherings of prospective students or potential donors. "Mendon is a winner. When your children choose Mendon to further their education, they're joining a winner. When you support Mendon financially, you're part of a winning team."

Now some of the state's columnists and commentators were picking up on the president's theme in critical analyses of the college's status. "If the football team is but a reflection of the college," said an Indianapolis editorial writer, "we wonder what is happening in other departments at Mendon."

As the negative publicity snowballed it began flattening customary support for the institution. Alumni were up in arms. Postpaid fund solicitation envelopes were coming back without contributions inside. Instead there were bitter notes.

"Don't bother to ask me for more money," one disgruntled alum wrote, "until you get your priorities straight! I thought I was supporting a quality academic institution, not a football factory."

"I don't go around bragging that I'm a Mendon alumnus any more," another penned across an otherwise blank contribution slip. "As a matter of fact, I don't even admit it!"

Members of the college's Board of Trustees were getting an earful from influential contributors who threatened to withhold payment on their pledges for the Centennial Campaign.

Student recruiters were encountering resistance from parents. Some objected to the apparent hypocrisy of a college affiliated with a church getting caught for lying about rules it had broken. Others questioned whether the evident emphasis on athletics was at the cost of academic programs and, if so, whether their children should bother to enroll at Mendon unless they were athletes. And athletes were reluctant to seek admission to the college because they feared possible NCAA sanctions might hinder their opportunities to participate in sports.

This had not been a happy springtime at Mendon, despite the approaching climax of the centennial observance—today's graduation ceremony which marked the end of the college's one-hundredth academic year. It should have been a grand occasion. To outward appearances, maybe it was. But the graduates, their families, the college staff—everybody in attendance—sensed a depressing pall hanging over the campus. They felt disappointed, embarrassed, cheated. The degrees conferred today represented diligent effort on the part of students and considerable sacrifice by their parents. And now they seemed tarnished by the controversy that had the whole state ridiculing their college.

Members of the Board of Trustees weren't just embarrassed. Though most tried to conceal it, they were infuriated. A special executive session of the Board was held on the campus this morning. Ken wished he'd been there. He would have liked to see Edwards squirm. He wondered what he'd say at the closed-door session to calm things down. The president was a smooth operator, though. Ken supposed a few trustees would get worked up, but Edwards would have them eating out of his hand by the end of the meeting.

Afterwards, when Edwards made introductory comments at a noontime dinner for trustees and their spouses, he seemed a bit subdued, Ken thought. But he quickly turned on the charm.

"I must thank each and every one of you trustees who have given so much of yourselves to this institution. And I would certainly be remiss if I didn't acknowledge the support of the spouses of these men and women. I know much of the time and effort our trustees devote to this college comes at the expense of their families. Your understanding and your willingness to share is greatly appreciated. That kind of service and support has sustained Mendon College for a century."

He went on in that vein for several minutes and then said grace, asking God's blessing "on the food of which we are about to partake, on this institution which You have nurtured through a century of service to young men and women, on this occasion when we celebrate the accomplishments of our graduates and send them out into the world, and especially on these men and women who have given so much of themselves in selfless service to others."

They can't have given him too bad a time, Ken thought. *If they did, he wouldn't be telling them and their spouses and God how great they are.*

At Ken's table were three male members of the Board and their wives. There was no discussion of the morning's closed session of the Board. Neither was there any mention of the difficulties that had necessitated the meeting. The trustees were amiable and interested in other happenings on the campus. But their comments and questions were carefully posed to avoid responses that would draw the conversation toward anything controversial.

As he was sliding his fork under the last morsel of apple pie, Ken felt a hand on his shoulder and turned to see Board Chairman John P. Bennington behind him.

"Dr. MacKenzie, pardon me. I don't mean to spoil the taste of that last choice bite."

Ken slid his chair back and stood up. They shook hands. He hadn't encountered Bennington earlier in the day. In fact, the two had spoken to one another only a few times during the four years Ken had headed the PR office. Before that, they had never met.

"I'm sure it will keep. And I'll be better off if I don't eat it anyway. Good to see you, sir."

"Well, I won't take much of your time now. I'm on my way to the registrar's office. He has to refresh my memory on procedures for handing out degrees. But I'd like to talk to you for a few minutes later in the day, before you leave the campus. Could we get together after the ceremony?

"Certainly, sir. Where would you like to meet?"

"How about your office, Dr. MacKenzie?"

"That would be fine."

"Thanks. I'll see you then."

With that, Bennington turned and walked from the room.

Now what is this all about? Ken wondered. *I hope Edwards wasn't so convincing this morning that Bennington is going to ask me to try to do something to repair the damage with the press. I'm not going to get involved in that. Edwards got us into this mess. He can get us out.*

His uncertainty about what Bennington wanted to discuss distracted his attention through most of the commencement program. After the ceremony he lingered long enough to congratulate graduates and parents he knew, then walked briskly to his office. Standing on the administration building steps, where they customarily met after commencement, was Donna. He'd been so preoccupied with Bennington's request to meet that he'd forgotten to call her about changing plans.

"Hi, Ken. It was a wonderful ceremony, despite all the recent trouble. Actually, it was sort of a refreshing diversion. Don't you think so?"

"Oh, yes. Sure."

His distraction was apparent.

"Is something wrong?"

"Uh, no, not really, Donna. It's just that I've had my mind on other things. Bennington asked to meet with me after the ceremony. He's the Chairman of the Board, you know."

"Yes, of course. What does he want?"

"I don't know. That's what I've been thinking about. Perhaps he wants me to try to repair the damage Edwards has done with this athletic mess. That's the only reason I can think of. Anyway, I'll know soon. I'm supposed to meet him at my office in a few minutes."

"I know how strongly you feel about what's been happening, Ken. And none of it's your fault. You tried to warn Edwards.

Remember, whatever Bennington wants you to do and whatever your response is, I'm with you."

He smiled, extended an arm, and she slid into it. The hug was brief, but revitalizing.

"Thanks, Donna. I know you are, but it helps to hear it. Oh, can you wait for me in the lobby? I hope Bennington won't take long."

She smiled and walked down the corridor in one direction while Ken went the other.

Moments later, Bennington arrived.

"Thank you, Dr. MacKenzie, for agreeing to see me."

"Just call me Ken, please. I try to save that doctor stuff for students. Let's sit over here."

Ken pointed to a pair of chairs between the doorway and his desk. He never sat behind the desk during one-on-one discussions, a practice he'd followed since his earliest days as a teacher and advisor of students.

"I'll try not to take more than a few minutes of your time," Bennington began. "So I won't beat around the bush. You're aware the Board of Trustees met this morning."

"Yes, sir."

"As you know, the session was closed and we are not yet ready to make public what happened there. But I must tell you. To put it very briefly, Ken, the Board asked President Edwards to resign."

Bennington paused and noted the astonished look on Ken's face.

"Apparently that's not what you expected. However, we fail to see how he can continue to lead this institution after the mess he's gotten it into with the attempted cover-up of the NCAA investigation. Edwards admitted to me privately that you advised him to be up front with the press but he disregarded that advice. Had he done as you suggested, all of this would have been avoided. We would have been embarrassed by the investigation, of course, but we would have taken a step toward repair of the damage by being honest and open about it.

"Now we are in a really bad situation. What has happened has had an adverse effect on recruitment of students, on solicitation of funds, on campus morale. We believe it's necessary to get rid of the man who caused the problem as a first step in restoring Mendon's reputation. President Edwards's resignation will be effective August 1."

Ken's face still reflected his puzzlement.

"Relax, Ken. I'm not going to ask you to serve as president."

"Uh, no. I was pretty sure of that." He smiled.

"But I'm sure you're aware we're going to need all the help we can get to restore this institution's image. Edwards also admitted to me that, when you disagreed with his plan for handling the athletic mess, you submitted your resignation as director of public relations. I understand when you agreed to take the position five years ago you had an agreement with President Scott, stipulating you could return to teaching here any time after two years at the PR job."

"Yes, I have a contract to that effect," Ken responded. "And I plan to return to the classroom this fall. My responsibilities in the public relations office terminate at the end of this month."

"That's what Edwards told me. However, I'd like to ask you to reconsider. I'm aware you have an excellent reputation as a teacher. I know that's your first love. And, if I can't persuade you otherwise, we'll be pleased to have you back in the classroom. But I'm hoping you'll agree to stay on in public relations for a while. It shouldn't be as difficult with Edwards gone. Please don't hastily say no. Sleep on it and let me know next week."

Ken hadn't dreamed this would happen. The end of his administrative responsibilities had been in sight. He didn't like what was happening.

"I do appreciate your confidence in me, sir. My first reaction is to say no, emphatically. But, if you wish, I'll give it some thought and have an answer next week. I'll need to talk it over with my wife. To do that, of course, I'll have to reveal some of what you told me about this morning's meeting. You may be sure both she and I will keep the matter in strictest confidence."

"I'll appreciate that, Ken. I do want you to know all of us on the Board are grateful for your service to the college, both in the classroom and in your recent administrative role. We hope you'll agree to stay on in public relations. If not, we'll understand and consider ourselves fortunate to have you on the faculty again. Thanks for hearing me out. I'll give you a call about the middle of the week and you can tell me what you've decided."

With that, Bennington extended his hand, then left.

Ken followed moments later and found Donna in the lobby, sitting on a bench alongside a large window overlooking the central campus mall, bathed now in the warm glow of the late afternoon sun.

"It's so peaceful here right now, Ken. I've really been enjoying this beautiful view. Sit with me for a minute and tell me what happened. Does Bennington want you to spend your last couple weeks in the PR office repairing damage?"

He looked up and down the hall to be sure they were alone.

"Bennington doesn't want these to be my last couple weeks in the PR office."

Now it was Donna who looked astonished.

"He asked me to stay on for a while," Ken continued. "That doesn't interest me in the least, but I did tell him I'd think about it a few days before giving my decision."

"I guess that's pretty bad news, huh? You've been so anxious to get back to teaching. It's a shame to have this pressure put on you now to stay in PR."

He shrugged his shoulders.

"There is good news, though. But it's confidential. For now, we can't breathe a word to anyone."

He checked the hallway again to see if someone might have come into the building.

"Edwards is leaving."

"What? How?" Donna couldn't believe what she was hearing.

"The Board fired him. He'll be gone by August."

"Wow! But will that affect the decision you have to make?"

"Well, if I were to stay in PR, it would be a lot more pleasant without Edwards around. But I can remember Kirchener, too. And I don't know who's going to follow Edwards. So, no, I guess it really won't make any difference.

"With the college's present problems and with Edwards leaving, there's a strong case to be made for my staying in PR to help out for a while. It's going to be another tough decision. It will boil down to whether I want to do what seems best for me or what seems best for the college. Bennington will call about the middle of the week. I'll need to have my answer ready then. Meanwhile, I'll need your help in coming up with the right answer."

"Oh, no. There you go again. You tried that once before when Scottie wanted you to take the job in the first place. I told you then it was your decision to make. That's still the case. I want you to be happy. Do what you think will accomplish that, and I'll be with you all the way."

"Thanks. You make it easy."

She wasn't sure what he meant, but she didn't ask. He'd tell her when he was ready. Arms around one another, they stepped out into the lengthening shadows and walked toward home.

CHAPTER 15

Clinging To Hope

JUNE 10, 1979

CAMBODIAN-THAI FRONTIER

"All Cambodian people must board the buses."

The amplified voice was stern, not at all friendly. The man shouting the order into the portable loudspeaker didn't look friendly either. And his comrades, holding automatic rifles and dressed as if ready for combat, appeared even more forbidding. But Kim Ang didn't worry. These were not Khmer Rouge. They were Thai soldiers.

"It is not safe for you here. We will take you to another camp. You will have better shelter and more food there. Get on the buses now!"

"Oh, good! We won't have to walk this time," Kim Ang said cheerfully to Aunt Lang.

Walking, it seemed, had been all she'd done for months. Her feet and legs were scratched, bruised, and weary from the difficult journey that ended just a few days ago. Step by tiring step, she had crossed her country from one end to the other, starting in Vietnam and proceeding northwest to the border with Thailand. The companionship of relatives had buoyed her spirits as the family group trekked from Sisophon toward the frontier, but the final few kilometers proved to be especially tiring and dangerous.

She'd never forget that treacherous journey through the no-man's land paralleling the frontier where fear lurked constantly in the shadows. She knew one wrong step could trigger a life-ending explosion. She feared she and her relatives might encounter Pol Pot soldiers. She dreaded the possibility their guide might desert them, or lead them to robbers rather than freedom.

And then it had happened. She was looking down, searching the groundcover for concealed deadly devices, when a sudden movement startled her. The guide was running away. And just ahead the trail was blocked by soldiers. They couldn't get away now. They had been seen. Besides, they were too weary. And if they tried to escape, they would be shot. They proceeded slowly toward the men with the guns.

Uncle Kim Eng, at the front of the procession, suddenly turned and shouted, "They don't speak Khmer! They're Thai! We're free!"

He interpreted the squad leader's instructions for his companions: "Keep moving down this trail. Go about one kilometer and you will see a camp. Report there and you will be given shelter and food."

With their burden of fear suddenly removed, they had continued down the path until they came to a slight rise. Before them, smoke from countless campfires hovered overhead, wrapping the horizon in a purple haze. Beneath, giving the whole scene a topsy-turvy appearance, were hundreds of flimsy shelters.

"It looks like the sky's on the bottom!" Kim Ang had exclaimed.

Indeed, the next layer of color below the haze was blue, as brilliant as the sky.

As they came closer, she realized the tents and huts making up the vast temporary city had been fashioned principally from plastic tarpaulins, all of the same bright blue color. Although these coverings, handed out by refugee agencies, afforded a measure of protection from the heavy rains of the wet monsoon, conditions in the camp hardly seemed better than on the other side of the border. Sanitation facilities were primitive. Too many people were in too small a space.

But at least here they had shelter, even if the roof and sides were nothing more than blue plastic tarps. Here there was hope. Here were dreams of new life in a new country, perhaps America.

And now today the promise of a brighter future was going to be fulfilled! They were going to a new place with decent housing, more food! And on this next leg of their journey to that better day, they wouldn't even have to walk!

Kim Ang, finally able to put the recent terror out of mind, counted more than a hundred buses as they approached the camp, rolled through the gate, and circled the ramshackle homes of the refugees. The huge vehicles were far better than any she had seen in her own country. She peeked inside one that stopped nearby and admired the upholstered seats. It was even air-conditioned!

"We're going to a better place, and we can ride!" Kim Ang shouted above the throbbing engines, some idling nearby and others powering the buses into the camp. "Things are getting better, Aunt Lang."

But Lang wasn't smiling. She wrapped her arms around her niece.

"Kim Ang, I've heard rumors, and I think now they must be true. I didn't say anything to you before because I wasn't sure. And I didn't want you to worry. I think we are not going to a better place. We are going back to Cambodia!"

"That can't be! We've come all this way. The Thais would never send us back through that terrible jungle filled with land mines and bad people. They said we're going to a better place, and I believe them."

Lang's hug tightened. "I hope that's right, Kim Ang. But Uncle Kim Eng heard a friend's transistor radio. The announcer said Thailand is sending the refugees back."

Apparently, most in the camp heard rumors they might be sent back across the border. Hardly anyone made a move to board the buses.

"You must get on the buses now!" the voice on the loudspeaker shrieked. "Now! Move now!"

As he spoke, other soldiers slung guns over their shoulders to free their hands, then moved into the crowd, grabbing children and old people and forcing them onto the buses. Unwilling to risk separation from their loved ones, the others reluctantly clambered aboard.

"It's no use," Uncle Kim Eng shouted to his relatives. "There's nothing we can do. Gather your things. We'll have to go. But be sure we all get on the same bus."

"What about my cousin, Nuom Yong, and her family?" Grandmother implored.

"We can't worry about them," Kim Eng replied. "We don't know where they are right now. They will have to take care of themselves."

Kim Ang refused to give up hope. Even as the bus rumbled along the highways all that day and into the night, she couldn't believe their destination would be the border.

"Where are we going?" she called out a window to a soldier when the bus stopped for gasoline.

"Bangkok," he responded, walking away.

But they had proceeded only a few miles before the driver turned onto another highway leading eastward, and she realized that couldn't be where they were headed.

"It must be another camp farther to the east," she then insisted.

Throughout the day she kept peering out the rain-splattered window at her side, hoping to spot a hopeful sign that another camp might be just ahead. Then darkness blotted out all images on the other side of the glass, and she could see nothing but the reflection of her own dejected face. Finally the continuous hum of the motor lulled her to an uneasy sleep.

Hours later a jolt brought her back to consciousness as the bus spun to the right and the wheels dropped off the pavement onto a rough, narrow dirt road. A glimmer of light through the window beside her indicated a new day had dawned. Silhouetted against the brightening sky were mountains, on all sides. Chances of another camp being in this place were slim. Her hopes sank.

The road became bumpier, and the bus moved more slowly until finally, with brakes squeaking eerily, it ground to a halt. The door swung open and a soldier climbed up the steps and shouted.

"Everyone out!"

No one moved.

He lowered his rifle, pointing it down the aisle.

"Get off immediately—or anyone left alive will have to clean blood off the seats before leaving!"

Instantly all gathered their belongings, squeezed into the aisle, and started toward the front of the bus. Outside more soldiers awaited them. Holding their guns ready to fire, they lined both sides of a path leading off to the south. There would be no possibility of escape. As she stepped down from the bus, Kim Ang noticed the path seemed to end abruptly where the first persons off were standing. They were refusing to proceed. As she moved closer, she saw why. The path ended at the top of a cliff so steep the only way to descend was by clinging to ropes and vines, or by lying on the ground and sliding down across the rocks.

"Move forward and go down! Go down!" the soldiers shouted. "There's your country, down there."

They fired warning shots overhead, and some people started over the edge. Children were lowered on the vines and ropes. Old people crawled along the rocks, trying to avoid miscalculations that would send them crashing down the cliff.

The rain, which had resumed, made the footing even more slippery. Kim Ang inched her way to the edge of the escarpment, then froze at the sight before her. The narrow way down the precipice was littered with debris—pots, rice sacks, clothing, blue plastic tarps—left by thousands who had been forced over the edge before her. Some of it may have been discarded intentionally to lighten burdens. Much of it had fallen accidentally during frantic efforts to avoid slipping. Many who had preceded her off the bus were still struggling downward. Off to the side, several bodies lay where they had fallen when shot by soldiers. Farther down, at the foot of the mountain, thousands squatted on the trail, unwilling to move farther.

Rising from the mists below were the smell of decaying flesh and the sounds of the sick, the dying, and the grieving. Occasionally an explosion echoed through the mountains when the press of new arrivals in the valley of misery forced someone off the trail and into the heavily mined terrain on either side.

"All right, get moving!"

As he yelled, the soldier shoved his rifle at Kim Ang and she sprawled to the ground, nearly slipping over the edge. She grabbed a rope and immediately began her descent. Nearby, her eight surviving relatives and her friend, Ay Leng, also were struggling down the precipice.

Uncle Teng was helping Aunt Lang and Uncle Kim Eng to lower their children to the first ledge on a rope. Kim Eng eased daughter Chhun Phon to the ground as Teng held the rope and lowered her. Now son Meng Ty was coming down the same way. Lang descended halfway to the ledge and encouraged her children as they came past. Uncles Hong and Tong were trying to help Grandmother as she skidded painfully across the rocks. Ay Leng was just above Kim Ang, using the same rope in her descent.

After reaching the ledge, the incline wasn't quite as steep and descent on foot became possible. Then, at the base of the mountain, they had to force their way among the masses who had gone before and now refused to move farther, hoping something would make it possible for them to climb back up the mountain and return to Thailand. None were willing to step off the narrow trail, blazed by the thousands of feet that preceded them. The area had been heavily mined by the Khmer Rouge, a fact attested to by sporadic explosions, shrieks of pain, and sobs of survivors.

"I think we should stop to rest," Uncle Kim Eng suggested after they tried to cram their way through the crowd for several hours. "Stand here while I check this spot for mines."

He sprawled on the ground and carefully examined the surface. Finally, satisfied the site was safe, he instructed the others where to sit and helped them place their tarps for temporary shelter from the driving rain.

"I talked to a man back there on the trail," he told the group as they huddled around a small cooking fire Uncle Teng had managed to light despite the wetness. "He knows this area. We are in the province of Preah Vihear, about 300 kilometers east of the camp we were in. The nearest roads are many kilometers from here. The jungle is dense, almost impassable. There is great danger from mines, and no one here knows the way through the minefields. This is the worst place the Thais could have taken us."

"Why did they take us here?" Uncle Hong demanded, almost as if someone in the group had been responsible.

"I can only guess," Kim Eng responded. "For one thing, I think they don't want us to get back to Thailand easily. They know if they took us where we came in, we'd soon try to cross the border again. From here, unless they let us go back up the trail, we'll have to go all the way into the middle of Cambodia, then back west to the border beyond Sisophon. That will take months. And another thing, I think

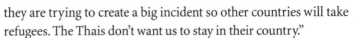

they are trying to create a big incident so other countries will take refugees. The Thais don't want us to stay in their country."

"So, should we get started back toward the middle of the country?" Hong asked.

Kim Eng pondered the question. "No, I think we should stay here as long as we can. Maybe when the rest of the world hears what happened, other countries will agree to take some of us and will pressure the Thais to let refugees back in. That's our best hope right now."

Kim Ang didn't want to stay. Yet she was afraid to leave.

"This is the worst day of our lives," she lamented, "worse even than when the Pol Pot soldiers made us go out of Phnom Penh. When we left there, we thought we were going for just a few days. Now I think we are going forever. We will all die. Yesterday we had hope. Today we have only despair. Already more than half of us are dead, and who knows how many will die now in this awful place?"

"The sounds and the smells here are terrible," Ay Leng joined in.

Hundreds—exhausted, undernourished, drenched, and desperate—lay along the trail, too ill to move. Their coughs and moans were incessant. The stench of rotting bodies, vomit, and excrement was overwhelming. People didn't even dare leave the trail to relieve themselves.

They had rested only about an hour when Kim Eng advised they move farther down the trail in hopes of finding a less crowded place to camp. Several more busloads of refugees had been disgorged at the top of the cliff, and the hundreds of new arrivals were now pushing their way in among the throng on the narrow trail.

Aunt Lang and six-year-old Meng Ty, standing at the edge of the family group nearest the jungle undergrowth, were folding their tarp in preparation to leave. An older man holding the hand of a child, probably his granddaughter, tottered along the path toward them, propelled by the surge of humanity behind. As the unsteady pair approached, Lang smiled and stepped back to let them pass.

Instantly, a thundering blast shook the jungle. Lang's body shot into the air. Meng Ty writhed in pain, screaming for help. The old man and child lay bleeding alongside Lang's half-folded blue tarp.

Kim Ang was the first to reach her beloved aunt. Blood poured from the jagged stump of what had been her left leg. Miraculously, she was alive. Cradled in her niece's arms, Lang spoke slowly, with great pain.

"Don't worry about me. Some day you will have a better life. Don't give up hope."

Kim Eng fought his way through the crowd and fell beside them. Kim Ang withdrew, and her uncle cradled the battered body of his wife.

"Don't go, Lang."

"I don't want to, my darling. But the pain is so great. I love you so much. You are …"

Her mouth stopped moving. Her eyes fluttered. Her lips formed a faint smile. She stopped breathing.

Kim Eng shrieked, then sobbed softly, uncontrollably. Kim Ang wrapped her arms around him, trying to bring comfort. Tears streamed down her own cheeks. She was devastated. The person she loved most was gone. Her uncle, the strong soldier who always helped the others through tough situations, was shattered.

Kim Ang looked up and saw Uncle Hong approaching. His hands and shirt were bloody. He squatted down and placed a hand on Kim Eng's shoulder.

"I'm sorry. Meng Ty has gone to be with his mother. He is dead, too."

Kim Eng's wife and now his son had been snatched from him in one horrible moment. The added measure of grief seemed to have no impact. He was dealing with more than he could bear.

Little Chhun Phon dashed through the crowd and threw herself into the mud at her father's feet. She grasped his legs and wailed.

Kim Ang withdrew her arms from her uncle while he scooped up his eight-year-old daughter. They clung to one another, heartbroken and trembling.

Kim Ang stood beside them, lifted her head and cried out, to no one in particular it seemed, perhaps to a God she didn't know:

"Why does all this happen to us? Why do we suffer so much? Why do we just get a taste of freedom, then have it snatched away?

My aunt was kind. Why is she dead? We are lost here in the wilderness. Our situation is hopeless!"

Hopeless, hopeless, hopeless— the word echoed back from the mountainside. Or did it just seem that way? Regardless, as the last reverberation faded, Aunt Lang's final words to her came flooding back. Kim Ang was sure she actually heard her speak again.

"Don't give up hope!"

"Forgive me, Auntie. I forget so soon. I won't stop hoping."

But now, here in this menacing wilderness, there remained only seven of the nineteen kinfolk who had started out together from Phnom Penh four years ago on this journey of misery. Hope might help. But it would take more than that for them to survive.

The Real Story
The Killer That Won't Quit

Designed originally as a defensive weapon, the land mine since World War II has been increasingly used to terrorize civilian populations. Unfortunately, the mines can't distinguish between soldiers and civilians, and they don't know when the war is over. Long after peace has returned the mines keep on killing.

That has been especially true in Cambodia where thousands have lost lives and limbs because of mines. Cambodia has 30,000 amputees—one for every 384 inhabitants. And it is estimated that there are still 10 million mines in the country.

Antipersonnel land mines contain from one-fourth pound to four pounds of high explosive encased in metal, plastic, glass, or wood. They are usually buried just below the surface of the ground and are detonated by foot pressure or a tripwire. Some, however, are placed above ground.

The Claymore mine, used during the Vietnam War, could be imbedded in earth or hung from trees and shrubs, about two to three feet above the ground. Made of plastic and set off by tripwires, the Claymores contain metal pellets that can be aimed in any direction and have a range of about 250 feet.

More than 300 kinds of antipersonnel land mines are manufactured in 44 countries, according to Human Rights Watch and Physicians for Human Rights. In recent years they have been produced at a rate of about 30,000 per day, and it is believed that more than 100 million mines lie unexploded in more than 50 countries. The American Red Cross estimates that 200 civilians are killed by land mines each week.

Land mines are small and inexpensive. They are sold today for about three dollars. But they are expensive and difficult to remove. A United Nations source says it would cost $200 billion to $300 billion to get rid of the mines scattered throughout the world. And demining Afghanistan by United Nations crews, for example, would take 4,300 years to complete at the current rate, according to the Red Cross.

For more details, see:

Joan D. Criddle and Teeda Butt Mam, *To Destroy You Is No Loss* (New York, The Atlantic Monthly Press, 1987), pages 257-258.

John Lloyd, "Antipersonnel Mines: The Time to Act Is Now," *1994 World Refugee Report* (Washington, D. C., U. S. Committee for Refugees, 1994), pages 33-38

Judy A, Mayotte, *Disposable People?* (New York, Orbis Books, 1992), pages 110-112

Haing Ngor with Roger Warner, *A Cambodian Odyssey* (New York, Macmillan Publishing Company, 1987), pages 378-379

Kevin Whitelaw, "Minefields, literal and metaphoric," *U. S. News & World Report* (Feb 3, 1997), pages 39-41

CHAPTER 16

Thankfulness and Anticipation

NOVEMBER 22, 1979
MENDON

"I've had a wonderful time today, Ken. I can't remember a better Thanksgiving Day. Can you?"

Donna's eyes sparkled in the candlelight. Except for a glow from the fireplace, the only light in the family room came from two flames dancing above empty cappuccino cups and dessert dishes.

Ken left the table, retrieved a piece of oak from the woodbox and tossed it onto the glowing embers. As the shower of sparks diminished and the new log burst into flame, he retreated to the sofa, leaned back, and contemplated the question.

"No, I really can't. I know I've never had a better dinner. And it was great having you all to myself. Families are fine, but I'm glad we were alone today."

After this morning's Thanksgiving Day service at church, they came home to change into casual clothes for an appetite-building hike at the Pinery. Relishing the beauty of the woods after an early-season dusting of snow, they wandered the trails longer than expected. By the time they returned to their car for the short drive back to Mendon, the sun had dipped to silhouette a nearby barn and cast a golden spell across the landscape.

Back home, darkness had fallen by the time Donna brought two steaming plates of turkey and dressing, cranberry, squash, and mashed potatoes to the family room. Ken had set up a table there so they could enjoy the coziness of the fireplace as they ate. Their dinner, with flickering flames and soft music, was a fitting end to a perfect day.

They'd decided to stay in Mendon for Thanksgiving this year, rather than travel to be with family. Ken planned to spend nearly all of Friday and Saturday at his office in Old Main, checking themes his freshman composition students turned in before their long holiday weekend. Donna hoped that, after completing preparations for next week's adult education class, she'd be able to get started on Christmas decorating. They'd make it up with their families next month, spending Christmas with Donna's parents in Wisconsin, then traveling to Michigan to end the year with Ken's folks.

Last June's decision to return to the classroom rather than continue in public relations had been easy enough for Ken to make. Telling Bennington was another matter. Ken liked the Board chairman and felt badly about having to disappoint him. Nevertheless, his conscience was clear. Scotty had asked him for a commitment of at least two years in the PR position, and he'd served five. Now it was time to return to what he most enjoyed, and what he believed was in the college's best interest as well—teaching.

"I'm thankful you're back doing what you like best."

Donna spoke softly, arms resting on the table as she admired her husband.

He didn't respond immediately. From across the room he studied the features he knew so well. Backlighted by the hearth's glow, her hair acquired an auburn tint. Soft light from swaying flames of the two candles played across her face, accentuating the fullness of her lips, the smoothness of her skin.

That's typical of her, he thought, *being grateful for something that makes me happy.*

Then, aloud finally, "Come over here and I'll tell you what really makes me thankful."

She curled up alongside and rested her head on his shoulder.

"I'm afraid I take my biggest blessing for granted too often," he continued, then paused, caressed her cheek, and added, "It's the beautiful woman who makes my home and my life so wonderful. I don't tell you, or show you, often enough that I love you."

"Sure you do."

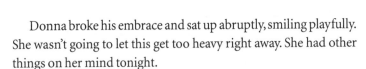

Donna broke his embrace and sat up abruptly, smiling playfully. She wasn't going to let this get too heavy right away. She had other things on her mind tonight.

"You told me twice already today," she persisted.

"I did?"

"Sure, this morning before church when I found your cuff links, then later when I agreed to have dinner tonight so we'd have more time at the Pinery during the day."

"Well, sure, but those were just responses of gratitude. They weren't real expressions of love."

"Oh?" She feigned wounded pride. "You don't really mean it when you say you love me?"

She reached out, pulled his head closer, and kissed his cheek.

"I'm just teasing, Ken. I do appreciate your expressions of love— when you show it in the things you do as well as what you say."

Her smile rekindled the embers of his desire. But she had no intent of fanning the flames.

"You want to know why I'm thankful?" she asked.

"Sure."

He lifted the hand at his side and kissed it. She had pulled back again, and it was the only target within range of his lips.

"Well, I'll tell you. As I said, I'm thankful for a husband who's happy with his work again. You're like a new man. I'm glad you don't have to deal with presidents and printers or worry about promotion and publicity problems. You're great when you're working with kids."

"I'm glad you're glad. I am happy. I do love working with kids."

"And that's not all. I'm grateful for your love. I really am. And for the happy home you've given me." She hesitated, letting her eyes affirm her words. "And I'm thankful for a man who has so much to share. I'm especially thankful the barriers between him and a greater sharing of himself have been removed."

Oh oh. All of a sudden this conversation is getting a little deeper. He smiled, but slight creases on his brow evidenced concern at the direction the discussion might be going.

"Explain that last sentence for me, please."

"Well, Ken, I just mean I'm glad you're doing what you like again, that the problems you've had to face the past five years are gone now—the problems that were keeping you from sharing yourself more fully."

"I don't remember refusing to share myself fully."

"No, I don't mean with me. You remember that blizzard a few years ago when the TV wouldn't work and we got this one? You remember I was upset because you spent so much out of our savings?"

Now he saw where Donna was headed. She was trying to steer him toward adoption again. He could feel the knots tightening in his stomach. She had him in a corner, and he knew it. He'd just confessed he didn't demonstrate his love enough. Having a child was her greatest desire. If he really loved her, how could he continue to stand in the way of fulfillment?

"Oh, I see. You've decided that, since I don't have too many problems at work any more, I could use a few more at home."

"Now you're teasing, Ken. You know I don't want you to have any problems, at work or at home. This isn't about having problems. It's about sharing love."

"When it comes to sharing, Donna, I don't know if I can do that—share you, I mean. If you have a child, am I still going to rate first in your life? Are you still going to be there when I need you?"

She knew the questions were serious. She was glad he could express these concerns openly.

"Ken, I've always hoped *we* would have a child, that this child would be *ours*, not mine. Of course, I'll always be there for you. That will never change."

Though he hadn't expressed it, Donna guessed he might be worried about sharing other aspects of his life, too. Maybe he feared an invasion of the time he reserved for his outdoor pleasures. Perhaps that negative possibility could be turned to a positive.

"Wouldn't it be fun to share your love of nature with someone else?" she asked. "Wouldn't you enjoy showing your son or daughter the wonders of the Pinery, or the way to tempt a trout with a dry fly?"

She let the questions sink in. He didn't respond. He wasn't

sure she expected him to. How could his answer be anything other than yes?

Now her eyes were speaking again, and their message was as clear as the one from her lips. They reflected her love, certainly, but her determination even more.

"You have so much to give." She spoke softly, but forcefully. "*We* have so much to give. I know if we give of ourselves to make some child happy, our love for each other will become stronger than ever. We've had a good life together, Ken. But it can be even better. We've got love to spare. It will be a shame if we haven't given any of it away before it's too late."

"Are you sure it's not too late already? I don't really want kids running around when I'm retired. I'm hoping that, a few years down the road when my preparation and teaching responsibilities lighten a bit, I'll have time to do some writing, some fiction perhaps. I couldn't write with a kid running in and out of my study all the time."

"We have plenty of time, Ken. You're only forty-two. By the time you retire, a child we'd adopt would probably be married."

"Then I'll be a grandfather, and there'll be even more little kids running around."

He was smiling now. Both realized the barriers he was trying to erect had too many holes in them. To all intents and purposes, the argument was over.

"Anyway, just to be on the safe side, if you're going to persist with this crazy idea, I think we ought to consider an older kid—one who's going to be married for sure by the time I decide to slow down."

"Does that mean it's OK, Ken? Can we try to find a child?"

Her eyes beamed. She threw her arms around him, buried her head in his chest, and cried.

"If it's going to make you this unhappy, forget it. I don't need a weepy wife."

"Quit teasing, Ken. You know I'm crying because I'm overjoyed." She squeezed him tighter.

"It's OK, Donna, for you to start looking into the possibility. If it's going to happen, it's going to take time. It's not a simple matter. There'll be a lot of difficult decisions to make, not the least of which will be—if it gets that far—which child is the right one. It's OK for you to start thinking and looking. Then we'll make the decisions as we go along."

"Ken, you don't know how much this means to me… ."

"Sure I do," he interrupted.

"No, let me finish. This is the nicest thing you've done for me, except maybe asking me to marry you. I've wanted so much to be a mother, to give you a child, and this is the only way I can do it. Knowing I can really made a difference in someone's life, do something that will make the world a better place, that means so much to me!"

She dried her tears on a sleeve of his sweater, rested her head on his chest. Their embrace tightened. They kissed. Then, still clinging to Ken, Donna twisted to face the hearth and watched in fascination as the fluctuating flames danced an accompaniment to her joy. She was sure she'd never been this happy.

Thank You, God, she prayed silently. *May this decision be one that will draw us even closer to one another, and to You. Thank You for the happiness of our life together. Let us share it soon with someone who desperately needs Your love, and ours. Spread Your arms now—across the country if need be, or even around the world— and bring us together with some child who needs a mother and a father, with the child you have chosen for us.*

CHAPTER 17

A Proposal, Of Sorts

NOVEMBER 23, 1979
KHAO I DANG REFUGEE CENTER, THAILAND

It's a miracle, Kim Ang thought. *I'm in a real hospital. How wonderful to be in a civilized place. There's nothing like this in all of Cambodia.*

Though her illness was more debilitating than any she'd ever experienced, she was actually grateful for the affliction. If she hadn't been sick she'd still be in the depressing and dangerous Mean Chey border camp controlled by the Khmer Serei. Those anti-communist soldiers weren't as malicious as the Khmer Rouge, but Kim Ang detested them. Like the Khmer Rouge, they regarded people merely as tools to be used to their own advantage.

From the horror of the Preah Vihear minefields where Aunt Lang and cousin Meng Ty were killed five months ago, Kim Ang with her surviving kin and Ay Leng had struggled back through the jungle to Sisophon. They had waited several days before starting out on the treacherous journey, wondering whether world reaction to the forced repatriation of more than forty thousand refugees would make the Thais let them back in. But that didn't happen.

So with thousands of others, they began the long trek back to the center of their country. Two days into their journey they were stopped by a Vietnamese patrol which, to their amazement, gave them food and told them which trails toward their destination had been cleared of mines. Nevertheless, nearly two months of arduous walking still confronted them.

And at Sisophon, where they arrived in early August, conditions were hardly better than while traveling. Food was difficult to obtain, and the likelihood of widespread famine increased with each passing day. Furthermore, news from the frontier revealed Thai attitudes toward the Cambodians hadn't changed. Chances of getting back across the border, and staying in Thailand, were nil.

Nevertheless, at Sisophon Kim Ang's uncles devoted themselves completely to formulation of another escape plan. They asked about routes and guides, the political situation in Thailand, the possibilities of resettlement in other countries. They spent hours discussing when and where they should make their move.

In October they learned that, after pressure from other countries and assurances of help from the United Nations and humanitarian agencies, the Thais reversed their policy of expelling Cambodians. Now they were actually establishing camps for refugees inside Thailand at a safe distance from the border.

Meanwhile, Grandmother's cousin, Nuom Yong, also had returned to Sisophon with some of her family. They, too, had been forced down the cliff and through the minefields at Preah Vihear with tragic consequences. Nuom Yong's husband and two of her sons were killed when a mine exploded. Her daughter was wounded by a piece of shrapnel from the same blast. The tragedy reduced Nuom Yong's family group to herself and her daughter, her son, daughter-in-law, and seven-year-old grandson. She was grateful, however, that two daughters, with the children of one, had escaped to Thailand earlier and had already resettled in the United States.

Nuom Yong, too, was determined to make another bid for freedom, and her son, Dap Hong Taing, eagerly joined Kim Ang's uncles in contriving a plan. Finally, about a month ago, the two family groups and Kim Ang's friend, Ay Leng, assembled to begin their second escape attempt.

At the last moment, however, Hong Taing's wife, Tan Chhun Ly, refused to go.

"I'm not going to go back through those minefields again," she told her husband. "Look what happened to your father and your brothers. That will not happen to me. And you will not endanger the life of our son again either. We will stay here."

The ensuing argument was vehement.

"I have a commitment to my mother and sister to take them to safety," he pleaded. "Don't force me to decide whether my obligation to my mother is more important than my love for my wife and my son. We have suffered so much. There is no future for us here. We will all die of starvation soon. You must come with me."

But she wouldn't listen, and his anger mounted. He turned suddenly and, with his mother and sister, followed his cousins westward out of the city toward the frontier. The remnants of the two families plus Ay Leng, now just eleven persons, were swallowed up in a long procession of refugees plodding to the border.

For most, the second escape attempt was less strenuous than the first. But Kim Ang and Hong Taing's sister, twenty-year-old Chhun Sang, struggled to keep pace. The shrapnel, still inside Chhun Sang's left thigh, caused great pain. Walking was difficult, and finally she had to be pulled in a cart her brother had improvised from bicycle wheels to transport luggage. Though all in the group were malnourished, Kim Ang's health was especially precarious. She had contracted Beriberi. Soon neuritis and muscular atrophy made it impossible for her to walk without the aid of crutchlike sticks. Eventually she, too, had to be pulled in the cart with Chhun Sang.

Hopes of the group soared when they finally neared the frontier again. But they were quickly dashed when Khmer Serei soldiers blocked the trail. To them refugees were merely bait for food that agencies distributed in the border region on the basis of the number of people in each camp.

So, almost within sight of freedom, the long line of Cambodians was diverted to the no-man's-land encampment of Mean Chey. Here they were captives again, this time not of the communists but of the enemies of communism.

But then, just when their spirits had bottomed out, when their hopeless situation and the pain of the two young women was greatest, a crack appeared in the wall separating them from freedom. Three days ago a team of doctors and nurses appeared at Mean Chey to identify sick and wounded refugees who could be treated in a new field hospital at Khao I Dang, a huge refugee camp being opened in Thailand, eleven kilometers beyond the border.

Thai soldiers accompanying the medical team ordered the Khmer Serei to approve the transfer of Kim Ang and Chhun Sang. On the following day they, and Grandmother, were among five thousand at-risk refugees—the sick, old persons, and unaccompanied children—who became the first residents of Khao I Dang. Kim Ang and Chhun Sang made the trip on mattresses placed in the flat bed of a truck, while Grandmother rode on a bus.

Yesterday the Khmer Serei permitted relatives of the evacuees to join them at the new camp which had been hastily developed to accommodate 200,000 refugees. Ay Leng, too, was approved for transfer to Khao I Dang and was now among those safely inside Thailand.

There is much to be thankful for, Kim Ang thought as she lay on the hospital cot at Khao I Dang. *What would have happened to me if the doctors didn't bring me here?*

But, despite her gratitude, Kim Ang still worried.

Will we be able to stay this time? she wondered. *Or will the Thais change their minds and force us back across the border again? My body couldn't take that. I would surely die.*

As she lay with her eyes closed, pondering that possibility, she felt a hand on her shoulder.

"Kim Ang."

It was Uncle Kim Eng. And standing beside him was Hong Taing.

"How do you feel?" her uncle asked as she blinked her eyes, adjusting to the light behind the two figures.

"Oh, better today. The pain is not as bad. The medicine is helping. What day is it?"

"Friday," Kim Eng responded. "You and Chhun Sang and Grandmother have been here two days. The rest of us came yesterday. Remember?"

"Oh, sure." She scrunched to a sitting position. "How are Grandmother and the others?"

"Everyone is fine now. Do you feel well enough to talk with Hong Taing and me? It is something rather complicated."

She didn't respond immediately, and her brow wrinkled as she pondered what complications had arisen, and why she, lying here in

143

a hospital, should be asked to talk about them? She studied the faces of both men before replying.

"I guess so. I'm all right."

"If you become too tired, tell us and we will come back later," Kim Eng said. "But what we want to talk about is very important. The sooner we discuss it, the better it will be for all of us."

His voice was softer now. Obviously, he didn't want others to overhear their conversation.

"You know Hong Taing's wife and son did not come with us when we escaped this time."

"Of course."

"And do you remember that Hong Taing's sister Chhun Ping escaped several months ago and has reached America?"

"Yes. She's there with her son and daughter and her youngest sister."

"That's right. And now Hong Taing has learned his sister filed papers to bring him and his family to America."

"That's wonderful!"

"Yes, but there is one problem."

"What is that?"

"All of the family is not here. Chhun Ping didn't know Hong Taing's wife and son aren't with him. When she made out the papers, she listed them along with Hong Taing, his other sister Chhun Sang, and their mother."

"So? What has that got to do with me? I don't think there is anything I can do, lying here in a hospital."

"Hong Taing needs to have a wife," Kim Eng explained. "He would ..."

"You want me to marry Hong Taing?" Kim Ang blurted incredulously.

Kim Eng placed a hand on her arm, trying to calm her.

"No, not really," he said. "He just wants you to pretend to be his wife."

Hong Taing moved closer.

"Let me try to explain," he said. "The papers my sister made out will go to American immigration officials here. They will see the names of two people on the list who are not with us. They will say none of my family can go to America because there is a problem with the papers. I do not care for me. But my mother is getting old. She can't live in the difficult conditions in Cambodia. And my sister Chhun Sang deserves a better life. Please help me."

"If you agree to help Hong Taing," Kim Eng interjected, "it could help our family, too. It's more likely we can go to America if a relative is already there, someone to file papers for us like Hong Taing's sister did for his family. If you reach America with Hong Taing, you can make out papers for us to go to America, too. I have talked to Grandmother and to your Uncle Hong. They hope you will do this."

Kim Ang turned from her uncle and stared at Hong Taing.

"So you want me to say my name is Tan Chhun Ly and I am your wife?"

"That's right," Hong Taing responded. "I will tell you all about my family and my house and all the things you need to know to answer questions the immigration people may ask."

"But I have already told one of the workers here my name is Savang Kim Ang. She asked my name when they brought me to the hospital."

"I was afraid of that," Kim Eng mused. "But I think it can be explained. You can tell the immigration people Savang Kim Ang is a name you used with the Pol Pot people so they wouldn't know who you really are. You needed a different name because your parents were wealthy and you were afraid they would kill you. When you came here, you said your name was Savang Kim Ang because it had become a habit to give that name. You were in great pain and weren't thinking clearly."

"Yes, certainly. That makes sense," Hong Taing chimed in.

"Will you do it?" Kim Eng asked.

Kim Ang turned to Hong Taing.

"How about your son? He's not here either. What will you do about that?"

"One of my friends here has a little boy Meng Fou's age, and he told me his son could pretend to be my son. He wants very much for the child to get away from the danger here. He says if he and his wife are able to come to America later his son can go back to them. If not, at least he'll have a better life."

"And how about me, a 17-year-old girl, pretending to be a 26-year-old mother?" Kim Ang persisted. "How could I get away with that?"

"You look older than your age," Hong Taing countered, "especially since your illness. And you are a very mature young woman. Besides, the Americans seem to think we all look younger than we are. They won't suspect anything."

"Will you do it, Kim Ang?" Kim Eng asked again.

She hesitated. "How long would I have to keep on pretending?"

"Only until we get to America," Hong Taing answered. "Then, when we are settled, you can leave and go to live with other relatives if you wish. You know my uncle, Nuom Peng Sy, and his family. They are also your cousins. I believe your family and his visited often. They're living near my sister Chhun Ping in America now."

"I think it would be best for all of us," Kim Eng added.

"And if I am caught lying to the American immigration people," Kim Ang asked, "what then? What will happen to me?"

"You won't be caught," Kim Eng assured her. "Hong Taing and I will coach you well. There is no danger."

Kim Ang wasn't so sure. But Grandmother and her uncles and little cousin Chhun Phon were the only family she had left. How could she refuse to help them have a better life? Besides, pretending to be Hong Taing's wife might hasten the day when she would reach some peaceful place where her dream of an education could come true. If she said no, would there be another chance to go to America? Meanwhile, would the Thais push them back across the border again? She couldn't risk that happening. There seemed to be no alternative.

"Yes, I'll do it," she said softly, without enthusiasm, adding under her breath, "and I hope I won't regret it."

The Real Story
A Respite for Refugees

In the aftermath of Thailand's heartless expulsion of more than 40,000 refugees, the doors to freedom for those fleeing Cambodia opened wider. The plight of those forced down the cliffs and through the minefields at Preah Vihear focused worldwide attention even more keenly on victims of the Cambodian holocaust.

Though the Thais' cold-hearted eviction of the refugees may have been unpardonable, it was understandable—at least to those who view the American response to Haitians in subsequent years as so. Thailand, about three-quarters the size of Texas with a population of three and a quarter times as many, was a magnet for refugees from all sides. During the preceding decade more than 600,000 refugees from Laos, Vietnam, and Cambodia sought refuge in Thailand.

Thai officials feared that widespread acceptance of the refugees in camps on their territory would only encourage more to come. Besides, they contended that those who fled Cambodia, if not Vietnam and Laos as well, did so because of U. S. policies during the 1970-75 war. They clearly believed their bigger and stronger ally had a greater responsibility.

Amid the international outcry that followed the Thais' callous expulsion of the refugees, the United States and other countries, as well as the United Nations, did promise to help.

Thailand agreed to move temporarily many of the refugees from camps at the border to centers farther from the fighting. And several programs, coordinated by the United Nations High Commissioner for Refugees, were established to assist refugees in the Thai camps.

The door didn't stay open long, however. In February 1980 Thailand closed its border to Cambodians. A year later it implemented its policy of "humane deterrence," under which new refugees from Vietnam and Laos were placed in holding centers with barely tolerable conditions and those from Cambodia were sent to camps at the border.

For more details, see:

Joan D. Criddle and Teeda Butt Mam, *To Destroy You Is No Loss* (New York, The Atlantic Monthly Press, 1987), pages 258-263

Virginia Hamilton, ed., *Cambodians in Thailand: People on the Edge* (Washington, D. C., U. S. Committee for Refugees, 1985), pages 10-13

Arnold R. Isaacs, Gordon Hardy, MacAlister Brown, *Pawns of War* (Boston, Boston Publishing Company, 1987), pages 169-174

Henry Kamm "Thais Readmit 1,000 Cambodians for Later Resettlement Elsewhere," *The New York Times* (July 11, 1979), page A1

Henry Kamm, "Cambodians Are Eager to Leave, but Fear Leaders," *The New York Times* (Nov. 21, 1979), page A3

Court Robinson, "Buying Time: Refugee Repatriation from Thailand," *1992 World Refugee Survey* (Washington, D. C., U. S. Committee for Refugees, 1992), pages 18-19

Court Robinson, *Something Like Home Again: The Repatriation of Cambodian Refugees* (Washington, D. C., U. S. Committee for Refugees, 1994), pages 3-5

CHAPTER 18

Angels at Millbrook

JANUARY 20, 1980
MENDON

As far as Ken was concerned, this was the way to spend a winter Sunday afternoon—cozy fire in the fireplace, footrest up on the recliner, most of today's newspaper on the floor at his side and the rest on his lap.

Donna was still busy in the kitchen, packaging up leftovers from dinner and putting dishes away. For the past two months, she'd thought little of anything except adoption. She had contacted several agencies, asked questions, filled out papers, made calls to be sure all was in order and to check on progress. She was enthused about moving ahead, with Ken's willingness, toward the day when they'd bring a child into their home. But she was discouraged to realize the process was going to take a lot longer than she anticipated.

Today, however, she did have her mind on other things. She slipped the last of the leftovers into the refrigerator and walked through the short hallway to the family room.

"Ken, I hope you're planning to go with me to the meeting at church this afternoon."

He glanced up from the sports section.

"What meeting?"

She tried not to sound annoyed.

"The meeting Rev. Greenwood mentioned at the end of the sermon this morning. The meeting about Cambodian refugees."

"Oh, come on, Donna. Do you know what day this is?"

"Sunday."

"No, not just Sunday. It's Super Bowl Sunday. The Steelers are playing the Rams, and that's the last football for a long time."

"What time does the game start?"

"Five o'clock, but there's a bunch of pregame stuff before then."

"The meeting's at three, Ken. You'll be home before kickoff. All that pregame hoopla is boring anyway."

"Well, that's a matter of opinion. I've really been looking forward to spending the afternoon right here. This only happens once a year."

"It's been happening for four months. And three weeks ago, on New Year's Day, it happened for about 24 hours straight."

"Oh, come on, Donna. You're exaggerating a bit, aren't you?"

"Well, not much. But I want you to go with me, Ken. There's a real need for churches to sponsor refugees. Someone's going to be there from Lafayette to tell about it, a man whose church is sponsoring a family."

"I really don't have time to get involved in something like that now."

"But we can find out what's necessary before deciding. We don't even know how much time or effort is needed."

"Donna, you go. Then when you get home you can tell me."

He lifted the paper and buried his head in the sports section again.

She said nothing, and he glanced up across the top of the paper. Her face reflected disappointment and frustration. Sometimes, he knew, she feigned that pout for effect, but this time it was genuine. She really was upset.

"Ken, I hardly ever ask you to do anything like this. I've been concerned about those people who lost everything. I don't know if there's anything we can do. But before we say we won't do anything, I think we should find out what needs to be done. I just want to get information. And I want you to be with me."

Watching the Super Bowl wouldn't be enjoyable if he and Donna were at odds. And he did have to admit she rarely twisted his arm to do anything like this.

"OK, Donna, I'll go. But if the meeting isn't over by 4:45 I'm walking out and coming home to watch the game."

An hour and a half later at Mendon's United Methodist Church, Ken was already checking his watch when Rev. Greenwood introduced David Cranston to about thirty of his parishioners. The MacKenzies were among the last to arrive, and Ken insisted on sitting behind those already gathered at the front of the sanctuary. Cranston, a florist and member of First Presbyterian Church in Lafayette, appeared a bit nervous.

"I'm more at home in a greenhouse than here in the shadow of a pulpit," he began. "I'm not a preacher. I'd starve if I had to make a living by speaking. And until last week I couldn't have imagined myself standing here, asking for help. This is completely out of character for me."

Ken had to agree. Cranston was no polished speaker. It was apparent he'd feel more comfortable someplace else. But he seemed sincere.

"I do need your help," he went on, "but not for me. When we're finished here I can go home to my family in a warm and comfortable house, a house where we feel secure, in a country where we have more blessings than we're able to count. But there are thousands of families who don't have those blessings. They can't go home. They're refugees.

"Maybe you and I can't make a difference for thousands of families. But I hope you'll give consideration this afternoon to just one family, a family that's lived through nearly five years of terror. I'm sure you've read and heard what happened in Cambodia. This family has lost more than half its relatives. Most were murdered. Some died of starvation, others of disease brought on by malnutrition and overwork as slaves."

Out of the corner of his eye, Ken saw Donna edge forward in the pew. She obviously didn't want to miss a word. *This guy has her spellbound*, he thought.

"Last summer," the visitor continued, "this family escaped to Thailand. But Thai soldiers made them go back—through a minefield. Their newly-won freedom was lost. And then in one cruel moment an explosion killed a husband and two of his sons. Now that man's widow needs your help. She risked her life again in another bid for freedom. So far, the Thais have let her stay and she's in a camp with her surviving son, her daughter-in-law and grandson, and her daughter. The daughter was wounded by the same mine that killed her father and brothers. If these people don't get to another country soon, it's possible they'll once more be forced back across the border."

Ken looked at Donna again. *She's going to get me caught up in this thing for sure*, he told himself. *I never should have agreed to come here.*

"A Cambodian woman supported by my church in Lafayette is another daughter of the lady," Cranston continued. "Her dream is to be reunited with her mother and surviving siblings. The family of her mother's youngest brother also will be coming to this area. Holy Trinity Episcopal Church in your town has agreed to sponsor that family."

Cranston gave the names and ages of the five persons he hoped the Mendon Methodists would sponsor, then went on to describe what would be involved.

"You'd provide temporary housing, food, clothing, and the basic necessities of life until they can get on their own feet," he told them. "You'd also introduce the family to its new community, help to find jobs, and arrange for language training. But most important of all, you'd be a source of personal comfort and encouragement until the family is able to be self-sufficient.

"I guess you could say the main things needed are a little money and a lot of love."

For more than half an hour Cranston responded to questions: How much is "a little money"? For what kinds of jobs are members of the family qualified? What kind of housing is expected? How long will the sponsorship commitment continue? Where will the family get language training? What kind of food do they eat? How about health care costs? How readily will these people adapt to life in the United States?

Then, when it seemed there were no further questions, Donna raised her hand and asked, "How did you happen to get involved in this?"

"That's a rather long story," Cranston replied. "My involvement began when our church decided to sponsor some Cambodians a couple months ago. But let me go back a little farther.

"I don't know if you believe in angels, but it seems to me an angel certainly must have been behind all of this. You can argue with me about that, but the first person to get involved was a most unlikely candidate for helping refugees. I know him, and he never was the type to be concerned about other people's problems.

"This all started in an unlikely place, too—a little town called Millbrook. It's about ten miles west of Lafayette. Most people don't even know it exists. There's not much there, just a couple dozen houses and a Baptist church. I doubt the church has more than thirty members, but one of them is this acquaintance of mine. He happened to hear about the need for sponsors of Cambodian refugees and called an agency in Indianapolis to see what could be done to help. I was dumbfounded when I heard that, but it's true. Something changed this man. If you don't believe it was an angel, OK. But he talked the other people in this tiny little church at Millbrook into sponsoring a family.

"Then, a few days after the family arrived, the agency in Indianapolis called this guy and said they had an urgent need for three more sponsoring churches. If they didn't find them right away, they said, the refugees might be sent back to Cambodia. So he got on the telephone, and one of the people he called was me. I decided if this man who never cared about helping people is doing this, maybe I ought to think about it, too. I talked to some friends in my congregation, and we decided we could do it if a little church in Millbrook could.

"That's how I happened to become involved. And that's why I'm here today, asking you to help. If you do, there may be days you'll have regrets. There will be problems. But I can assure you they'll be outnumbered by your blessings. Invariably when I talk to persons involved with refugees, they tell me it's done more for them than the people they tried to help. I've found that to be especially true for me.

"But I've talked enough. It's time to go so you can discuss these things among yourselves. I've given Pastor Greenwood a manual with detailed information that will be helpful if you decide to sponsor the family. If you have other questions, I'll be glad to respond by telephone or come back and answer them. Thanks for listening to me. God bless you."

With that Cranston left the sanctuary, and Rev. Greenwood moved to the podium.

"Most of you heard my sermon this morning when I used the last part of the twenty-fifth chapter of Matthew as my text. So I don't think I need to say more about how I feel about this. Do you have questions or concerns?"

"Yes, sir, I do." The voice came from the left, a couple rows ahead. Ken recognized the man but didn't know his name. "I think it's fine to help people, but there are lots of them closer to home we can help. I don't think we have to bring foreigners in here and add to our unemployment problems. Bringing in these Asians will just make it tougher for people already here who need help."

"Would anyone like to respond to that?" Rev. Greenwood asked.

Help could be provided to persons already in the community and to refugees at the same time, Ken thought to himself. But he didn't say anything.

"As most of you already know, we're having a hard time meeting our budget," another called out. Ken knew this one. It was Jud Hartman, chairman of the church's Finance Committee. "I won't agree to sponsoring any family of refugees until we have all the money we need to operate the church and can meet our local obligations. Then we should raise the money necessary for sponsoring refugees before we commit ourselves. You can't just go ahead and agree to do something like this without having the funds first. That would be completely irresponsible."

Ken squirmed in the pew and raised his hand.

"Doctor MacKenzie," said the pastor.

"I'm no do-gooder. Maybe helping a refugee family is a good idea, and maybe it isn't. But if it's something we should do, how can we sit back and wait until we meet all our other obligations, then raise all the money for this before deciding to do anything? I don't recall the Good Samaritan telling the robbery victim he'd be back to help after he'd taken care of all his other problems. Seems to me if helping refugees is what needs doing, we should try to figure out how. If we can't move ahead on faith, what kind of church are we?"

When he'd finished, Ken couldn't believe he'd said that. Neither could Donna. She moved closer, reached out and squeezed his hand.

"I agree with that." Duane Landon was speaking now. Ken hadn't really seen much of Duane since their last fishing expedition of the summer. "I'm convinced this is something we ought to do. If there's agreement here today, Shirley and I are willing to head a committee to get things going."

Others quickly followed with offers of help. Donna was one of them. So was Barbara Moore, the church's youth activities director.

"You're all aware my husband Tom and I live just up the street in a house the church owns," Barbara said. "We've been talking it over, and it really is too big for us. We can move into an apartment Tom's folks have. Then the house we're in now could be used for the refugee family."

"That's a very kind gesture," the pastor commented. "But before we go farther, I believe we should take a vote to see how much support we have for proceeding with a sponsorship."

"I move that we agree to sponsor the Cambodian family," Donna offered, "that a committee be formed to handle planning and arrangements, and that Duane and Shirley Landon serve as chairpersons."

The motion was seconded and approved by nearly two to one on a show of hands.

"There needs to be some assurance that money intended for other purposes doesn't end up supporting these strangers," Hartman then insisted. "I move that contributions for the refugees be kept in a special account, completely separate from other church funds so there's no possibility of comingling. There should be no possibility of other money being siphoned away to help refugees."

Though most were displeased by the apparent spirit of the motion, many felt the idea had merit. With a separate fund, church accounts would be protected from use by the refugee committee to be sure, but at the same time money given for the refugees wouldn't be used for other purposes. The measure passed by a slim margin, and several persons made pledges on the spot to get the fund started.

"Well, it appears we have resolved to take this step," Pastor Greenwood noted. "We have a committee and we have promises of financial support. If this fund is to be maintained separately as directed by the last motion, we need a treasurer to handle it. Are there any volunteers?"

The wheels were turning in Ken's mind. *Sure as I'm sitting here*, he thought to himself, *Donna is going to get me involved in this thing. Handling the money won't be a big job. I'll be doing my part, and I won't have to get personally involved with the refugees when they get here.*

He raised his hand. "I'll do it," he called out.

CHAPTER 19

Sweet Sorrow

SEPTEMBER 8, 1980
BANGKOK, THAILAND

Kim Ang thought this day would never come. When she agreed last November to take the place of Hong Taing's wife, she expected she'd be in America within a month or two.

At first, everything went well. Competent care, along with modern medical procedures and drugs, speeded her recuperation and her discharge from the hospital. Perhaps years would pass before her body fully recovered from the abusive overwork and undernourishment of the Khmer Rouge regime, but now she was as healthy as most at Khao I Dang.

The interviews with American immigration officials, too, had gone without a hitch. Hong Taing and Uncle Kim Eng had coached her well.

"The Americans will try to trick you," Kim Eng had cautioned. "They'll take you into a room alone and ask you about very specific details. For example, they may ask if the hinges on the front door of your house in Sisophon are on the right side or the left side. Then they will take Hong Taing into the room and ask him the same question. And they will do the same with the others in the family. Obviously, you must all give the same answers."

For Hong Taing and his mother and sister, of course, there would be no problem. But Kim Ang and Seng Meng, the eight-year-old child who would take the place of Hong Taing's son, needed to spend many hours with Hong Taing, learning details of the family, its home, and its affairs. They had plenty of time together because Hong Taing convinced relatives of Kim Ang and Meng that the two should move to his hut immediately so there would be no suspicion they weren't who they would claim to be. As Hong Taing provided information about the family's former home and activities, he had them repeat the facts time after time. Kim Eng then assumed the role of an immigration interrogator and put them through mock interviews to prepare for the questioning they would undergo.

The effort paid off. When she completed her final session with the Americans, Kim Ang was certain there was no suspicion she was not really Tan Chhun Ly. Meng was asked few questions by immigration officers, and there was no apparent skepticism concerning him either.

Chhun Sang's recovery, like Kim Ang's, was rapid. After they'd removed the piece of shrapnel from her thigh, doctors told her she'd been very fortunate. The jagged piece of metal had barely missed the femoral artery. She would always carry a scar, reminding her of the tragedy that snuffed out the lives of her father and brothers, but that would be the only physical consequence. Soon able to be up and walking, she had left the hospital before Kim Ang.

All the hurdles seemed to have been cleared, and Hong Taing was told the family would probably leave for America in February if all passed their physical examinations. The exams weren't very thorough, and the health of each appeared to be the best it had been in years. There was no reason to expect a problem. But then came the shattering news that Nuom Yong's chest x-ray revealed the possibility of tuberculosis.

Tests confirmed the 60-year-old woman did have the disease in an early stage. She was hospitalized only briefly and soon was able to resume normal activities, but the delay continued.

Hopes that had soared suddenly plummeted. Though Kim Ang worried about leaving Grandmother and her uncles to live halfway around the world with people she hardly knew, she was eager to get out of Khao I Dang. More than 100,000 persons now crowded the camp, making it the largest city of Cambodians in the world.

She didn't mind big cities, but Khao I Dang had few of the customary city conveniences. Crammed along its red clay streets were thousands of flimsy shacks, hurriedly thrown together from bamboo sticks, palm leaves, and blue plastic tarps. Trees no longer provided shade. They had all been cut down for firewood. Dust filled the air during dry weather, and rain turned the ground to red mud.

Conditions were bad enough in the daylight, but nights at Khao I Dang were downright dangerous. In the dark, old grudges were often settled with knives, women were raped, and anybody might be robbed—especially when it rained. With raindrops pounding on roofs of plastic tarp and corrugated metal, drowning out all other sound, persons of evil intent could easily approach the huts, reach through the flimsy walls, and grab whatever or whoever was there.

The months of waiting did yield one benefit. Kim Ang knew attainment of her goal, an education in America, would require understanding a new language. English classes were offered in the camp for a small fee, but she didn't have the money. So she sprawled on the ground outside the tent where instruction was given and listened carefully. Then, in every spare moment, she studied the lists and practiced saying the words.

At first she wondered how anyone could learn this strange language. There were so many rules—and so many exceptions to the rules. Sometimes the letters "gh" sounded like "f" and other times they had no sound at all. "Tough" and "rough" rhymed with "stuff," but the last sound of "dough" is like "go" and "bough" like "cow." And "now" and "cow" were pronounced one way, while "low" and "slow" were different. And how can "sow" and "sew" and "so" all sound the same but have different meanings? And why does "sow" sometimes rhyme with "go" and mean to plant seeds, other times rhyme with "now" and mean a female pig? How would she ever figure out which word meant what, and why certain letters sounded one way in one word and another way in others?

But eventually, she acquired a vocabulary of several hundred words. Although she couldn't understand what the camp's English-speaking aid workers said to one another when she'd try to eavesdrop, she could comprehend all the words and phrases she heard the teacher say as she crouched outside the canvas classroom.

Finally, in mid-August camp doctors proclaimed Nuom Yong to be completely recovered, and the family again was cleared for departure. Only one of the five wasn't on edge during the final weeks, wondering if something would happen again to delay them. That was eight-year-old Meng. He dared not object to his father's decision that he go, but he longed for something to happen so he wouldn't have to leave his real parents.

Last night Kim Ang had gone to bid Ay Leng farewell, and the parting had been tearful. Since the thump of the dud rocket that brought them together on the streets of Phnom Penh six years ago, the girls had been closer than sisters. After the decision that Kim Ang would leave with Hong Taing's family, they tried to ignore the fact that separation was merely a matter of time. But there was no denying the reality now.

"Ay Leng, I'll miss you. Even when my own sisters were alive, I didn't feel as close to them as I do to you."

"Yes, it's the same with me," her friend responded. "We've been through a lot together. We escaped to Vietnam and then to Thailand, twice."

They recalled past experiences. They expressed concerns about what the future might bring.

"I don't want to be away from you," Kim Ang sighed, "but my family insists I go with Hong Taing so I can file papers for them to come to America, too. And I do want to go. There is no future here. My grandfather's dying wish was that I go to someplace like America and get an education. My Aunt Lang's last words to me were, 'Don't give up hope.' I have to go. But I hope you will come to America soon, too, Ay Leng. Then we can be together again."

"That won't happen, Kim Ang. I have no relatives in America, or anywhere. I'll stay here until we're all sent back again. But don't worry about me. I'll be all right. I'm happy for you. You were a friend to me when I had none other, except my mother. Now I'm all alone, but I have memories. I'll remember you always. But go now, Kim Ang. It's too painful to talk more about parting."

The friends clung to one another, weeping. Then Kim Ang pulled herself away, slipped through the opening in the blue tarp at the doorway, and ran back to Hong Taing's hut, the red mud of the street pulling at her sandals as if trying to hold her back.

That was the last she saw of Ay Leng. Kim Ang didn't expect her friend to be among the hundreds of hugging and crying relatives at the departure point this morning. And she wasn't. The waving and watching, while the bus rolled toward the camp gate carrying her best friend away, would have been far too painful.

Many who stood alongside the buses, waiting to board, carried bundles loaded with life's necessities: bags of rice, cooking pots, mats for sleeping, everything they thought might be needed to start a new life in America. They refused to believe the authorities who told them those things weren't necessary. Wasn't that what the Khmer Rouge said when they forced them out of the cities five years ago?

As names were called out, the departing Cambodians climbed aboard the buses. Grandmother and little cousin Chhun Phon wiped tears from their eyes when they hugged Kim Ang. But her uncles merely smiled and offered words of advice and encouragement. She was, after all, their eventual ticket to freedom.

Somehow the people and packages all managed to squeeze aboard the buses. As Kim Ang settled into her seat, the door at the front swung shut and the engine roared. A blur of waving hands and handkerchiefs flashed by the windows, and Khao I Dang was out of sight.

Now, aboard the huge Boeing 747, Kim Ang felt the excitement and apprehension mounting. Most of the four hundred refugees who filled every seat had never been inside an airplane. Would this gigantic machine really fly? How would it ever get into the sky?

Little Meng seemed least concerned about that. Kim Ang let him sit next to the window, and she took the center seat. At her left was Chhun Sang, and across the aisle in the center section were Hong Taing and his mother.

Finally, the plane rolled slowly backwards, came to a stop, then lurched forward as it began the long taxi to the end of the runway. There it paused again before the whine of jet engines grew louder. Suddenly, it thrust ahead, gathered momentum, and hurtled down the runway. Kim Ang felt herself pushed against the back of the seat as the nose lifted. She leaned across Meng and looked out the window just in time to see the ground rapidly fall away. Within moments the rice paddies were tiny swatches of green, roads and rivers were thin ribbons, and buildings were no more than specks.

The world below that had brought her so much pain was sinking farther and farther away. Then the plane sliced into a blanket of clouds, and the place of her suffering vanished completely. Up here there was only bright sunshine, blue sky, and billowy white clouds. *Surely, things are going to be better.*

The Real Story
Khao I Dang, a Sad Ending

In October 1979, after the Thais authorized the United Nations High Commissioner for Refugees to establish holding centers inside Thailand for Cambodian refugees, one at Sa Kaeo soon was crowded with 30,000 who had been in a Khmer Rouge-controlled area south of Aranyaprathet.

Early in November construction of another was begun to accommodate refugees who had camped north of Aranyaprathet in an area controlled by the Khmer Serei (Free Khmer), anti-communist guerrillas. Taking its name from a nearby mountain, Khao I Dang, this camp within two months had a population of 110,000.

The initial plan for moving refugees into the camp, after it was ready and fully staffed, was to have 10,000 per day walk from the frontier in groups of 200 at five-minute intervals. But many of the first 5,000 were too ill or weary to walk, so buses and trucks had to be used.

Among the first at Khao I Dang was Haing Ngor, a Cambodian doctor who described the camp in his book, *A Cambodian Odyssey*. "At night the camp was unsafe," he said. "There were revenge killings, robberies, and rapes. Thai villagers came over the fence at night to sell goods, and Thai soldiers fired at those who wouldn't give them *bonjour* (bribes). Under the dirt floors of the shacks were storage holes and tunnels. Most of the families in camp had something or someone to hide. During the day, when the Westerners were there, the camp had a better character. It was a place for life to begin again, for bargaining at the market, for praying at the temple."

During his stay at Khao I Dang, Dr. Ngor worked with Western physicians to care for sick and injured refugees in the camp hospital. After his resettlement in the United States he received an Academy Award as best supporting actor for portraying Dith Pran, Cambodian colleague of *New York Times* reporter Sidney Schanberg, in the Warner Brothers Film *The Killing Fields*. The ending of the film was shot at Khao I Dang.

Dr. Ngor considered *The Killing Fields* a way of telling the world about what had happened in Cambodia. "If I die from now on, OK," he told a writer for *The New York Times*. He lived long enough to become involved in humanitarian efforts that helped thousands of his countrymen who remained in Cambodia. But in 1996 he was murdered on a Los Angeles street.

For more details, see:

Haing Ngor with Roger Warner, *A Cambodian Odyssey* (New York, Macmillan Publishing Company, 1987), pages 416-422

Court Robinson, "Refugee Protection in Thailand and the Closing of Khao I Dang," *1986 World Refugee Survey* (Washington, D. C., U. S. Committee for Refugees, 1987), page 54

Gail Sheehy, *Spirit of Survival* (New York, William Morrow and Company, Inc., 1986), pages 32-34, 150-161

Gail Sheehy, "The People America Forgot," *The Washington Post* (June 27, 1982), pages C1, C4

Molyda Szymusiak, *The Stones Cry Out: A Cambodian Childhood, 1975-1980* (New York, Hill and Wang, a division of Farrar, Straus and Giroux, 1986), pages 236-245

Peter Webb and James Pringle, "Thailand Opens the Gate," *Newsweek* (Dec. 3, 1979), pages 77-78

"Pol Pot's Lifeless Zombies," *Time* (Dec. 3, 1979), pages 55-56

PART II

WE MEET, AND THE ANGELS SING

CHAPTER 20

Coming Together

Donna couldn't believe the Cambodians were finally coming. She'd almost given up hope.

"Ken, can't you get out of tonight's faculty meeting? I really wish you'd go to the airport in Indianapolis with me. They'll be there at 6:15."

"Sorry. I need to present the English Department's course-change proposals. Anyway, Duane says there shouldn't be too many of us. And there'll just be room for you and Duane and Shirley and the five Cambodians coming back."

He was right. Duane planned to take his van, and there'd be room for eight passengers if they put the luggage in the carrier on top. Of course, she and Ken could drive down in their own car, but Duane had suggested few go so as not to overwhelm the newcomers.

"How about coming over to the Hampton House after your meeting?"

The church-owned house at 518 Wentworth Avenue had gone by that name ever since the congregation acquired it eight years ago through a bequest of Charles Hampton, a charter member. Neither past occurrences inside nor present appearance outside distinguished the unremarkable structure from others in the block. But Donna believed it soon might be the site of life-changing experiences for a Cambodian family and several Mendon Methodists.

"Sure, I'll be there soon as I can."

Ken did want to meet the Cambodians. After all, this project was important to Donna. He'd support her, as long as he could do it without getting too involved. Duane and Shirley and Donna could be the ones for that.

Even though Ken wouldn't be at the airport for the welcome, Donna's enthusiasm was at a peak. This had been a long time coming. The Refugee Family Committee had been all set to welcome the Cambodians seven months ago. A week after agreeing to sponsor the family they learned the arrival probably would be in February.

Duane's organizational skills and the devotion of his corps of volunteers paid off. All the necessary tasks were checked off with time to spare. The house was spruced up and completely furnished with donations from members of the congregation. The pantry was stocked with enough food for weeks. Volunteers were all set to provide transportation when needed, serve as tutors, shop for clothes when the family arrived, help find employment. Ken reported more than a thousand dollars in the special refugee fund, with additions coming in every week.

Then, in mid-February, the disappointing call came. Duane Landon responded to the ring, anticipating a request for service or questions about a new TV set. But the caller was Becky Richards, Indianapolis contact person for the Immigration and Refugee Program of Church World Service.

"No, I'm sorry, Mr. Landon, the family isn't on the way. I'm afraid they've been placed on hold. The only information I have is that it's a medical hold. They could be cleared any day, or maybe not for months. When I know more, I'll call."

Committee members were disheartened. And they knew the Cambodians were now burdened with more anxiety and distress. Months went by and there was no further word. Then two days ago, just as Duane and Shirley were finishing dinner, Mrs. Richards called again. This time Shirley answered.

"There's good news tonight. Your family's on the way!" was the message.

Shirley lost no time in spreading the word. Within seconds she'd enlisted Donna's help in contacting members of the committee. Now it was just a matter of setting in motion the plans made long ago.

Shirley's next call was to David Cranston in Lafayette. She was sure the Cambodians sponsored by his church would be thrilled to know their relatives were finally on the way.

"Yes, they already know," Cranston said. "Word usually travels faster among the refugees than through agency networks.

"Will they be at the airport?" Shirley asked.

"They wouldn't miss it!"

Indeed, they were at the terminal when the Landons and Donna walked in at 5:45.

"This is Dap Chhun Ping," Cranston said, introducing a Cambodian woman who appeared to be about thirty. "She's one of the daughters of Nuom Yong, the grandmother in the family you're sponsoring."

Chhun Ping had been in America nearly a year and still lacked confidence in her ability to communicate in English. She smiled and nodded but didn't speak.

"Meng Hong is Chhun Ping's son," Cranston continued. "He's nine."

The boy extended his hand, obviously familiar with the way westerners greeted one another. His seven-year-old sister, realizing she would be next, retreated behind her mother.

"And this vanishing lady is Kim Ngim."

The child peeked from behind her mother's skirt and smiled.

An older girl, a teenager with a striking resemblance to the older woman, stood behind the others. Cranston took her arm and guided her to the front of the group.

"Finally, and perhaps most important to you," he said, "is this young lady. Her name is Chhun Heang. She's what we Americans sometimes call the caboose. Chhun Heang is Nuom Yong's youngest daughter. She's fourteen."

The girl smiled, and Cranston continued. "Chhun Heang came to America with her sister, Chhun Ping, and she has done very well in her first year of school here. Duane and I have agreed Chhun Heang will live with her mother in Mendon now. You'll be responsible for one more person, but you're fortunate to have a translator right in the family."

Though the compliments embarrassed Chhun Heang, she stepped

forward confidently to meet the three adults.

"I pleased meet you, sir," she nodded to Duane.

Then, moving to Donna, "You pretty lady. I happy know you."

As she approached Shirley, the girl sensed an immediate mystical attachment. Shirley felt it, too. Chhun Heang didn't speak. Instead, she placed her hands together, raised them to her forehead, and bowed in the traditional oriental gesture of greeting and respect.

Her head still bent, she spoke softly.

"Thank you for bring to me my mother."

Shirley was near tears. She took the girl's hand and drew her closer. The two embraced.

"You speak English very well," Shirley said finally.

"Not so good. I make much mistake. But I try do better."

"You do just fine. And you'll be a big help to your family. We don't speak Khmer, so we'll need your help, too."

"Your attention, please," a voice on the public address system interrupted. "American Flight 265 from San Francisco has landed and passengers will be disembarking at Gate 19."

Chhun Heang held Shirley's hand as the group started toward the gate.

Tension mounted. What if they didn't make the connection after their trans-Pacific flight landed in California? Would they really be there when the door opened? Chhun Ping and her children took up a position from where they'd have a good view of the deplaning passengers. Chhun Heang, still holding Shirley's hand, was a few feet away. Donna and Duane stood behind Shirley.

Then the door opened, and the passengers of Flight 265 began filing into the corridor. They kept coming and coming. But none were Asian. The stream of humanity continued for ten minutes, and then it stopped. Chhun Ping, her brow furrowed, said something to the children in Khmer. They turned to the four Americans and Chhun Ping spoke again, this time in English.

"They not here. What we do?"

Suddenly, Chhun Heang, who had been peering down the passageway, let go of Shirley's hand.

"There they are!" she shouted.

Coming down the tunnel from the plane was a little boy. In back of him were a man, apparently his father, and an older woman who was undoubtedly his grandmother and the man's mother. Behind them were two young women.

Seconds later a jumble of hugging, crying, rejoicing bodies clogged the gate. Donna wondered if Chhun Ping and Chhun Heang would ever release their mother. Finally, each let go with one hand and widened the embracing circle to bring their brother and one of the younger women into the jubilant reunion.

Donna noticed the welcome for the little boy and the other woman was lukewarm, at best, compared to that of the others. But she thought little of it. Maybe the neglected young woman was the sister-in-law. The greeters would naturally feel closer to their mother and siblings. Perhaps the child should have gotten more attention, but Chhun Ping had children of her own and Chhun Heang was still a child herself.

One thing, however, did stick in Donna's mind—the beauty of the woman who was all but neglected by the others. And she looked so young! But, except for the grandmother, all of the Cambodians looked young to her.

Tugged toward the waiting Americans by Chhun Ping and Chhun Heang, one on each side of her, Nuom Yong dabbed at the tears on her cheeks.

"This my mom!" Chhun Heang announced proudly. Then she turned to her mother and the two spoke in Khmer.

"Mom say she grateful you make her free," Chhun Heang translated.

The older woman pressed her palms together, placed her hands atop her nose and bowed to the Americans.

"This my brother, Hong Taing," the girl continued, pulling the man to the front of the group of newcomers. Then she introduced each of the others.

"This Chhun Sang. She my sister. She older than me."

That was quite obvious. *She must be in her twenties*, Donna thought.

"This my sister-in-law, Tan Chhun Ly. She older than Chhun Sang."

Older? That surely wasn't obvious to Donna. If anything, she looked even younger than Chhun Sang. But perhaps anyone so beautiful would look younger.

"And this my nephew. His name Meng Fou."

The child smiled shyly.

The introductions completed, Duane suggested the group head to the baggage carousel to pick up the family's luggage.

"No more," Chhun Heang pronounced. "This all they got."

Donna quickly assessed what each of the five newcomers was carrying. The grandmother had a bundle, about the size of a picnic basket, wrapped in a multicolored piece of fabric. Each of the others carried a small satchel similar to the one she'd used for taking her gym suit and shoes to college physical education classes. That was it. Besides the clothes on their backs, all the earthly possessions of these five people were in the one bundle and four little handbags.

But they were smiling. Donna was amazed. She turned to David Cranston.

"After all they've gone through, how can they smile?" she asked. "Half their relatives and friends have been killed. Here they are in a strange, new place. All they have is in those few little bags. They really have nothing to smile about."

"They have one another," Cranston replied. "Now they have freedom. And they have hope."

Duane was embarrassed he'd assumed there would be more luggage. He smiled sheepishly.

"Well, OK," he said. "We can get those things in the van without any problem. But before we go, let's make sure we have all the necessary papers. Chhun Heang, please ask your family to show me their I-94s."

The girl translated, and Hong Taing reached into his satchel to produce five small slips of paper which proved each of the refugees had entered the country legally. Duane checked the documents, then handed them back to Hong Taing.

"Tell your brother we will make copies of these tomorrow," Duane advised Chhun Heang. Each of you should always carry your copy with you. We will also keep copies in the church office. Hong Taing should keep the originals in a safe place at your house."

Chhun Heang translated as Hong Taing tucked the I-94s back into his satchel.

In the parking lot, the groups that were to ride to Mendon in the two vehicles separated amid a babble of Khmer and English directions and parting phrases. As Chhun Heang climbed into Cranston's car, Donna reached out and grasped her arm.

"Wait a minute, Chhun Heang. You should be with your mother. I'll ride with Mr. Cranston."

"That OK," the child responded. "I be with mother all time after get there."

"No, you should be with her now. You can tell her about America on the way. Besides, Duane and Shirley need someone with them who can translate."

That convinced the girl. She was delighted not only to be with her mother but also with Shirley, and she sat between the two in the middle seat of the van. Hong Taing rode up front with Duane. In the rear were Chhun Sang, the boy they called Meng Fou, and the girl the Americans assumed was Hong Taing's wife, Tan Chhun Ly.

Cranston followed the Landon's van back to Mendon. When the two vehicles rolled to a stop in front of the Hampton House, Donna was surprised to see Ken waiting on the front porch—surrounded by a group of Cambodians. She started up the front walk while the others were still getting out of the cars.

"You're early," she called to him. "And who are all these people?"

"Yeah, the meeting didn't last long."

He waited for her to reach the porch steps before continuing.

"This is Nuom Peng Sy and his family. They're sponsored by Holy Trinity Episcopal Church, and he's Nuom Yong's brother. This lady, Kim Phang, is his wife. I'm afraid I can't tell you the names of all five children. We've been practicing English while we waited for you."

"Well, wouldn't you know. Some people love their work so much they don't know when to quit!"

Donna put an arm around Ken, kissed him on the cheek, and turned to the Cambodians—almost in a single motion. But before she could speak they darted down the steps to greet their newly-arrived relatives.

On the front walk below, shouts of joy erupted—just as they had at the airport gate. Ken and Donna stood alongside the Landons and David Cranston, viewing the celebration from the porch. Finally, Nuom Yong slipped out of the cluster of Cambodians on the walk and stood at the foot of the porch steps, staring up at the house. She spoke rapidly in Khmer. When she paused, Chhun Heang explained:

"My mother not believe this her house. Too big. Too nice."

"Well, you tell your mother this *is* her house," Duane assured. "Let's go in and see it."

Inside, as the Americans guided the newcomers from room to room, eyes widened and the rapid-fire Khmer expressions of amazement grew louder.

"I don't understand a word they're saying," Donna commented, "but from the looks on their faces and the sounds of their voices, it's obvious how they feel."

Inclusion of Chhun Heang in the family certainly was going to help, and not just with translating. She was familiar with most of the American gadgets that typically baffled newcomers. She showed her family how to turn the lights on and off, how to open and close the curtains and drapes. In the kitchen she demonstrated how to get water from the faucets and how to use the stove and refrigerator.

"My mom don't believe light in refrigerator go out," Chhun Heang chuckled to Shirley. "I tell her, put head in and I close door. You see."

The bathroom was even more amazing. Chhun Heang flushed the toilet and her relatives oohed and aahed. She said something in Khmer, and they all began to giggle.

"Hong Taing think that for wash feet," Chhun Heang said, pointing to the toilet. "I tell him what for."

After she'd provided an introduction to the bathtub and shower, she turned to the sponsors.

"No worry. I explain need put curtain inside so water not go on floor."

The next marvel introduced was the washing machine. Ken listened to the chatter in Khmer, then turned to Donna.

"They don't think that thing really works. You can see it all over their faces. I'd like to be here when they pull the first load of laundry out of the machine."

He'd probably be on the campus when that happened, but another miracle could be performed right now.

"Chhun Heang, show them the vacuum cleaner," he suggested. "It's in that closet."

The girl dragged an old machine, almost an antique, out into the room. Ken pulled a sheet of paper from his pocket and tore it into tiny pieces of confetti which he threw on the floor. Chhun Heang flipped the switch and the noisy motor drowned out all other sound. She pushed the vacuum toward the paper until the wide nozzle swallowed all the pieces. There were more oohs and aahs.

"Well, maybe that's enough for tonight," Duane remarked. "We'd better not reveal all our marvels at once. Just one more thing. We need to show them the telephone."

They went back into the kitchen where the phone was mounted on the wall.

"Show them how it works, Chhun Heang. You can dial the church office. Pastor Greenwood should be there now. There's the number."

He pointed to the bottom line of a large card taped to the wall next to the phone. On it were names and corresponding numbers the family might need: "Fire, Police, Ambulance, Duane and Shirley's house, Duane's shop, Donna's house, Church office."

Three rings sounded in the receiver which the girl held out so the others could hear.

Then a voice: "Hello."

"What I say?" Chhun Heang gasped.

"Just tell him who you are," Duane responded.

"I Chhun Heang. You help my family. Thank you."

"Welcome to Mendon, Chhun Heang," the voice on the phone said. "I'm looking forward to meeting you and your family tomorrow."

"Oh, thank you. Goodbye."

She put the receiver back on the hook.

"For emergencies," Duane advised Chhun Heang, "everybody in your family should know how to say your address in English. It's 518 Wentworth Avenue."

"I explain to them," she said. "They learn fast."

"Well, OK. We'll go now so you can get some rest. If you need us, call on the telephone. Tell your family Shirley and Donna will come tomorrow morning at 10 o'clock to show them the city and take them shopping. They will take Hong Taing to the Social Security Office to apply for cards, too. He will need to have all the I-94s for that. Donna and Shirley will make copies of the I-94s then, too."

"OK, I explain," the girl replied.

The Americans started toward the door, along with Chhun Ping and her two children who would return to Lafayette with Cranston. At the doorway, Chhun Heang took Shirley's hand.

"My family not talk English yet. But they very happy. This more than they dream. So nice house. So good people. They want say thank you, but not know how. I say for them now. Thank you. Thank you."

She brought her hands together and raised them to her face, bowing low. Behind her Nuom Yong mirrored the expression of respect and gratitude. Tears welled up in her eyes and trickled down her cheeks.

Donna's eyes misted, too. Doubting she would make it down the front steps without help, she put an arm around Ken and held on tightly.

But in the car on the way home, she started to hum.

"What's that song?" he asked.

"One of my dad's favorites when I was a kid. Glenn Miller's band recorded it the year I was born. It's a love song, but dad would sing it to me as a lullaby. I only remember the first few lines. They seem just right tonight."

She started to sing softly:

> We meet and the angels sing,
> The angels sing the sweetest song I ever heard.
> You speak, and the angels sing,
> Or am I breathing music into every word?
> Suddenly, the setting is changed,
> I can see water and moonlight beaming,
> Silver waves that break on an undiscovered shore.

She hummed the rest, her head nestled against Ken's shoulder. When she stopped, the droning motor seemed to take up the tune. She snuggled closer.

"I've never been happier. This is the best thing we've ever done, Ken. Thanks for being with me tonight."

CHAPTER 21

A Quick Divorce

NOVEMBER 12, 1980

Ken MacKenzie smiled as he recalled his decision to be responsible for the church's Refugee Family Fund so he'd have an excuse not to be personally involved with the Cambodians. Since the family arrived, he'd been at the Hampton House several times a week.

"The kids need help with their schoolwork," he'd tell Donna, "so I'll go along with you tonight."

But she noticed they spent as much time playing games as working on studies or English vocabulary. And he seemed to be enjoying it as much as the kids. He'd even introduced Meng Fou and Chhun Heang to trick or treating on Halloween. Despite a steady drizzle, the three of them covered seven blocks in the neighborhood of the church.

"You'll be the one to take them to the dentist to get the cavities filled," Donna warned when she saw the two big bags bulging with candy.

She herself had been with the Cambodians nearly every day of the past two months. Often she'd be at the Hampton House for several daytime hours, then go back at night. Duane and Shirley were principally responsible for the family, and others on the committee were doing much of the routine legwork necessary for getting them off to a good start. They'd taken them to a hospital in Lafayette for physical examinations, registered with the Benton County social services and health services departments, and enrolled the younger children in elementary school and the entire family in English as a Second Language classes at the Adult Learning Center. Two of the ladies led expeditions to clothing stores and made sure family members would be warm during the approaching winter months.

When it came to buying food, old shopping habits weren't easily broken. For the Cambodian women, visits to the market had been a daily ritual. Finally they were convinced that here, with the refrigerator, they could keep food longer and make fewer trips to the stores. Now they went twice a week with Donna and Shirley to buy food.

But that obligation took little of Donna's time. Most of her many hours with the family were devoted to establishing and operating a business that would provide a means of income.

One afternoon when she and the Landons talked to Hong Taing about employment possibilities, they learned he'd been a chef. Duane offered to contact owners of restaurants in town to see if Hong Taing might be able to get a job at one of them.

However, that evening when Donna recounted the afternoon discussion at the dinner table, Ken had another idea:

"Hong Taing could go into business for himself."

Donna typically had a positive attitude. She rarely pooh-poohed Ken's suggestions, regardless of how ridiculous they appeared to be. But this seemed a bit far out.

"Open his own restaurant? That would take a little more cash than you've got in the treasury right now, wouldn't it?"

"Well, it wouldn't have to be a restaurant, at least in the beginning. How about a takeout business? He could do eggrolls and a few other oriental dishes. I bet there'd be a lot of interest. I know kids at the college wouldn't mind supplementing dining hall food with something different once in a while. A lot of them probably would just as soon have eggrolls instead of pizza occasionally for a study break. Right now there's no place in town to get oriental food."

"That's not a bad idea," Donna admitted. "But wouldn't it have to be prepared in a licensed facility? He couldn't just make it in the family's kitchen."

"How about the kitchen at church? That's been approved by the health department."

"Right." She hesitated. "But there's going to be a language problem. He still only knows a few words of English, and none of his customers will be speaking Khmer."

"Yeah. I guess that would be an obstacle."

"Unless," Donna cut in. "Unless someone who speaks English spends a lot of time with him to get things going, shows him how things work in the kitchen, orders the ingredients, decides prices, does some advertising, serves as a go-between with customers."

"And who would that be?"

"I suppose it could be me."

When Hong Taing heard the suggestion the next day, he was excited. Duane and Shirley thought it was a great idea. A few days later Duane and Ken purchased a freezer and another refrigerator and stove so the food prepared at church could be stored, reheated, and distributed from the family home. The appliances were placed in a room at the front of the house, and a sales counter was installed in the doorway. Hong Taing was in business.

His sister Chhun Sang and wife, Chhun Ly, helped at the church kitchen. Donna handled business aspects of the operation and also volunteered to be what she called "the official taster"—the product sampler and quality controller. She'd sometimes suggest changes to make the food more appealing to American consumers.

Chhun Sang and Chhun Ly's English was improving rapidly, and Donna believed they'd be able to handle sales in a few months. When they first began to market the oriental delicacies, Donna felt she needed to be at the Hampton House during the busiest afternoon and evening hours. Lately, she'd begun pulling back, mostly because Ken convinced her that if members of the family realized they had to communicate in English they'd learn faster.

But she still spent several hours a day with the Cambodians. She knew the business would need her attention for some time. And she'd taken a special interest in Chhun Ly. The young woman was making wonderful progress in her language study and seemed to be far ahead of the others in adapting to the challenges of a new way of life. Her eagerness to learn encouraged Americans who knew her to want to help more.

But there were some things about Chhun Ly that Donna still couldn't quite figure out. The day after the family arrived in Mendon, when Donna took her to the supermarket, Chhun Ly found a door bolt in the hardware section and asked if she could buy it.

"For bedroom door," the young wife explained.

Perhaps she wants to keep her in-laws from interrupting intimate moments, Donna thought to herself. *But it's strange this would be the first thing she'd want to buy in America.*

And then there was Meng Fou's first day of school. When he came home, Chhun Ly didn't even greet him.

"I guess I'm hardly an authority on raising kids," she told Ken that evening, "but I can't imagine having my little boy walk in after his first day of school in a strange new land and not at least say something like, 'Well, how'd it go today, buddy?'"

Those incidents were puzzles. But they didn't really bother Donna. One thing did, however. That was Chhun Ly's moodiness. She often seemed troubled. A certain amount of anxiety would be expected, but in Chhun Ly's case it seemed to occur at the wrong times. She wasn't anxious about the things that seemed to bother the other Cambodians. She was making a good adjustment to life in America. But many times she appeared to be off in another world, worried, apprehensive. Something was wrong. Donna just couldn't put her finger on what it was—until a week ago.

At about two o'clock one afternoon, after she'd spent four hours with Hong Taing, Chhun Sang, and Chhun Ly in the church kitchen, she decided everybody needed a break. At least that's what she said when she invited Chhun Ly to come home with her for a cup of tea. The young Cambodian woman seemed relaxed and happy while working alongside her husband and sister-in-law. But during the drive to the MacKenzie home her mood swung. She spoke only when questioned, and her responses were terse.

While Donna busied herself in the kitchen, Chhun Ly sat at the dinette table and stared out the window, looking at nothing in particular. Obviously preoccupied, she seemed unaware of Donna's presence. Even the whistling of the teakettle didn't seem to break the spell. She just kept staring, seeing nothing.

"A penny for your thoughts."

Donna smiled at the girl as she slid a tray with a teapot, two cups, and a plate of cookies onto the table. Chhun Ly turned toward her but made no response.

"That's what Americans say when someone thinks much but says nothing." She paused. "What are you thinking, Chhun Ly? Is there a problem?"

"No, I OK."

Donna always spoke slowly to the Cambodians, and tried to use simple words. She took even greater care now, to be sure she was understood.

"Chhun Ly, I know you had much trouble. I know it is hard to come to a strange place, to learn a new language, to do things in different ways. You have been doing very well. You are learning English faster than any of the others. You understand the American way of doing things better than the others. But I think there is a problem that troubles you."

"I OK. No problem."

"I want to be your friend, Chhun Ly. You can trust me. I know something is wrong. Something makes you unhappy. If you do not say what it is, I cannot help. Tell me why you are not happy."

"I happy."

The interrogation seemed to be getting no place. Most would have given up by now. But once Donna made up her mind to get to the bottom of something, she wasn't easily deterred.

"Chhun Ly, there is a problem. I can see you are not happy. There are people here who can make things better. I can help you. I want to help you. Don't you believe me?"

There was no response.

"If you do not want me to tell anyone else about the problem, I will not. Please let me help you. I want you to be happy."

She reached out and took the younger woman's hand.

"Chhun Ly, you are safe here. I am your friend. Ken is your friend. You can trust us."

Still no response. The warm, dark, troubled eyes stared into hers. Donna waited. Chhun Ly's lips quivered.

"I sorry. I no want make problem. I no want give you trouble. Everything my fault."

Donna slid her chair closer and held both of the young Cambodian's hands.

"Chhun Ly, honey, you will not make me unhappy, no matter what you say. If there is a problem, we will fix it. If it is your fault, that is OK. Everybody makes mistakes. I do things wrong, many times. Now tell me what troubles you."

The girl's eyes met Donna's. The words finally came out, slowly, softly, little more than a whisper. Donna could scarcely hear them.

"I not Hong Taing's wife."

Donna had cautioned herself not to show disapproval, or even surprise, no matter what she might hear. She squeezed Chhun Ly's hands, and she smiled.

"The bolt you wanted to buy at the supermarket, that was to keep Hong Taing out of your bedroom?"

"Yes."

"So you are not Meng Fou's mother."

"That right."

"And you are not twenty-seven years old."

"No. I eighteen."

"And your name. Is it Chhun Ly?"

"No. That name of Hong Taing wife. My name Savang Kim Ang."

"Oh my, having a different name for you is going to be hard to get used to. Anyway, I think for now, until we get things straightened out, you should still be Chhun Ly. Will that be all right?

"Is OK. That my name now."

"We will get all these things worked out, honey. I will help you. Is there more you want to tell me?"

Relieved that the truth was finally out in the open, that she had a sympathetic listener who possibly would even help her, the girl began reciting, as best she could with her limited English vocabulary, the story of what had happened—the years of Khmer Rouge terror; the murders of more than half her relatives, of her mother and father and two sisters, and probably her two brothers; the escapes to Vietnam and Thailand; the perilous journeys through the minefields; the dream of coming to America. She explained why Hong Taing's real wife and son were not with him and why he needed to replace them if he and his mother and sister were to be reunited with the sisters who had reached Lafayette.

"In Thailand, Hong Taing tell me when get to America I live someplace else," she continued. "But now in America he say I must stay his house. If I tell sponsor what happen, he say he stop my family from come to America."

"You have relatives in Thailand?" Donna asked.

"Yes, grandmother, three uncles, and cousin. They in refugee camp. They tell me if I come America with Hong Taing I make papers so they come America, too. Now that never happen. It my fault. I make big problem. I make you trouble, too."

"No, it is not your fault. How could anyone blame you? You're still hardly more than a child. You did what your family asked. You did what you thought was right. I will help you fix the problem. I will talk to Ken, and to Duane and Shirley, if that is all right. They can help us to decide what to do. Will that be all right?"

"OK."

"We must not let Hong Taing's family know you told me anything. But do not worry. Everything will be all right. We will fix the problem as soon as we can. If there is trouble before we decide what to do, you come right to my house or to Duane and Shirley's. OK?"

"Yes. Thank you for help me. You good friend."

"Thank you for letting me be your friend, honey. Now don't worry. Everything will be all right."

Back at the church kitchen, Donna explained their longer-than-anticipated absence to Hong Taing and Chhun Sang with the simplest words possible and an amusing array of gestures and sign language.

"We had problem, with car. So sorry. No understand how to fix. Take much time."

In the next breath she offered a silent prayer: *Lord, I know I'm not supposed to lie, and I'm not setting a good example for this young woman. But right now the truth just doesn't seem to be a good idea. Forgive me.*

Then, aloud again, "I cannot stay now. I have some business I must do. Thank you for having tea with me, Chhun Ly. I will see you all later. Goodbye."

At home, Donna fumbled through the kitchen drawer beneath the telephone where she kept a list of phone numbers. Ken called the drawer's contents her "masterpiece of mishmash." But she seemed to know where everything was. She quickly pulled the list from a jumble of other papers and ran her finger down it until she came to "Richards, Becky—CWS Rep., Indianapolis." She reached for the phone and dialed the number.

"Mrs. Richards, this is Donna MacKenzie in Mendon. Our church is the sponsor of Nuom Yong's family."

"Yes, of course. How are things going?"

"Well, I'm afraid we have a small problem."

"Oh? Is it something I can help with?"

"I hope so. We need some advice, at least. I've just learned Hong Taing's wife is not his wife. I mean, Chhun Ly is not Hong Taing's real wife. She just pretended to be his wife so he and his family could come to America. She's not a 27-year-old mother. She's just a teenager, an 18-year-old girl. It's a rather complicated story, but they were sent back to Cambodia from Thailand and then escaped again to Thailand. Hong Taing's real wife wouldn't go the second time. Meanwhile, his sister reached America and filed papers for him to..."

"Oh, yes," Mrs. Richards cut in. "I'm beginning to get the picture. He needed a wife and he talked her into pretending. And the little boy, is he really Hong Taing's son?"

"No. He's the child of a friend. The friend wanted to be sure the boy would get out of Southeast Asia, so he let Hong Taing take him."

"OK. Well, first of all, Donna, this isn't unusual. After their horrible past and the bleakness of their future if they don't make it to a third country, it's understandable these people will do almost anything for a chance at a better life. Your family certainly isn't the first to reach America under false pretenses."

"I'm glad to know that. I was worried about being in trouble with the government."

"No, I don't think there's any danger of that. And, as far as the little boy is concerned, I see no problem at all. That situation will undoubtedly take care of itself. Perhaps his parents will reach America and he'll be reunited with them. Otherwise Hong Taing will be responsible for raising him."

"And how about Chhun Ly?"

"That definitely is a problem. There's good reason to be concerned about her. Perhaps, rightly or wrongly, Hong Taing believes she really should be more than a make-believe wife. You really must get her out of the house as soon as you can and find someplace else for her to live. Will that be possible?"

"Uh, well, yes, probably. We really haven't thought about it, of course."

"Well, I'd suggest the key people on your committee get together right away and see what can be done. Of course, besides getting Chhun Ly out of the house you'll need to maintain a good relationship with the rest of the family. That won't be easy. Hong Taing may be afraid. He may well be angry. You're facing a tricky situation, one that will need careful handling."

"Yes, I see what you mean. I really appreciate your advice, Mrs. Richards. We'll see what we can do."

"I'm sure you'll do fine. Let me know how you come out."

"I will. Thanks. Goodbye."

Moments later, Ken walked in.

"Hi. Got a kiss for a tired man? Busy day on the campus."

Donna slipped into his arms and, after the kiss, kept an arm around his waist and her head on his shoulder.

"I need an extra hug."

"Bad day?"

"Oh, not bad exactly. But interesting."

"Tell me about it."

"Well, Chhun Ly isn't Hong Taing's wife."

She looked up for Ken's reaction. His face registered curiosity more than surprise.

"Whose wife is she?"

"Nobody's. She's just an 18-year-old kid."

"Well, I think I better hear the whole story. Come on out to the family room and sit down. I have a feeling this is going to take a while."

They sat on the sofa while Donna recounted the events of the afternoon.

"I just got off the phone with Becky Richards in Indianapolis. She says it's really important that we get Chhun Ly out of the Hampton House. We need to find someplace else for her to live."

"Yeah, I can see that. Got any ideas?"

"Yes."

That's all she said. Ken waited for more.

"Well?"

"Why not with us?"

She studied his face again for reaction. There wasn't any. And he didn't raise an objection. But that didn't mean he agreed.

"We have the room," Donna continued. "She's a really nice girl. She's been through so much. She's been robbed of most of her childhood. She still needs parents. She needs steadiness. She needs love. We could give her that, Ken. I think …"

"Whoa. Slow down. I thought that's the direction you were headed. You don't have to sell me. If that's what you want, it's OK with me."

Later, at a hastily-called conference in Pastor Greenwood's study, Donna and Ken related the day's surprising developments to him and the Landons. Donna told of her conversation with Becky Richards and the advice that Chhun Ly live elsewhere as soon as arrangements could be made.

"Ken and I have a suggestion. We'd like to have Chhun Ly stay with us."

"You're willing to do that?" the pastor asked.

"No problem. We have the room. We'd love to have her."

"That'd be great!" Duane exclaimed, with obvious relief. "It would be a wonderful solution to a big problem."

"Well, there'll still be other problems," Ken responded. "We have to get her out of the Hampton House and into ours. That's likely to be embarrassing to the rest of the family, especially Hong Taing. And for an Asian there's nothing worse than losing face. We need to minimize that as much as possible. It's not going to be easy."

"Got any ideas?" Duane asked.

Ken thought for a moment. "Well, first of all, of course, we need to carefully consider exactly what we're going to say and do. I think we should talk about that now. And, if possible, I'd suggest we make the move tomorrow. The sooner the better."

"Sounds good to me," Duane said. "Shirley and I can be there."

"I don't think you should," Ken countered, to the surprise of the rest in the room. "You're the family's principal sponsors. They're going to feel threatened. They may have a sense of guilt. They need to have someone to turn to. You have to be the guys with the white hats. Donna and I'll be the bad guys. We'll need to have Pastor Greenwood with us because he represents the church. The church, after all, is the official sponsor. They need to know that what's happening is a decision of the church."

"Yes, that makes sense," Rev. Greenwood agreed. "But what's our approach? How are we going to lay this on them?"

"We'll have to wait until the kids are home from school," Donna observed. "I hate to put Chhun Heang through the ordeal of translating this news to her family, but I don't see any alternative. I think she'll have to be there.

"Then, I'd suggest we emphasize that Chhun Ly didn't come to us. They need to understand some of us were suspicious and it was only after intense questioning that she admitted the truth.

"And I believe we have to convince them there'll be no problem for them. We need to assure Hong Taing that we admire him for bringing Chhun Ly and Meng Fou to America, that what he did was a good thing. We need to demonstrate that we still love them, that we want to continue to be their friends and help them every way we can."

"Good approach," Duane observed. "And how about us? What do Shirley and I do?

"Well, here's what I'd suggest," Ken responded. "An hour or so after we've left, you show up and be the sympathetic listeners. You let them know you understand how they feel. But at the same time you try to move them toward healing the rift that's undoubtedly going to be there. "You can hear what they're saying and be sorry for what's happened, but it's important to try to get them to look at the other side of the coin, too. In other words, you listen to their side of the story and then present ours. But I don't think you should push too hard. Just say it once. It's more important that you remain their friends. You'll need to walk a fine line. Your job won't be easy."

"Seems like a good plan," the pastor commented.

"If you get any better ideas," Donna assured, "be sure to let us know. Otherwise, Ken and I'll meet you here tomorrow at three-thirty, Pastor Greenwood. Hopefully, we'll have Chhun Ly moved out by five. Duane and Shirley, probably you should be there about six.

"And in the meantime, keep praying."

CHAPTER 22

Merry Christmas

DECEMBER 24, 1980

Removal from the Hampton House of Kim Ang, the girl the MacKenzies had known as Chhun Ly, didn't end her turmoil. But it started Ken and Donna's. And, strangely, they didn't seem to mind.

"You sure you can handle all this?" Pastor Greenwood asked as they greeted him on the way out of church last Sunday. "Seems like you've been under a rather heavy load of stress the past month."

"Well, there haven't been many dull moments." Donna smiled as she grasped his hand and held it briefly. "But, actually, we've been tremendously blessed."

Kim Ang, between Ken and Donna and a step behind, peered between them at snow swirling beyond the open doorway and shivered at the thought of stepping out into the cold. Donna slipped an arm around the girl, the hug drawing her into the circle of friends.

"When we're with this beautiful young lady," she continued, "and realize all she's gone through, how could we be anything but grateful for all the blessings we have? Considering what she's had to deal with, a little stress and strain is nothing."

"Donna's right," Ken chimed in. "Besides, stress isn't always unpleasant. If you're doing something worthwhile, if you can feel good about it, stress can be OK. I know some people wouldn't understand that. But I think you see what I mean."

"I certainly do," the pastor replied. "You've discovered first-hand what Christ was getting at when He said it's more blessed to give than to receive. Sorry, I didn't mean to start off on another sermon. But yes, Ken, I know what you're experiencing."

"I've changed," Ken admitted, "and I owe it all to these two charmers. You probably didn't know Donna practically dragged me to that first meeting about sponsoring a family. And I only offered to take care of the money so I wouldn't have to get more involved. Then this other lovely young lady comes into my home, and I learn that what I thought were problems are nothing compared to hers."

"Kim Ang has been a real joy for me, too," Donna added. "Something else you probably didn't know—Ken and I had been hoping to adopt a child, an older one. My idea mostly. But progress was discouragingly slow. So I asked God to do something about it. I haven't told Kim Ang yet, but she's definitely an answer to prayer."

Nevertheless, though the stress may have been OK, the problems were real. They had to be dealt with. Since the decision to bring Kim Ang into their family, Ken and Donna had confronted one challenging situation after another. The first, taking Kim Ang out of the Hampton House and bringing her to their own, seemed to have gone well enough. Explaining their action to Hong Taing hadn't been easy, but everything seemed to go as planned. There had been no hitches. There was no argument. The Mackenzies and Rev. Greenwood heaved a collective sigh of relief as they drove off with Kim Ang and her few possessions.

But the next day it became apparent that Hong Taing did feel embarrassed and threatened by what they had done. When the Cambodian families gathered for their English class at the Adult Learning Center that morning, he accused his uncle, Peng Sy, of telling church sponsors Kim Ang was not his wife.

"You want her to marry Meng Tieng," Hong Taing shouted in Khmer.

"I am not looking for a wife for my son," the uncle retorted, "and I said nothing to your sponsors, or anyone else."

The accusations and denials continued, and the two men had to be placed in separate rooms for their morning lessons. Kim Ang said nothing about the incident, but at the dinner table that evening Donna sensed the girl was troubled.

"Problem at school today, Kim Ang?"

"No. No problem."

Donna didn't persist. But later in the evening she went to Kim Ang's room to see if she needed help with her vocabulary list. Kim Ang was squatting on the floor, rocking back and forth, her face a map of despair. Donna sat beside her, reached out and took her hand.

"Kim Ang, what's the problem? Come on now. Remember Ken and I can help."

"Nobody can help. I make big trouble. Hong Taing angry to his uncle today. He say bad things. It all my fault."

For half an hour Donna sat with her, hugging her, reassuring her.

The next evening she took Kim Ang to the home of Peng Sy and his wife, Kim Phang, hoping a visit with the cousins would help to dispel her depression. Moments after they arrived, Donna realized she'd done the right thing. Chhun Leng, the older of Peng Sy and Kim Phang's daughters, was the same age as Kim Ang. And she had inherited her father's sense of humor. Her infectious, carefree disposition soon had Kim Ang smiling, then laughing as they recalled childhood experiences.

Chhun Leng's three brothers—Meng Tieng, 20; Meng Phok, 15; and Meng Yu, 13—were more serious, but outgoing. And six-year-old Chhun Ny was a pixie, a miniature version of her older sister. She was alongside Donna on the couch most of the evening.

What a wonderful family, Donna thought to herself. *They're so content, with so little, in this humble house Holy Trinity's parishioners provided. I really need to spend more time here with Kim Ang.*

But while Kim Ang's gloom was lifting in the house on the other side of town, the phone rang at the MacKenzies'. Ken answered. The voice on the other end was obviously that of a Cambodian. He sounded far away.

"Savang Kim Ang live this house?"

"Yes, but she's not here now. Can I help you?"

"My name Haing Hok. I cousin Kim Ang. I live California, Long Beach. I think Kim Ang have problem. Her family want Kim Ang come California, stay my house. That be OK?"

Ken hesitated. *How in blazes does news travel so far, so fast, with these people?* he asked himself.

"Well, uh, that would be a big decision. It would have to be Kim Ang's decision. And if she wants to go, we would have to do a lot of checking first—with the agency that brought her to the United States and with the government. I'm not sure she can just pack up and go. We're still working on clearing up her status here."

Ken wondered how much of what he was saying the man understood.

"I think better she be here. Not so big problem," responded the distant voice.

"Well, Mr. Haing, I'm not so sure of that. Besides, Long Beach is a big city. This is a small town, and I think Kim Ang will get a better start here. She wants very much to have an education, and she will get a good education here. She is with people who like her very much and will take good care of her. But I will tell Kim Ang you called."

He pressed his finger to the hook, cutting off the phone connection, but stood there several minutes holding the receiver, wondering what complications might follow Haing Hok's call. If Kim Ang were to leave, Donna would be devastated. And he'd miss her, too. In just the few days since she'd been with them, he'd begun to experience the joys and satisfaction of parenthood.

Sure, there were problems and responsibilities. Nevertheless, he doubted anything he'd ever done before was this worthwhile. But what would happen to Kim Ang if she left? Would she stand a chance of achieving her dream of an education and a better life without the kind of attention he and Donna could give? He doubted it.

When Kim Ang came home with Donna and learned of the call, she didn't return it. But the possibility she might have to move again, to another strange new place, unsettled her. Minutes after she walked in the door, her boosted spirits were deflated.

The next week Haing Hok called again. This time Kim Ang was home. All she told Ken and Donna about the conversation was that her distant cousin planned to come to Indiana soon, presumably to take her back to California with him.

"Kim Ang, he can't take you to California unless you say it is OK," Ken counseled. "He cannot force you to go with him. In America we call that kidnapping, and it is against the law. If he tries to make you go when you don't want to, he'll be put in jail."

"I must do what my family want," Kim Ang replied. "I think my grandmother send letter to Haing Hok and tell him take me California if he think that good idea. It up to Haing Hok."

"How about your dream of going to school?" Donna asked. "You told us a few days ago about your grandfather's dying wish, that you get an education. If you live in California with your cousins, will that happen? I think they will make you get a job and you will never go to school. If you stay here, you can start high school soon. And then you can go to college."

"You are in America now," Ken persisted. "You are eighteen years old. You do not have to do what your family wants."

As soon as he spoke the words, he realized his mistake. In her culture, you don't go against the wishes of your family. Displeasing your elders just isn't done. Kim Ang didn't respond, and he quickly changed direction.

"What would you like to do, Kim Ang?"

"I want stay here." She paused, biting her lower lip. "But I must go."

"Why?" Ken asked.

"I make trouble. Hong Taing angry to his uncle. Everybody not happy. If I go away, trouble go away."

"Kim Ang, that's not so," Donna countered. "You did not make the trouble. It is not your fault. And if you go away, the trouble will still be here. If you go, you will be punishing yourself for something you didn't do."

"We not talk more now. It not help. We wait, see what Haing Hok say when he come. I go study English."

She went to her room and closed the door.

A few days later, with Christmas less than a week away, the spirit of the season was missing at the MacKenzies'. The tree Kim Ang had helped to decorate, with lights of many colors and sparkling ornaments, seemed out of place. Carols, played over and over by all the radio stations, sounded hollow. This would be no merry

Christmas; that seemed certain. Kim Ang was despondent. Ken was discouraged. Donna was close to tears.

The last of eight bongs from the old grandfather clock was still reverberating when Kim Ang came into the family room to say goodnight to Donna and Ken.

"Honey, come on out here and sit with us for a while," Donna coaxed. "This is Friday, and you can sleep late tomorrow. It's so early to go to bed."

"No. I sleep now. When I sleep, I have no troubles."

She turned and went to her room.

"Too bad that isn't true," Ken observed after the girl left.

He and Donna might be able to escape their problems by falling asleep. But they knew it seldom worked for Kim Ang. Often, in the middle of the night, they'd hear her cry out as nightmares transported her back to the horrors of Cambodia.

Ken slept restlessly that night. At six in the morning he gave up trying to doze off again. Downstairs he found Kim Ang already up, sitting on the living room sofa, a large picture book on her lap. It was open to a full-color, two-page spread of the Grand Canyon.

"America beautiful place."

"Sure is. You feeling better this morning, Kim Ang?"

"Little bit."

"OK if I sit down and talk with you for a while?"

"Sure. OK."

For nearly an hour they exchanged stories about what transpired before they were drawn together here in this Indiana college town. Kim Ang wanted to know about Ken's life before he met Donna, how they met, why they didn't have children of their own, why he liked teaching, what he had to do to become a teacher, whether he didn't want to live in a bigger city.

Ken tried to avoid questions that would resurrect memories of the Khmer Rouge misery. He asked about her childhood, the good things she could remember about Cambodia, the kind of city Phnom Penh had been when she was a little girl, whether she had ever seen the ancient temple ruins of Angkor Wat, what her first impressions of America were.

"Would you tell me about your family?" he asked.

"Most all dead now," she said.

"Yes, I know. I'm sorry. I should have asked more clearly. I mean your family who are still living—your grandmother, your uncles, your cousin. Are they at Khao I Dang now?

"Yes. But I hope they come America soon. Haing Hok say he fix it so they go California."

"They could come to Mendon, too, Kim Ang."

"No. I have no money to sponsor."

"You don't have to be the sponsor. We can find a church to be the sponsor. Just like our church is the sponsor for Nuom Yong's family."

"Nobody here do that for my family."

"Yes, somebody here will do that. Trust me, Kim Ang. If you stay here, I will find a church to sponsor your family so they can come to Mendon. OK?"

"I want stay here. But I not know."

"If I promise Haing Hok I will find a sponsor for your family, perhaps he will say it is OK for you to stay here. Remember, you have a good chance to get an education if you stay in Mendon. In California I do not think you will go to school."

"You want me stay?"

"Yes, of course. Very much. And Donna will be sad if you go away. She loves you very much. You are like a daughter to her."

"You, Donna best friends I ever have." She hesitated, then smiled. "I stay."

By the time Donna came downstairs, Ken and Kim Ang were rummaging through a box of photos, hunting for a picture of Kim Ang in front of the church. Ken had snapped it the Sunday after the family arrived, and she asked if she could send it to her relatives in Thailand. When the search uncovered a photo of Ken and Donna on their honeymoon, Kim Ang broke up with laughter.

"That you?"

"Well, certainly."

"Donna same almost. You more hair, more brown then. Not so many lines on face, too. Look too young to be marry."

Donna came in from the kitchen.

"What's so funny? You don't sound like the two people I was listening to yesterday. How come you're both so happy this morning?"

"We've had a long talk. Kim Ang says she wants to stay with us."

Donna leaned over the back of the sofa and wrapped her arms around them.

"Your eyes smile, but tears come out," Kim Ang observed.

Dabbing at her face with a sleeve of her robe, Donna finally was able to speak.

"I'm so happy, Kim Ang. That's wonderful news!"

Placing her head between theirs, she drew them together and kissed each on the cheek. Then, pulling herself slowly to her feet, she wiped her eyes with her sleeve again on the way back to the kitchen.

But the joy didn't last long. Five minutes later Donna was startled by a cry from the living room. When she returned to investigate, Kim Ang was holding a picture of Ken's father. Suddenly she sank to the floor at the foot of the sofa, shrieked again, pounded the floor with her fists, and began sobbing uncontrollably.

Ken bent and touched her shoulder.

"What is it, Kim Ang? What's the trouble?"

She never heard the words.

"Just hold her, Ken," Donna suggested. "She needs to cry. As long as we've known her I've never seen her cry. I doubt if she ever has. She has all that horror bottled up inside, and it needs to get out. Just hug her and let her cry."

Ken slid to the floor, his back against the sofa, and cradled the hysterical young woman in his arms. Donna sat on the sofa behind them, letting Kim Ang know with an occasional touch that she, too, was there. She let Ken do all the talking, and he said little—just an occasional phrase of encouragement when the sobs subsided enough to be heard:

"It's OK, Kim Ang. It's all right to cry. You'll feel better. We're here to help now."

They sat that way—Ken on the floor holding the girl, Donna on the couch—for nearly an hour before the wailing drained enough grief and misery to enable Kim Ang to regain a semblance of composure.

Donna slid down to the floor then to relieve Ken, put her arms around Kim Ang, and continued to voice soft reassurance:

"Things are going to be better, honey. We're with you now. We're going to take care of you."

After several minutes, still holding the young woman, she finally dared ask, "Do you want to tell us what upset you?"

Kim Ang pointed to the photo lying beside her on the floor.

"Look like grandfather. He die. No food. If I bring food, he no die."

"But, Kim Ang," Donna interrupted. "Chhun Sang told me the story she heard about how your grandfather died. She said when he was starving you were far away."

"Yes, but if I hide from Pol Pot soldiers I can bring food."

"Kim Ang, you can't keep blaming yourself for every bad thing that happens. There was nothing you could do to help your grandfather. Really now, you didn't even know he was dying until your uncle came to you. Even if you knew, there was nothing you could do. The Khmer Rouge would have killed you."

Donna's recitation of the facts chipped away at the guilt that had triggered the outburst, and with further reassurances of love and support Kim Ang felt better. She was smiling again by the time Ken called them to the dinette for brunch.

That had been four days ago, and now on Christmas Eve the three were plummeting downward again on the emotional roller coaster. Haing Hok was in town. The cousin from California called Kim Ang from Peng Sy's house and asked her to meet him there this afternoon.

"We're going with you," Donna announced when Kim Ang told her of the call. "You're not going over there to talk to that man alone."

Hok, they discovered when they arrived, was actually a friendly, outgoing young man, probably in his late twenties. His English was not as good as Kim Ang's, though he'd been in America much longer. He claimed to have a good job as custodian at a school in Long Beach and to have brought several of his relatives to that city to live. He hoped Kim Ang's grandmother and uncles would come there soon.

There were no arguments, no harsh words. Ken knew enough about Cambodian customs by now to realize Hok would avoid confrontation. Most Cambodians were too polite to disagree openly, especially with strangers. They were more likely to say what they thought the other person wanted to hear.

After he'd sounded off during their phone conversation, Ken was certain Hok wouldn't confront them now about moving Kim Ang to Long Beach. But he was just as sure that's what the cousin from California had in mind.

And, in English, Hok said nothing about Kim Ang leaving. However, there was a lot of conversation in Khmer, and Ken could tell by the expressions on Cambodian faces there were many things he and Donna weren't being told.

In the car on the way home, Kim Ang confirmed Ken's suspicion.

"Hok tell Peng Sy he want me go California. Then be easier my family go there. If I go, make papers for them, then come faster."

"Why didn't he say that to us?" Donna asked.

"That's not the Khmer way, honey," Ken responded. "The last thing Hok would try to do would be to provoke an argument with us."

"If he want me go, I must go," Kim Ang said matter-of-factly. "If I not go, my family very angry."

Donna turned, reached across the back of the seat, and took Kim Ang's hand.

"This is hardly how I thought your first Christmas in America would be, honey. Christmas is supposed to be a time of joy. I hoped today and tomorrow would be two of the happiest days of your life. Now I'm afraid it's a sad time for all of us."

Ken seemed most despondent of all. In the waning hours of the afternoon he retreated to his study and pretended to be busy, shuffling through files that needed no attention and held no solution to the problem that troubled him. When Donna came to the doorway, he was slouched in his chair, back to her, just staring through the window into the vague shadows of dusk.

"Ken, we probably should change into something a little more dressy for the candlelight service," she said, assuming he'd lost track of the time.

"I'm not going."

"Oh, Ken, please. We can't stay away from worship, on this night especially, just because things don't seem to be going the way we want them to. What kind of example would we be setting for Kim Ang?"

He didn't answer. But he knew she was right. He pulled himself out of the chair and went upstairs to change.

At church, the Christmas pageant fascinated Kim Ang.

"That baby born in barn?" she whispered to Donna. "No have house?"

"That's right. And when he was still a little boy he was a refugee, just like you were. A bad king wanted to kill him, so he had to go to another country."

"What mean, Savior, Christ the Lord?"

"It means he's God's son, and he came to the world to save us. It's really a long story. I'll tell you more later."

At the end of the service, as the congregation sang "Silent Night" in the darkened sanctuary and a single flame passed from candle to candle down the rows of pews, the ever brighter light lifted Kim Ang's spirits. Her dark eyes sparkled, reflecting the glow of the candle she held.

"Oh, wonderful. One little fire make much light when people give to others."

Ken pondered her observation. *Well put, honey. That's pretty much the essence of Christmas. You've seen something here that many of us have missed.*

Back home after the service Kim Ang was still upbeat, so much so that she asked Ken and Donna to take her back to Peng Sy's house to talk again to her cousin Hok.

"I don't think that's a good idea," Donna replied. "You're starting to feel a little better now. If we go back there again, you're just going to be even more depressed."

"I OK. I want go back."

Ken agreed with Donna. "No need to go through all that again, Kim Ang. You'll just get more upset. Besides I'm not sure I want to see him again. I might become angry and say something bad."

"It be OK if we go."

"Kim Ang, let's just spend Christmas Eve here together. We'll have some of the cookies we made—and some hot chocolate, too. You can help me. Ken will make a fire in the fireplace."

"No, please. I want talk more with Hok. Please call Peng Sy. See if OK we go there."

"When you make your mind up about something," Ken observed, "you really don't take no for an answer, do you? I give up."

He dialed the number, and Peng Sy's oldest son answered.

"Meng Tieng, this is Mr. MacKenzie. Kim Ang asked me to call your house to ask if it's all right if we come back for another visit."

"Sure, I think that be OK. We been talking here, and I think it be good idea if you come."

Fifteen minutes later they were back at Peng Sy's house. Meng Tieng met them at the door and brought them into the living room where Hok and the rest of the family were waiting.

"Hok and my father ask me to say something," Meng Tieng told them. "Maybe my English little better. OK?

"Sure, that's fine," Ken nodded to the young man.

"We do a lot of talking tonight," Meng Tieng continued. "Hok tell us what he hope for Kim Ang and her family. He want them all be in America and be happy.

"My family tell Hok how good Mr. and Mrs. MacKenzie be to Kim Ang, help her with problems, take her in own house, be just like father and mother.

"Then Hok say to us he think it be good idea Kim Ang stay here, live with you. He say it OK, too, you make papers bring her family to Indiana."

"That's wonderful!" Ken exclaimed. "We will certainly do our best to make Kim Ang happy—and her family, too."

Through the misty blur of tears welling in her eyes, Donna studied the faces in the room. She'd never seen such beautiful smiles. But none could match the beaming expression of Kim Ang. The woman and the girl left their chairs and met in the center of the room where they threw their arms around one another.

"See? I say be OK we come here."

"I shouldn't have doubted you, honey. Merry Christmas!"

The Real Story

Good Dreams and Bad

During the Pol Pot regime dreams brought a welcome escape from the horrors of the day, but Cambodians who survived the holocaust found that slumber invariably brought nightmares which plunged them back into despair. The bad dreams went on night after night, year after year.

Telling of the bad days-good nights period of his life, Pin Yathay reported in his book, *Stay Alive, My Son*, that sleep provided his only relief from illness and exhaustion. "Sleep allowed us to forget our misfortune and our hunger," he wrote. "Strangely, it was a real release, and not only for us—most people, as if escaping from the daytime nightmares, reported astonishingly beautiful dreams. I found it somehow reassuring. If I had been frightened of the nights as well as the days, I think I would have given up."

Teeda Butt Mam in her book, *To Destroy You Is No Loss*, recalled, "Dreams were my escape—a way to bend without breaking. Every night I relived happy family parties, school events, or childhood games. The worse my daylight existence, the sweeter my dreams."

But when the horror was removed from wakeful hours it appeared in nighttime dreams.

"Ever since coming to the United States I've had nightmares," Haing Ngor said in *A Cambodian Odyssey*. "If I thought too much in the daytime about what had happened, I had dreams that night... It didn't take much to set off my nightmares—the sound of water dripping from the faucet was enough. It put me back in prison, looking up at water dripping from a hole in a bucket. Almost every night I woke suddenly and sat up to make the dreams fade."

Nightmares haven't been the only enduring product of the Khmer Rouge terror and oppression. A number of Cambodians, particularly women, have suffered from functional blindness, vision loss caused by psychological factors. Those who had seen so much tragedy just didn't want to see any more, according to an electrophysiologist who studied the problem among women who, according to advanced brain wave tests, should have had perfect vision.

However, one psychiatric clinic that has treated hundreds of Indochinese refugees has noted that Cambodian women have shown a remarkable resiliency. "These women came in with the most serious problems and the highest level of depression," a psychologist at the Indochinese Psychiatry Clinic at the Brighton Marine Public Health Center in Boston said. "But after six months of treatment they showed the most dramatic improvement of any group."

For more details, see:

Joan D. Criddle and Teeda Butt Mam, *To Destroy You Is No Loss* (New York, The Atlantic Monthly Press, 1987), pages 101-102

Haing Ngor with Roger Warner, *A Cambodian Odyssey* (New York, Macmillan Publishing Company, 1987), pages 433, 440

Alexandria Smith, "Eyes That Saw Horror Now See Only Shadows," *The New York Times* (Sept. 8, 1989), page A10

Pin Yathay with John Man, *Stay Alive, My Son* (New York, The Free Press, a division of Macmillan, Inc., 1987), page 132

"The Resilient Widows of Cambodia," *Ford Foundation Letter* (February 1987), page 5

CHAPTER 23

A Busy New Year

No sooner had Kim Ang set the dish of chocolate ice cream in front of Ken than the telephone rang. Donna, still in the kitchen, licked the serving spoon as she lifted the receiver.

"For you, Ken. Want to take it in your study?"

By the time he returned, the ice cream had melted. Donna and Kim Ang had cleared the rest of the table, but they took their seats again.

The girl grinned. "You say hard ice cream not good. Now you got soft."

Ken shook his spoon at her in mock anger.

"I didn't know what busy was, honey, before you came here. But I don't mind."

He turned to Donna.

"That was Henry McAllister, returning my call. He's asked his elders at Elm Grove Baptist Church to meet with us a week from tomorrow. I explained what we'd say and what we hope they'll consider."

Ken had been spending a lot of time on the phone during the two months since the amazing turnaround in Haing Hok's attitude—the event Donna referred to as the "Christmas Eve Miracle." It had been a busy time for all three of them.

Donna still put in several hours nearly every day with Hong Taing and Chhun Sang, keeping their business going. Hong Taing hadn't yet spoken to his uncle, or to Kim Ang either. But when Donna was near there was no hint of the smoldering anger caused by the embarrassment of Kim Ang's removal from his home. Donna had made it clear that she understood his anxiety and anger. She expressed sadness that his wife and son weren't with him. He knew she understood his loneliness. She was not a target of his resentment. Besides, he couldn't afford to alienate Donna. His business wouldn't survive without her counsel and her ability to communicate with his customers.

Kim Ang, now one of Mendon High School's two newest freshmen, was engrossed in studies. Ken convinced the principal to let her and Chhun Leng enroll in afternoon classes at the start of the second semester a month ago. They continued with English as a second language at the Adult Learning Center each morning, then studied freshman English, general mathematics, and home economics at the high school.

Kim Ang was beside herself with joy when Ken drove her and Chhun Leng to their first afternoon of classes.

"My dream coming true!" she exclaimed as they entered the building.

She knew study in a different language wasn't going to be easy, but now she discovered she also lacked background knowledge other students could take for granted. She and Chhun Leng were four years older than most in their classes, but they were fourteen years behind in some respects. They drew a blank if anyone mentioned Little Bo Peep, or Yankee Doodle, or Abraham Lincoln.

Math was a snap, and home economics wasn't difficult. But English was something else. Trying to understand the stories and poems in the literature book was a real challenge. So was trying to write in English. But Kim Ang was determined to succeed. She often was at the desk in her room until two or three in the morning.

Meanwhile, Ken faced the challenge of finding sponsors for refugees with equal zeal. Determined to make good on his promise to find a church sponsor for Kim Ang's family, he began calling ministers and lay leaders the day after Christmas. Besides Rev. McAllister in Elm Grove, he talked to six pastors in Mendon and one in Itasca about considering sponsorship.

He contacted Becky Richardson, too, and asked her to send information that would be helpful for prospective sponsors.

"I'll put some forms in, too," the refugee agency representative offered. "You'll need them when a church agrees to sponsor. One's an affirmation of sponsorship. The church needs to complete that. The other's an affidavit of relationship. It has to be filled out by a relative. Maybe I'd better send a couple of each. From what you've told me, one of Kim Ang's uncles and his daughter really are a separate family. You'll need more forms. Perhaps you'll want to get a second church to sponsor them."

As it turned out, Ken had to call her back and ask for two more sets. On New Year's Day, Donna and Kim Ang persuaded him to go along to Peng Sy's house for another visit. Meng Tieng wasn't home, but all the younger children were there, eager to practice their English with Ken and Donna. During the conversation one mentioned another sister.

"She oldest. She not here," Chhun Leng added.

"Where is she?" Donna asked.

"She in camp. Thailand. Husband, three children, too."

"Would you like them to come to America?" Ken asked.

Peng Sy and his wife, Kim Phang, overheard. Her eyes widened. Chhun Leng turned to her parents, assuming the question was intended for them. Her mother responded in Khmer.

"They understand, but they not speak English good yet. They hope so much Chhun Huoy come America. You help?"

Ken thought he'd just been making conversation. Offering to help wasn't what he'd had in mind. But then, why not?

"Sure. I can't promise anything, but I'll see what I can do." He paused, smiling at Chhun Leng. "You haven't got any more relatives over there, have you?"

He'd meant it as a joke. She didn't smile.

"My mother has brother. He in Thailand, too. You find sponsor?"

"Uh, this brother, is he married?"

"Sure."

"Children?"

"Yes. Five daughter, one grandson."

"Oh well, if I can find two I probably can find four. Good thing I made eight calls already. Better make a few more."

"What say?"

"Nothing really. I'm just talking to myself, Chhun Leng. Tell your mother and father I will do what I can. But remember, I cannot promise churches will sponsor. I can only ask."

As he pulled away from the curb for the drive home, Donna reached across the seat and gave him a playful poke in the ribs.

"What's gotten into you, Kenneth? Am I still married to the same man, the one who didn't want to go to a meeting about sponsoring refugees?"

"Well, to be honest, there was a little misunderstanding back there. And I was sort of careless. But, really, I don't mind the way it turned out. Yes, I'm the same guy. Guess I've changed a little, though, since I met these people. Thought I was so clever, too, offering to take care of the money so you wouldn't be after me to do more."

He paused to check traffic at the first intersection, then continued.

"When they were on one side of the ocean with me on the other, it was one thing. But now we've met. I realize they're people just like you and me. They have feelings. They cry, they laugh, they hurt. They've got so little. And I have so much.

"All of a sudden, the things I've been doing all these years don't seem very important. I look in the mirror in the morning and ask myself, 'What have you ever done that's made a difference?' And I have to answer, 'Not much, really.' Well, now I see I can make a difference. I can help make somebody's life better."

During the past couple months he'd tried to make up for lost time. Besides following up on the eight December contacts with church leaders, he called nine more. All of them listened to his pitch, but not many were sympathetic. Some agreed to "give it some thought" or "see if there's any interest." Others had excuses right off the bat.

"I've asked four ministers today whether their congregations would consider sponsoring a family," he told Donna as they relaxed in the family room one evening. "These are all men who know about the Good Samaritan and the twenty-fifth chapter of Matthew. And do you know what they told me?"

"Well, no," she responded. "But I think I'm going to find out."

"One said it would be a really nice thing to do, but 'we have some other priorities now." Another told me his church is too small and too far out in the country. They have more than a hundred members. I should have told him what the two dozen or so people at the Millbrook church did; they're even farther out in the country. But I didn't."

"Just as well. It wouldn't have helped to argue or make him feel guilty," Donna agreed.

"The next one told me his denomination is big on disaster relief, and his church gives a lot of money to food programs and that kind of thing. I guess he figures that's enough to keep consciences clear. And the last one said his church just paid off the mortgage last year. Now they have to do a lot of maintenance they couldn't afford while they were making the payments."

He paused and threw up his hands.

"How come these clergymen can't see what Christ wants them to do?"

"Well, I knew a man once who didn't even want to go to a meeting to hear about refugees."

"*Touché*, Donna. You really know how to stick the sword in gently."

They both laughed.

Kim Ang, working on an English assignment at a table across the room, had been unable to concentrate during Ken's impassioned monologue and paused to listen.

"What mean *touché*?"

"Oh, I knew you were going to ask that," Donna replied. "How am I ever going to explain it? You said it, Ken. You tell her."

"It's a French word, Kim Ang… "

"You talk French?" she interrupted.

"No, just a few words. But in English we've borrowed words from other languages. Actually—Oh, I'd better not get into all that. I'll try to make it as simple as possible. *Touché* is French for 'touch.' Well, there is a sport called fencing. In that sport two people try to touch each other with pointed swords. When one of them is touched he or she lets the other one know by saying *touché*. And sometimes when people talk and argue a little bit, one says *touché* to admit the other person made a good point."

"What mean 'admit'? What mean 'made good point'?"

"Time out! Your turn, Donna."

She took over the impromptu English lesson, and Ken retreated to his study.

The four negative responses and several other putoffs had discouraged him. But for the past few weeks he'd been tracking encouraging developments in three congregations. One was the Elm Grove Baptist Church. Ken hadn't contacted Rev. McAllister until the last week of January, but the two hit it off right from the start. Ken liked the preacher's straightforwardness, his willingness to listen. He didn't beat around the bush, and he didn't drag his feet.

"I can't promise you we'll do anything," the clergyman had told him. "But if we know God is leading us, we'll surely do what He asks. I'd like to hear more about it. Could you and your wife come over to the parsonage tomorrow night? I'll have a couple of our leaders there, too."

After a discouraging start, Ken had made progress at Mendon Lutheran Church. His first contact there had been with Kathy Wenger, chairperson of the church board.

"Frankly, it would be tough to get any interest at our church," she said when he called. "I certainly wouldn't be able to do anything about it myself." There was a slight pause. "But I think we should give members of our congregation a chance to listen to you."

She scheduled a meeting and announced it in the bulletin that Sunday. But only two persons showed up. One was Kathy; the other Nelson Stephens, the pastor. Nevertheless, they opened another door that night, inviting Ken, Donna, and Kim Ang to talk to the adult church school class the following Sunday. That morning nearly half the class indicated they'd help with a sponsorship, and during the following week they met at the church to start planning. Only approval of the congregation was still needed to clear the way for a refugee family.

At St. Joseph's Catholic Church, Ken found both the priest and parishioners to be receptive right from the beginning, and by mid-February he'd held several meetings with them.

Last week was decision time at both churches. Monday evening,

Pastor Stephens called to report the Lutheran congregation approved sponsorship of a family, and on Tuesday St. Joseph's vote to sponsor was unanimous.

Most gratifying to Ken and Donna was the decision at St. Joseph's where close friends, Marilyn and Bob Gleason, spearheaded the bid for sponsorship. Kim Ang was thrilled, too. The refugees that St. Joseph's would bring to America were her grandmother and her uncles Hong, Tong, and Teng.

The Lutheran Church agreed to be responsible for Uncle Kim Eng and cousin Chhun Phon, now nine years old. When Chhun Leng translated the news last Tuesday, her mother was ecstatic.

Ken was relieved. With two sponsorships assured, he needed only two more—for the families of Kim Phang's brother, Seng Dao Tong, and her oldest daughter, Chhun Huoy—and he was counting on the Elm Grove Baptist Church to take one of those.

His main concern this week had been a snag that threatened to send Chhun Huoy and her family to France rather than America. In a letter to her parents, she said she and her husband had no contact with U. S. immigration officials but had twice been interviewed by the French.

Ken called the office of Congressman Frank Foreman to ask for help, and today a response was in the mailbox when he came home for lunch. He tore the envelope open and quickly scanned a copy of a cable from the embassy in Bangkok. Two sentences had been highlighted: "The family has no close relatives in the United States and therefore is not eligible for resettlement. A brother of the husband has resettled in France and the family may be eligible for resettlement there."

Ken threw the paper onto the desk in his study and reached for the phone. An aide to the congressman answered.

"I really appreciate your efforts," Ken said, "but the embassy people in Thailand seem to be missing a few facts. The woman's parents live here in Mendon." He hesitated, then added with a note of frustration, "How close do the relatives have to be?"

"Obviously, parents are close enough. We'll get a cable off to the embassy immediately," the aide assured him. "By the way, do you have a sponsor for the family?"

"A sponsor? We're working on it. I'm sure…"

"Tell him we'll sponsor the family." Donna, standing in the doorway, had been listening to Ken's end of the conversation.

"Just a minute, please," he told the aide, then covered the mouthpiece.

"What do you mean, 'We'll sponsor the family?'"

"It's no big deal. Don't keep the man waiting."

He lifted the handset to his head again.

"If it helps, just tell the embassy my wife and I will be responsible for sponsoring the family."

He hung up and turned to Donna.

"And where are we going to put two more adults, two young kids, and a baby?"

"You've got to have faith, Ken. There'll be a church to sponsor. If not, they can stay with us for a while. We'll make room."

CHAPTER 24

Ups and Downs

"Kim Ang, you can't carry all three sacks and not let me have any," Ken pleaded. He was embarrassed. Donna had asked them to go to the supermarket to get the things on her shopping list. Now at the checkout, while he was paying, Kim Ang quickly picked up everything they bought and started toward the door. She was determined to show her appreciation to the MacKenzies every way she could. Besides, in her country elders and males were to be respected.

Ken tried to take one of the grocery bags.

"In America, ladies are special," he tried to explain. "Men let them go first, open doors for them, things like that. Men are supposed to do most of the carrying, too. If I don't have any of the bags, people will think I'm a bad man."

She kept on walking, but he planted himself in front of her at the exit and took the sack squeezed between the ones in each arm. She wouldn't let go of those.

Outside, she came to an abrupt halt in front of a row of newspaper dispensers.

"Who that?" she exclaimed, relaxing her grip on one of the bags to point at a picture on the front page of one of the papers.

"Oh, that's Diana Spencer," he told her. "She's going to marry Prince Charles of Great Britain."

"She Donna's sister?"

"No, hardly. But Donna will be thrilled to know you asked."

"Hair same. Face look like Donna, too."

Ken took a closer look. There was a similarity. The caption

beneath the photo said women were flocking to hairdressers to duplicate Diana's charmingly simple coiffure. Amazing. Donna had worn her hair in that style for years.

At home it was Donna's turn to be embarrassed as Ken teasingly recounted the discussion in front of the newspaper boxes.

"And another thing," he added. "You need to talk to this young lady about American customs. She wouldn't let me carry any of the grocery bags. Can you imagine what people think when this little girl's struggling with three sacks and the guy she's with has empty hands?"

"Yeah, in a small town like this, word gets around quickly," she kidded. "Your reputation will be shot in no time. I'll see what I can do."

Ken feigned exasperation. He was grateful they both had a sense of humor. Without it, the past several weeks would have been almost impossible.

There had been turnarounds in the situation of Peng Sy and Kim Phang's daughter Chhun Huoy and her family. After Ken's call in February, Congressman Foreman's office reported the family would be interviewed by Americans. Things were looking up.

Then her parents received a letter saying she and her husband still hadn't talked to American officials but had been interviewed again by the French. Peng Sy and Kim Phang worried that Chhun Huoy and her husband would give up and accept resettlement in France if that opportunity were offered first.

Even more discouraging had been the ever-changing status of Kim Ang's grandmother and uncles. First had come the disheartening news last month that Uncle Kim Eng and his daughter would be resettled in California rather than Indiana. Becky Richards's call with that information was the first inkling Ken and Donna had that Haing Hok obviously hadn't given up his plans to bring Kim Ang's relatives to Long Beach.

Ken was furious. He couldn't believe the man would make a Christmas Eve promise to let the relatives come to Indiana, then go back to California and renew his efforts to resettle them there.

The sponsors at the Lutheran church were discouraged. They expected Kim Eng and Chhun Phon would arrive there any day. Ken smoothed it over somewhat by convincing them they'd be happier with a larger family. He persuaded them to sponsor instead Kim Phang's brother Seng Dao Tong and his wife, five daughters, and grandson.

Two days later Mrs. Richards called again. A Church World Service representative in Los Angeles had confirmed Haing Hok was still trying to bring Kim Ang's grandmother, Chen Yi, and her uncles Hong, Tong, and Teng to Long Beach.

"The person out there told me Haing Hok is a son of Chen Yi," she said. "That's what it says on the affidavit of relationship he filed, and they say they have no reason to believe otherwise. So they think he's as close a relative as Kim Ang. And he filed first."

Ken decided he'd have to talk to Hok himself.

On the phone, the Cambodian professed innocence.

"They no understand," he insisted. "I no say I Chen Yi son. I say cousin. They mix up."

Ken doubted that. He knew if Hok could lie to his face on Christmas Eve, he wouldn't have trouble doing it on the telephone.

"You have to make them understand, Hok. You promised me Kim Ang's grandmother and uncles would come here."

"Yes, that what I hope, too."

"Well then, will you go to the Church World Service people in Los Angeles tomorrow morning and make them understand you are just a cousin of Chen Yi, not a son?"

"Sure. I do that. Can talk Kim Ang, please?"

"Kim Ang, Hok wants to speak to you."

He handed her the phone. She said little, and what she did say was in Khmer. When she hung up, she was obviously troubled. But she wouldn't say why. He'd yelled at her, no doubt. Unwilling to argue with an older American male, he vented his wrath on the young Cambodian woman.

A few days later Kim Ang was even more upset after another call to the West Coast. She phoned to welcome Uncle Kim Eng to America and wish him well. However, he immediately criticized her for leaving Hong Taing's home and said she had disgraced her family. She left the phone in tears.

The following week Ken called Becky Richards again to check on the status of Kim Ang's grandmother and uncles. Becky contacted Los Angeles and got back to him in an hour.

"No change," she reported. "Haing Hok has been in touch with them again, but he still claims to be Chen Yi's son. I don't think there's anything else we can do."

Ken sighed. "I guess you're right. I hate to give up, but he's got us over a barrel."

He hung up, then seconds later lifted the receiver and dialed the Gleasons.

"Marilyn, this is Ken. I've got bad news. Just had Becky Richards check with CWS in LA again. That jerk is still lying and there's no way to prove it. Nobody will believe the truth. I'm afraid the family's going there. I'm sorry. I've embarrassed you and Bob and disappointed your friends at St. Joseph's. Now I don't know what else we can do. We'll just have to give up."

"It's not your fault, Ken," she responded. "They'll be disappointed, but they'll understand. You've done all you can. There's nothing else to do—except pray. We'll do that."

That had been a Monday. On Wednesday morning the phone rang in Ken's office at the college just as he was winding up a conference with one of his students.

"Dr. MacKenzie, this is Becky Richards. Are you sitting down?"

"Yes. Is the news that bad?"

"Not at all. It seems the people in Los Angeles have finally uncovered Haing Hok's lie. Now they won't let the family go to Long Beach. They're coming to Indiana."

"Wonderful! You don't know what this means to Donna and me, and to Kim Ang, and the people at St. Joseph's!"

"Oh, I think I do. I know how hard you've been working on this one. I'm just delighted for all of you."

"How long have we got?"

"I'd say at least a week. It's hard to be more specific than that."

Within minutes he was home. He was too excited to break the news to Donna on the phone. He wanted to see her reaction, to

share her joy. He wasn't disappointed. They couldn't wait to tell Kim
Ang either, so they drove to the Adult Learning Center and had her
called out of class.

Her jubilation more than made up for the stress generated by
the long-distance struggle with Haing Hok. When she went back to
the classroom, they watched through the window in the door as she
broke the news to the other Cambodians.

Their next stop was at the Gleasons where they shared the news
with Marilyn.

"Well, you've made a lot of people happy this morning," she told Ken.

"Not me. I'd given up. But I remember somebody saying they
were going to pray."

Later, when Chen Yi and her three sons finally arrived on a flight
from San Francisco, Donna and Ken stood alongside the Gleasons
at the Indianapolis International Airport terminal. Kim Ang beamed
as she brought her four closest surviving relatives toward them and
made the introductions.

"This my grandmother. And this Uncle Hong. Uncle Tong. This
Uncle Teng; he one year older than me. I tell them you their
sponsors." She nodded to the Gleasons. "I say Marilyn and Bob very
good people, help them have good start in America."

She took Donna's hand and pulled her closer to her kin.

"I say to grandmother and uncles, you and Ken do many good
things—work hard so they come America, find sponsors for other
Cambodians, too. I say you like mother, father for me."

When the family arrived at its new home in an apartment
building near the center of Mendon, just two blocks from the
Catholic Church and five from the MacKenzies' house, Kim Ang
was able to help Marilyn and Bob and other St. Joseph's parishioners
introduce her grandmother and uncles to their new surroundings.
With a week off from school for spring vacation, she had plenty
of time.

Donna and Ken were uncertain whether she'd return to their home
or stay with her grandmother and uncles. A few days before the family
arrived they had tried to get a reading on Kim Ang's feelings about
where she wanted to live. They didn't want to press too hard. It would

be difficult enough for her to decide. But she'd been with Ken and Donna five months by then and, despite the stress that moved in with her, she had brought them more happiness than they'd thought possible. Donna felt she had to express how she and Ken felt.

"Kim Ang," she began. "Before your family comes, we want to tell you some things. You need to know we love you very much. You have become part of our family. You have made us very happy. When your grandmother and uncles are here, you will still be welcome to stay with us if that is what you want. We would like that."

She paused and looked at Ken, wondering if she had said too much. He took it as a cue to add his thoughts.

"You will need to decide what is best for your family, Kim Ang— and for you. In your culture, family is very important. And that is good. But we hope helping your family will not stop you from getting an education. If staying with us makes it easier to make that dream come true, you can live here and still spend time with your family."

"Whatever you decide," Donna interjected, "we will always love you, Kim Ang. We will always want to help you, whether you live with us or somewhere else."

"I love you, too," Kim Ang responded. "You very good to me. When little girl, I don't know if mother, father love me. Here I know. But I cannot say now what I do. I must wait for grandmother, uncles. They decide."

Ken and Donna knew that's the way it had to be. She'd be obliged to respect the wishes of the older members of her family. If Chen Yi and the uncles wanted her with them, she'd have to stay there. They could only hope her family would consider her best interests. When the family arrived, there was no discussion of where Kim Ang would live. She went with her grandmother and uncles, and Ken and Donna knew she'd be with them all that week. They wouldn't know more until the week ended and it was time for Kim Ang to go back to school.

By Tuesday, though, the silence and emptiness in the big old house on Center Street were getting to Donna. She had to talk to Kim Ang. She could wait to ask whether her foster daughter would be coming home, but she had to know if she was all right. After several rings, Kim Ang picked up the phone at her grandmother's apartment. She sounded weary.

"Kim Ang, this is Donna. How are things going?"

"Everything OK."

"You sound tired, honey. Have you been sleeping all right?"

"No, I not sleep."

"Have you been too excited to sleep, or have you been sick?

"No, not excited. Not sick. Got some red spots, and itch. But not sick. Just not enough time for sleep. Too much work. I need do everything."

Donna had been concerned this would happen. She wondered from the beginning whether the grandmother and uncles would take advantage of Kim Ang. Besides that, she'd been worried about what seemed an obsessive urge to please the grandmother. Before the family arrived, a dozen parishioners from St. Joseph's spent an entire day cleaning the apartment. When Donna and Ken took Kim Ang to see it that night it was spotless. Nevertheless, Kim Ang insisted on going back, alone, the next day "to be sure everything OK." When she came home six hours later, she confessed she'd rescrubbed all the floors and cupboards.

Now, besides her own apparently unhealthy obsession, Kim Ang was being victimized by what seemed to Donna to be a demanding grandmother and three inconsiderate uncles.

"What all did you have to do?" Donna asked.

"Need do cleaning, cooking, pick up everything, wash the clothes."

"You're using the washing machine in the apartment building, aren't you?"

"No. Need put money in that. Grandmother say cost too much. I do in bathtub."

"Is it all done now?"

"No. I have more. But no problem. I can do."

"Don't you wash anything else over there, Kim Ang," Donna ordered. "We'll bring the clothes over here and use the washing machine. You get everything together that needs to be washed, and I'll pick you up in five minutes."

Back home, Donna checked the rash that had broken out on Kim Ang's back and applied a salve. Then she insisted the weary young woman go to her room and get some sleep while she washed, dried, and folded the laundry. She was still folding towels and bedding when Ken came home three hours later.

"I thought you washed yesterday," he greeted her.

"This stuff isn't ours. It belongs to Kim Ang's grandmother and uncles."

She recounted her phone conversation with Kim Ang.

"She's in her room now, sleeping. She's hardly had any sleep since they came. They've been making her do everything over there. That can't go on, Ken. I know I said we shouldn't interfere or pressure them about Kim Ang staying with us. But we have to talk to them. I think Hong understands English well enough so we can get across our concerns."

That night when they took Kim Ang and the laundry back to the apartment, Ken took Hong aside and explained their concern.

"We are happy you are in America," he began. "We hope you will have a good life here. We want all of your family to be happy. We have tried very hard to bring happiness to Kim Ang."

"Yes, you help very much," Hong agreed. "Thank you."

"Many things are not the same in America as in Cambodia," Ken continued. "You already know that. But there are some things you may not know. One is especially important. To be successful in America, you need a good education. And it is important that women go to school, too. Donna and I are afraid your mother will not let Kim Ang go to school. That would make us very sad. And it would not be good for your family. If Kim Ang has a good education, she will be able to help you more."

"Yes, I know education important," Hong acquiesced. "My father tell Kim Ang that when he die. I know he want her go school."

"Donna and I are worried, too, that if Kim Ang stays in your house and does all the work, she will not be able to study. If she lives in our house, we can help her with her studies. We think it is very important that all of us, my family and your family, do as much as we can so she will have a good education."

"I think that right," Hong nodded. "It not up to me to say, but I talk to mother."

When Saturday arrived, Ken and Donna were still wondering whether Kim Ang would come home. School would resume Monday. Kim Ang's books were here. She wasn't. They'd just have to wait and see what happened. But it wasn't easy.

Today was even more difficult. They had hoped Kim Ang would be with them for this morning's Palm Sunday service. They missed having her in the pew between them. At home after church, Donna kept looking out the front window, hoping to see Kim Ang coming up the street. But there was no sign of her.

"She's not coming back," Donna sighed as the clock struck midnight and Ken started turning out the lights. "I'm so afraid her dream's over. If she stays with those three men and her grandmother, she'll be nothing but a housekeeper. And that'll be the end of her studies."

He put an arm around her as they walked through the darkened house. But he didn't know what to say.

Upstairs, Ken was already in bed and Donna was fluffing her pillow when she heard a sound below. Then a voice:

"Hello. Sorry I late. I home now."

Kim Ang was standing at the bottom of the stairway. Donna came down, two steps at a time, and threw her arms around the girl.

"I wasn't sure you were coming back, Kim Ang. Are you going to stay?"

"Yes. We do lot of talk about that. Grandmother want me stay her house. But Uncle Hong say he think be hard for me go school if live there. He say school important. He remember what Grandfather tell me night he die. He know you love me. He say you feel bad if I not with you. Finally, Grandmother say OK I live here."

Donna hugged her again.

"Welcome home, honey." She dabbed at a tear in the corner of her eye. "Better get to bed now. Tomorrow will be a busy day."

Kim Ang smiled. "I think you mother now, for sure. Only mother say that."

CHAPTER 25

Yellow Roses and Other Blessings

SEPTEMBER 22, 1981

Not everybody in Mendon appreciated Ken's determination to improve the lot of his fellow man. In the doorway of Dugan's Hardware one day last spring, he nearly collided with someone who didn't.

"You're the guy bringin' all them gooks in here, ain't ya?" the man snarled.

He looked familiar, but Ken didn't know him. Apparently he didn't want an answer to the question. He kept walking toward a pickup parked in front of the store. But as he jerked open the door of the truck he yelled back, loud enough to be heard above the street noise:

"Blasted foreigners are takin' all the jobs an' us white folks are goin' hungry."

Before Ken could respond, the truck door slammed. The starter whined and the engine caught, then raced a couple times before spinning wheels kicked up dust and debris along the curb.

Ben Dugan smiled and shrugged his shoulders as Ken stepped up to the counter.

"That guy doesn't like you much."

"No, guess not, Ben. Doesn't look like he's a native American. If not, he's on thin ice talking about foreigners. At one time or another that's what all of us were, or our grandparents at least."

"Well, don't let it get you down."

"I don't. The Cambodians here are starting their own businesses or taking jobs other people don't want. My guess is they'll eventually be our employers rather than take our jobs."

Ken had anticipated there'd be some resentment. Too many Asian faces had shown up too fast to suit some people. Three weeks after Kim Ang's grandmother and uncles arrived, the family of Kim Phang's brother, Seng Dao Tong, came to Mendon.

But at the time of last May's doorway confrontation Ken wasn't overly concerned with reactions from bigots. He had other worries. The Americans in Thailand still hadn't interviewed Peng Sy and Kim Phang's daughter Chhun Huoy and her family. And despite the initial bright outlook for sponsorship of the family by the Elm Grove Baptist Church, nothing seemed to be happening there either.

But Henry McAllister called a week later. Lack of action by his elders had disappointed him, too. He decided he'd preach a sermon on the Good Samaritan and invited Ken to take part in the service.

"Would you give an introduction, tell a little about refugees and your involvement with them, what it's meant to you?" he asked.

The next Sunday morning Donna and Kim Ang were with Ken at the Elm Grove church. After Pastor McAllister read the familiar parable from the tenth chapter of Luke, Ken stepped to the platform. He reminded the congregation of the horrors that forced thousands to flee from Cambodia. He recounted his own lack of concern:

"I closed my eyes, and my mind, and my heart," he said, "and I walked by on the other side. But God was patient with me. He gave me another chance."

He told about his church's decision to sponsor a family and his continuing reluctance to do anything. He confessed he agreed to take care of the money for the sponsorship effort only so he'd have an excuse not to get more involved. He described how his attitude changed when he met the refugees and learned of the trouble they'd endured:

> One of them is with us this morning. Her name is Kim Ang. When she was thirteen, her world fell apart. She was separated from her family and everyone she knew, then forced to work as a slave. Heavy burdens and long hours of work gave her constant pain. She never had enough to eat. She always was afraid. And for good reason. Her

parents were murdered by communist soldiers. So were her only two sisters. Her grandfather died of starvation. An uncle, aunt and two-year-old cousin were killed, just because the uncle was a doctor. Another aunt and her child, also two years old, died in a land mine explosion. Kim Ang doesn't know whether her two brothers are alive or not.

During the past several months, my wife and I have learned not only about Kim Ang's terrible past, but we have come to know her as a very special young lady whose first concern is for the happiness of others. Knowing her and having the opportunity to help her have been among the greatest blessings of our lives. You see, I discovered when I was willing to cross the street and offer help I was the one who received the blessing. That has made it easier for me to ask others to join in bringing love and hope to refugees who have suffered so much. And that's why I'm here today.

In a crowded camp in Thailand there's a family of five—a mother and father, two little girls, and a baby boy. They've suffered the same kind of hardships as Kim Ang. They need someone who's willing to cross the street, to extend a hand, to say 'I will help.' If the Good Samaritan were here, he would. But whatever became of the Good Samaritan? Please listen carefully as Pastor McAllister considers that question with us.

Ken stepped down and sat alongside Donna and Kim Ang in a second-row pew while the pastor began his message. As his sermon unfolded, Rev. McAllister paraphrased St. Luke's account of the parable, then emphasized its implication that doctrine is significant only when it's applied.

"The lawyer who was testing Jesus," he explained, "had a correct understanding of the doctrine. He knew what he had to do to inherit eternal life. But he hadn't done it. Jesus told him he had to put that knowledge to use."

Then he focused on the lawyer's second question, "Who is my neighbor?" He pointed out that wasn't actually what the man wanted to know.

"He really is concerned about the limits of his responsibility," the pastor explained, "about how little he can do and still get by. He's got it all backwards. The question isn't 'Who is my neighbor?' It's 'Will I be his neighbor?' And the question we need to ask this morning is not whether the poor man down the street, the unsaved woman next door, or the refugee who needs help is my neighbor. What each of us needs to ask is, 'Will I be his neighbor?' My prayer is that, when that question is answered this morning, the Good Samaritan will be found right here, living within many of you."

Just before the benediction, Rev. McAllister invited parishioners to meet with Ken, Donna, and Kim Ang after the service to learn more about refugee sponsorship. Nearly all the church's elders and several others remained. Some were merely curious, but the questions of others showed a genuine interest in getting involved.

Afterwards, on the way back to Mendon, Ken turned to Donna.

"How do you think it went?" he asked.

"It?"

"Yeah. You know, my introduction to Henry's sermon."

"Oh, that. It was OK, I guess."

He frowned. She smiled and jabbed at his arm.

"Just kidding. I thought it was great, really—but not as good as the sermon."

"Well, he's had more practice."

"Kim Ang liked it, too," Donna added. "She says you ought to be a preacher."

Ken glanced in the rearview mirror.

"Well, honey, since you moved in I've changed a lot. But not that much. I think I'll stick with teaching for a while."

The jovial mood was short-lived, however. That afternoon Meng Tieng and Chhun Leng came to the MacKenzie home and translated part of a letter their parents had received from Chhun Huoy:

"We are so discouraged. Nothing happens. We are afraid we will never get out of this camp. Or we will be sent back to Cambodia. We have decided to go to the first country that will let us in. If the French say to us first we can go there, then that is what we will do."

The next evening, however, their spirits zoomed upward again when Henry McAllister called to report his elders had voted to sponsor Chhun Huoy's family.

"That's great, Henry!" Ken exclaimed. "Now all we have to do is pray the Americans approve them for resettlement before the French do."

Weeks went by with no further developments. But in June a letter from Chhun Huoy told her parents that she and her husband had completed two of the three interviews required by the U. S. Immigration and Naturalization Service. Then there was another long lapse before the next shot of good news. It came on the first Monday of August when Ken took a call from Becky Richards:

"You'll like what I have to say, Dr. MacKenzie. Chhun Huoy and her husband and children are coming. They'll arrive in Indianapolis Friday."

But there was another call on Tuesday.

"Becky Richards again, Dr. MacKenzie. I hate to say this, but the family's been put on medical hold. And there's no further information.

"They didn't give you any idea what the problem is?" Ken asked.

"No, so we have no idea how long it'll be before they're cleared. It could be a couple days, a couple months, or ..."

"Don't say it. With a church to sponsor them now, they just have to come. This has to be terribly discouraging for them. Their hopes have been boosted, then shattered, so many times. And now this. But there's nothing we can do, I guess. Congressman Foreman can't help us on this one. We'll just have to be patient."

The delay discouraged Ken, but he was thankful the problem didn't need his attention. He and Donna had others to deal with. Kim Ang's continuing insistance that she was responsible for Hong Taing's unhappiness was more troublesome than they'd at first anticipated.

"She still thinks it's her fault," Donna reminded Ken one evening. "I can't seem to get through to her. She always blames herself for anything that goes wrong. Nothing I say makes any difference. It's almost like she enjoys persecuting herself."

"I think she gets a little help in that respect."

"What do you mean?"

"I mean she's not the only one blaming her for whatever goes wrong."

"Who else?"

"Her grandmother, I think. Maybe her uncles, too. Have you noticed she seems more upset after she's been with them?"

Donna thought for a moment.

"Now that you mention it, sure. It's not just Hong Taing's attitude that troubles her then. It's family pressure, too."

Ken nodded. "It's mostly family pressure. At Christmas Haing Hok was going to take her away. That was due to family pressure. Then a few months ago her uncle arrives in California, and when she calls him what's the first thing he says?"

"He chews her out for being ungrateful to Hong Taing and leaving his house."

"Right. Then her family arrives and they see Hong Taing's resentment. They must know it's not her fault, but they don't let on to her. They're embarrassed because of Hong Taing's bitterness. They're really the ones who put her in the spot she was in. But they need a scapegoat. And she's it."

Donna nodded. "That all seems to fit. It's not all her grandmother's fault, though. Cultural disparity is involved in this. Chen Yi has been through so much, suffered so much. Now she finds herself an old lady in a strange new world. She wants things to be like they were in the old country. I'm sure that's why when Kim Ang is with her grandmother she gets an earful about how she disgraced the family."

"Yes, but I wish we could get her to fight back. She's just letting them dump on her. Then she feels guilty and depressed because she can't please them."

"She won't fight back, Ken. It's the same as if she were an abused child. You know, abused children often try desperately to please the persons abusing them. Sometimes the more they're abused the more they try to please."

They were convinced they'd identified the cause of Kim Ang's latest trouble, but they knew they couldn't eliminate it. They couldn't confront Chen Yi and her sons. Nor could they discourage Kim Ang from spending time with her closest relatives.

Perhaps they could help her to understand she wasn't the problem. But that wouldn't be easy. They hadn't forgotten Kim Ang's determination to move away last December when she first blamed herself for the trouble with Hong Taing. She had stayed, but not because she was convinced she wasn't at fault. She stayed because, for the first time since Aunt Lang died, she felt loved. For now all they could do was be sure she knew they loved her. And, as soon as the time was right, they'd see if they could help her work through the trouble.

Two weeks ago, amid the excitement of beginning another school year, Kim Ang's depression diminished. The necessity of using English at home with the MacKenzies was paying off in improved comprehension, and teachers felt she no longer needed the morning English classes at the Adult Learning Center. She was pleased to be the first of the local Cambodians to become a full-time high school student. Though the load of five subjects was challenging, she was thrilled to be back in the classroom where she could concentrate more on grandfather's hopes and be less concerned about grandmother's admonitions.

On Wednesday of that first week of school Kim Ang was late getting home. The last class of the day ended at three o'clock and the walk home took only fifteen minutes. But at five there still was no sign of her. Donna was becoming worried. She reached for the phone and had just started to dial the number for the high school when she heard the back door open and close.

"Kim Ang, is that you?"

"Yes. Sorry I late."

"Where have you been?"

"Grandmother's house," the girl called back as she piled her books on the bench alongside the door and hung her jacket in the closet.

Donna didn't respond. Further questions could wait until Kim Ang came into the kitchen. She wondered what effect this visit with her kinfolk would have on the girl. She'd been so happy the past few days. It would be a shame to have her sink into depression again. She was sure that would be the case though. Rapid footsteps in the hall leading to the kitchen alerted Donna to be prepared. But she wasn't ready for what she saw. Kim Ang was smiling and seemed about to burst with joy.

"Guess what!" she exclaimed.

Donna hesitated. What could make this girl so happy? The last time she'd smiled after seeing her grandmother was at the airport in Indianapolis.

"Well, let's see. Chhun Huoy's family is coming," she responded finally.

"No, that not right."

"How many guesses do I get?"

"You never guess. I tell you. My brothers alive! They in Thailand!"

She threw herself into Donna's arms, almost upsetting a bowl on the edge of the counter.

"Oh, wonderful! I'm so happy for you!"

Still holding both Kim Ang's hands, Donna stepped back.

"How did you find out?" she asked.

"Grandmother have letter from friends in camp. They say Pheng and Heng there. They run away when find out Khmer Rouge look for them. They go far away, find good people who say Pheng and Heng can pretend be their sons. In that part Cambodia, Pol Pot people not so bad. Work hard, but not kill. When Vietnamese come, they see chance get away. They escape later than me, go different camp than me."

"Do you know which camp they are in?"

"Sure. They tell in letter to grandmother. Can they come America, you think?"

"Oh, I hope so, Kim Ang. I'm sure Ken will check into that. Perhaps Marilyn and Bob's church will sponsor your brothers, too. If not, we will ourselves. Don't you worry."

The next morning Ken called Becky Richards to check on procedures to expedite the resettlement of Kim Ang's brothers. She interrupted before he had a chance to ask.

"How did you know they're coming?"

"Who's coming?" he countered.

"Chhun Huoy and her family, of course. Are you expecting someone else?"

"Well, yes. I might be. But first tell me about Chhun Huoy. When is she coming?"

"The family's due at Indianapolis next Monday evening, the twenty-first. Scheduled arrival is 7:45. Now tell me who else you might be expecting."

Ken told her about Kim Ang's brothers.

"Wow, that's great! We'll just need the usual sponsorship papers. Send them to me right away and I'll try to get things going."

As soon as he was off the phone, Ken hustled Donna and Kim Ang into the car and drove to Peng Sy and Kim Phang's home. This wasn't the kind of news to break on the phone. Dinner could wait. From there, he called Henry McAllister. Then Kim Phang called her brother, Seng Dao Tong. Peng Sy told his sister, Nuom Yong, and Kim Ang called her grandmother.

They had all shared the anxiety during the months of uncertainty, the disappointing delays, the frustrations on both sides of the ocean. Now they wanted to take part in the happy ending. All the Cambodians in Mendon were determined to get to Indianapolis to welcome Chhun Huoy's family. And they did.

Yesterday a caravan of two vans, the Mackenzies' Buick, and the Lutheran Church's Sunday School bus filed down route 65 to Indianapolis, carrying the Cambodians and sponsors from their four sponsoring churches—St. Joseph's Catholic, Holy Trinity Episcopal, Mendon Lutheran, and Mendon United Methodist. Henry McAllister and his wife were there, too, along with two of the sponsoring couples from the Elm Grove Baptist Church.

The plane was on schedule and first through the gate was five-year-old Kim Pov, small for her age but obviously fearless and independent. She was thirty yards ahead of the rest of the family. Her sister Kim Leng, 7, walked alongside Chhun Huoy. Baby brother Chhun Sy squirmed in his mother's arms, head and legs protruding from opposite ends of a loosely-wrapped blanket. Their father, Meng, carried a small satchel in each hand.

At the gate they were engulfed by the welcoming tide of relatives and friends. Kim Phang and her granddaughters wrapped their arms around one another and squeezed themselves into a single lump of love. Peng Sy took his infant grandson and held him triumphantly over his head.

The MacKenzies stood against the concourse wall opposite the celebration, basking in the joy of the welcome. Ken slipped an arm around Donna and pulled her closer.

"I've never seen such happy people. We've had a few problems getting them here. But this sure does make it worthwhile."

She leaned her head on his chest and he raised his hand to caress her cheek. It was wet. He squeezed her closer.

"By the way," he added, "in case I haven't said it before, thanks for dragging me along to that meeting at church."

Though still warmed by last night's joy, Donna was dry-eyed this morning when Kim Ang left for school. At the door, the girl paused and turned to her.

"You make Peng Sy and Kim Phang very happy. Their family all here now. Thank you for be so good to my people."

"You're welcome, honey. But it's made us more happy than you and your people. We should thank you." She paused, smiled and waved the back of her hand toward the door. "Now off to school with you before you're late."

"OK, Mom. Bye."

They both laughed.

But an hour later Donna was misty-eyed again. From the front door, she followed the blurred image of the Mendon Floral delivery truck as it backed slowly out of the drive. In her hands were a bouquet of bright yellow roses and a card with a handwritten message:

> Kenneth & Donna,
> The long wait is over now. We are all happy to
> be together again. Thank you very much for
> your efforts. May God continue to bless you.
> Peng Sy & Kim Phang's family

The Real Story
An Old Argument

In his book *A Nation of Immigrants*, President John F. Kennedy pointed out that "every American who ever lived, with the exception of one group, was either an immigrant himself or a descendant of immigrants."

Be that as it may, public opinion polls in the 1990s reveal that anti-immigrant sentiment prevails among a majority of Americans. They claim that immigrants take their jobs, raise their taxes, crowd their schools, and don't fit in with the rest of us.

But those opinions aren't new. Before the United States came into existence, some Americans were saying things like that. In 1751 Benjamin Franklin was convinced the Germans would not assimilate. He asked why they should "be suffered to swarm into our settlements and, by herding together, establish their language and manners to the exclusion of ours."

Immigration proponents and restrictionists both cite seemingly valid statistics to prove their points, and the debate goes on. But what's at stake, as Bernard Weisberger wrote in the February/March 1994 edition of *American Heritage*, is the essential nature of the United States of America.

Contending that America is different from other nations, Weisberger says, "Some sneer at the statement that we are a nation of immigrants as a cliche; all nations, they assert, are made up of mixtures of different peoples. So they are, as new tribes and races displaced old ones by conquest or by random migration. But the United States was created by settlers who arrived from elsewhere, who deliberately and calculatedly invited and urged others to follow them, and who encouraged the process in ways that were unique."

In a 1990 *Wall Street Journal* article, Julian L. Simon points out that "public opinion has always opposed immigration, and for the same reasons it does now. Magazine articles in earlier decades, and public-opinion polls more recently, show bigotry to have been the main driving force, according to research by Rita Simon of American University.

"Nowadays it is no longer acceptable publicly to state crude racist arguments about color, ethnicity and religion," he continues. "'Cultural homogeneity' is the contemporary codeword for racist opposition to immigration. Supposed dangers from terrorism, crime, disease and social disorganization also are used to arouse antagonism against immigrants."

For more details, see:

William Dudley, editor, *Immigration: Opposing Viewpoints* (San Diego, Calif., Greenhaven Press, Inc., 1990)

Gil Loescher and John A. Scanlon, *Calculated Kindness: Refugees and America's Half-Open Door, 1945-Present* (New York, The Free Press, A Division of Macmillan, Inc., 1986)

Julian L. Simon, "Bring on the Wretched Refuse," *The Wall Street Journal* (Jan. 26, 1990) page A14

Bernard A. Weisberger, "A Nation of Immigrants," *American Heritage* (Feb./March 1994) pages 75-91

CHAPTER 26

Wings of the Wind

OCTOBER 24, 1981

Aware of the horror Kim Ang had endured in Cambodia, the MacKenzies never suspected a mere two-day separation from them would distress her. Not until weeks later, after Rev. Greenwood had a long talk with their nineteen-year-old foster daughter, did they realize the mistake they'd made.

"What she went through in Cambodia," he told Ken and Donna, "hasn't made her immune to emotional upheaval. To the contrary, because of her experiences, little things you or I wouldn't even notice could disturb her tremendously.

"Remember, when she was still a child, she lost her parents and at least half her close relatives. She was separated from the remaining familiar faces and sent away as a slave. Then, when she finally found her way back to what was left of her family, the only one who really showed her any love was blown away by a land mine. Now, for the first time since that happened, she feels loved again. And when you go away she's deathly afraid something will happen. She's afraid you won't come back."

"Oh!" Donna exclaimed. "We should have realized that. Of course! Everything you say makes sense."

The trouble had occurred the previous weekend. And, as it turned out, fear of losing Donna and Ken was only part of the problem. Nevertheless, it wouldn't have occurred if they hadn't gone out of town and left Kim Ang behind.

Besides teaching her once-a-week class this fall, Donna had agreed to handle promotion of Mendon's evening adult education program. And that meant she had to be at Indiana University in Bloomington the first Saturday of October for a conference on broadcast publicity. She and Ken decided to make a weekend of it. Hoping to work in some hiking, they left early Friday afternoon after reserving a cabin at Brown County State Park for Friday and Saturday nights.

Concerned about a possible recurrence of Kim Ang's depression, Donna arranged for her to spend the weekend with Duane and Shirley Landon. She was to go there after school Friday. But, when the MacKenzies returned to Mendon Sunday evening, they learned she never reached the Landon's.

"She called us late Friday," Shirley told them, "and said she was going to stay at her grandmother's."

"That's bound to mean trouble," Ken sighed.

But when Kim Ang came home Sunday night there was no evidence of a problem. She did explain though why she didn't stay at Duane and Shirley's.

"Cambodians say I bad woman if I sleep at houses of other Americans."

That made sense. They'd forgotten the cultural disparity again.

"Of course. I understand," Donna assured her. "But, after this, please tell us if we ask you to do something that's not right. We have to understand your culture, too."

She decided she wouldn't ask Kim Ang how things went at her grandmother's. If there had been problems, as she suspected, she'd see the results soon enough.

In the morning her fears were confirmed. There had been problems, but their manifestation wasn't merely emotional. When Donna came down to fix breakfast, Kim Ang was in the bathroom—retching.

"Kim Ang, what's the problem?"

"Feel sick. Stomach hurt."

She was in pain more often than not. Her knees hurt most of the time. Her back ached, too. The heavy loads she'd carried as a child, digging canals for the Khmer Rouge, were still a burden. But Kim

Ang rarely complained about those aches and pains. This was something unusual. Donna felt her forehead.

"I don't think you have a fever, honey. Where does it hurt?"

"Here." She pointed to her abdomen.

"Did you eat something at your grandmother's that might have made you sick?"

"Don't think so."

Donna was puzzled. Severe stomach pain. No fever.

"I'll call Dr. Humphrey and see if he'll take a look at you."

A hint of guilt crept over Kim Ang's face. She stared at the floor.

"No. I eat something."

"What did you eat?"

Kim Ang still wouldn't look at Donna.

"Don't know. Find in drawer my desk. Little bag. Have like sand inside. That what I eat."

Suddenly it dawned on Donna! Silica gel! Ken used to keep his cameras in that desk. When he bought the cameras, packets of silica gel were in the boxes. Ken just tossed them in the drawer, assuming they'd help keep the cameras dry there, too.

"Did the little bag have writing on it?" she asked. "Did it say 'Poison'?"

"Not sure. There was picture—head bone, two other bones in front like X. I think writing say, 'Danger. Do not put in mouth.'"

Donna put her arm around the trembling girl and led her to the phone in the kitchen. She called the doctor's office.

"Dr. Humphrey will see us in an hour, Kim Ang. He says the poison won't make you die, but he wants to do some tests. Why did you eat the poison? Was your grandmother giving you a bad time again about leaving Hong Taing?"

Kim Ang was staring at the floor again. She didn't respond.

"Honey, you can tell me. You have to trust me. I can't help if I don't know what the problem is."

Kim Ang kept looking down.

"Not help anyway. Nobody help. Grandmother want me marry. She try find husband."

Donna didn't know what to say. *Yes, that could be reason enough for the girl to attempt suicide. She's in a can't-win situation. If she marries, her dream will end. There will be no more education. And if she refuses to go along with the arranged marriage, she'll be an outcast. The few family members she has left will have nothing to do with her.*

Fumbling for comforting words, she put her arms around Kim Ang. "I'm sorry, honey. Perhaps Ken and I can talk to your grandmother."

"No. That not help."

Donna knew she was probably right. Her grandmother figured it was her responsibility to find a husband. Besides, marrying off her granddaughter could end the embarrassment she'd caused by leaving Hong Taing's house.

By Wednesday Kim Ang was feeling well enough to return to school. Fortunately, the silica gel wasn't as potent as the warning label made it out to be. Dr. Humphrey assured Donna there was no permanent damage.

Two weeks later the pressure seemed to be off. Kim Ang was less stressed. Apparently her grandmother hadn't found any good prospects. Ken and Donna hadn't attempted to discuss their concern with Kim Ang's relatives. But they'd prayed a lot.

This evening Ken was at his office, working on a course change proposal. Donna and Kim Ang were enjoying the coziness of the family room while a brisk autumn wind howled around the corners of the house. Donna, at one end of the sofa, was flipping pages of the *National Geographic* that came in today's mail. Kim Ang had curled up at the opposite end with her literature book.

"I try read this story three times already," the girl complained. "Still not understand."

Donna set the magazine aside, slid across the sofa, and leaned over to see what Kim Ang had been assigned to read.

"Oh, 'The Lottery' by Shirley Jackson. That's a very famous short story. I've read it several times, too. What don't you understand, honey?"

"Every year, on June 27, men put papers in little box. Then they pull out. See who is unlucky person. Everybody throw stones. Kill that person, I think. Why they do that?"

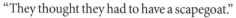

"They thought they had to have a scapegoat."

"What mean scapegoat?"

"That's somebody who takes the blame for all the other people. The people in the story think if they put all the blame on one person and kill that person, then everything will be OK. Only good things will happen then. Of course, they're wrong, but that's what they thought."

"Oh, I understand now. But that terrible. They not very smart people."

Donna moved closer and took Kim Ang's hand.

"You're right, honey. You know, your relatives are a little like that."

"What you mean?"

"You're their scapegoat. They may be trying to put the blame on you. They are the ones who arranged for you to come to America, pretending to be Hong Taing's wife. Then when we took you out of his house and he became angry, they blamed you. And now if your grandmother forces you to marry, that will kill your dream. If you marry and go away to live someplace else, maybe they think everything will be OK."

Kim Ang seemed to understand. She didn't say anything. But she smiled her appreciation for the insight. She stood up and walked to the window.

"Wind very strong. Make me afraid."

She came back to the sofa and sat next to Donna.

"You afraid when wind blow?"

"I used to be when I was a little girl," Donna replied. "Then my mother showed me something in the Bible. I'll show you."

She pulled the New English Bible from the shelf next to her, knowing that version would be easier for Kim Ang to understand, then thumbed through it until she came to Psalm 18.

"This is a song about God the savior. Remember, you asked me in church last Christmas what savior means? Then later I told you about Jesus, God's Son, and how He died to save us?"

"Sure."

"OK. Well, this song starts out telling God that we love Him, that we know He saves us and keeps us safe.

"A man named David wrote this. It's about when his enemies were all around him and he was in really bad trouble. Then he called out to God, and God came to him. Now listen to this part."

She ran her finger down the page and stopped at verse 10.

He rode on a cherub, he flew through the air;
he swooped on the wings of the wind.

"That's how God came to him, riding on a cherub. A cherub is an angel. Do you know what an angel is?"

"I think maybe have wings."

"Sure. Angels have wings—in pictures men have painted of them, at least. This verse says God rode on an angel, 'on the wings of the wind.'

"So you see, Kim Ang, that's why I'm not afraid of the wind anymore. If God makes His angels winds, if the Bible says angels are wind, then how can I be afraid of the wind? The harder the wind blows, the more I know God and His angels are near, watching over me, protecting me."

"Thank you for tell me that. Now I not afraid."

Donna slipped the Bible back onto the shelf, then turned again to Kim Ang.

"I'll tell you something else about angels, honey. I'm sure they had a lot to do with you being here in Mendon and living with Ken and me."

"How you know that?"

"Because of Mr. Cranston. Do you remember him? He's Chhun Ping's sponsor."

"Oh, sure."

"Well, after Chhun Ping went to Lafayette, Mr. Cranston came to tell us that you and Nuom Yong's family needed a sponsor. He had learned about refugees from a man who lived in a little town called Millbrook. In that town there's a very small church. Most people would say the church is too little to sponsor refugees. But it did. And when Mr. Cranston found out that tiny church was helping a family, he decided his church could, too. Then he came to our church, and we said if those churches were sponsors, we would be. And then you came with Nuom Yong.

"All of that happened because a few people in a little church decided they could do something. Why do you think they didn't just say, 'There aren't enough of us to help; let somebody else do it'?"

"Don't know. What you think?"

"I think angels were working there. I think God sent them to tell the man what he should do. And I think the angels helped him persuade the other people in the church to sponsor the family.

"I want to tell you something else, too, Kim Ang. For a long time I prayed to God, asking Him to help Ken and me have a child. We couldn't have one of our own, so I wanted to adopt a boy or girl."

"What mean adopt?" Kim Ang interrupted.

"Adopting is finding a boy or girl who doesn't have a mother and father and making that child a part of your own family."

"Oh, sure, I understand."

"Do you remember last year when I told Rev. Greenwood about wanting to adopt a child?"

"No, I not remember that."

"We were talking at the door on the way out of church. You probably didn't hear everything we said. You were thinking about going out into the snow and cold. Well anyway, Kim Ang, when Ken said it would be OK to adopt, I started to look for a child. But I couldn't find one. Then I prayed, 'God, please help me find someone who needs your love, and ours.' And do you know what happened then?"

"No. What?"

"That's when you came."

"You mean God send me to you when you pray?"

"Yep. That's what happened. So, you see, you're pretty special!"

She leaned her head on Donna's shoulder.

"Make me feel real good. Thank you for tell me that. I glad you talk about angel, too. Now I happy when wind blow. You really special. I glad you my mother now."

A tear fell on her hand and she turned to look up at Donna.

"Why you cry? I make you sad?"

"Hardly, honey. Except for Ken, you're the nicest thing that's ever happened to me."

CHAPTER 27

Another Exodus

"No good," Kim Ang mumbled as she tossed her report card onto the dining room table.

After becoming a full-time high school student last fall, she attacked her studies with the same intensity that had characterized her childhood huckstering efforts. But her grades for the first six-week period of study weren't what she'd expected.

She tried to slip past Ken who stood between the table and the door to her room.

"Whoa, wait a minute. Let me see that."

He scanned the card.

"Looks pretty good to me. You have a C+ in history, B+ in typing, an A in Algebra, and a C- in English.

"C no good."

"C is average. Average is OK."

"Not good enough."

"Well, come on, Kim Ang. You're expecting too much of yourself too soon."

"What you mean?"

"Tell me, what language is your history book written in?"

"You know. English."

"OK. And how long have you been speaking English?" He didn't give her a chance to answer. "Other students in your classes have been using English all their lives. Some are getting D's and E's. Give yourself a break."

"What mean give break?"

"I mean, don't be so hard on yourself, don't criticize yourself. It's good to want to do better. Keep trying to do better, Kim Ang. But don't get discouraged if you don't get a hundred percent right away. It's going to take time."

"OK, I remember that. You, too!"

He didn't consider her rejoinder impertinent. Rather, he saw it as evidence of a sense of humor buried too long beneath a heap of trouble and undeserved condemnation. He was glad she still had it. He tried unsuccessfully to fight back a smile as he feigned anger.

"And what do you mean, 'You, too?'"

"You say, 'Don't be discouraged if not successful as you want right away. It take time.' But you discouraged because my brothers not come yet. I hear you say that."

She was right. He was discouraged. And he had said so. The day after learning the boys were in Thailand, he assembled the necessary papers and sent them off to Becky Richards. She sent them on to Church World Service in New York for transmission to Bangkok. Then, nothing happened. Months went by and there was no word.

In January Ken asked Congressman Foreman's office for help. The legislator's cable to the embassy in Bangkok brought an alarming response.

"The limited number of spaces in the U.S. program for all Khmer refugees has been exhausted," the message said. "However, we have filed the documents for Savang Pheng and Savang Heng in the event we are able to consider them at a future time."

"What does that mean?" Ken asked Foreman's aide.

"Well, the Reagan administration isn't considering Cambodians for resettlement this year. There are provisions for letting in other Southeast Asians, but not Cambodians."

"So what can we do now?"

"Just wait, I'm afraid—and hope the administration changes its policy and decides to let some Cambodians in."

Another six months passed. Then one morning, when Donna was at church helping with vacation Bible school and Kim Ang was working in the kitchen, Ken picked up the ringing phone in his den.

"Professor MacKenzie," the voice on the other end said. "I have some news I believe you'll be happy to hear."

It was Congressman Foreman himself.

"Let me read from a cable I just received from Bangkok. It says, 'We have now received authorization to process qualified Khmer. I am pleased to inform you that Savang Pheng and Savang Heng have been approved for resettlement in the United States. Barring any medical or other problems, the Intergovernmental Committee for Migration will arrange for their onward movement to the United States where they will rejoin their grandmother and other relatives.'"

"Tremendous!" Ken shouted, loud enough to bring Kim Ang from the kitchen.

"Oh, pardon me, sir. Didn't mean to get carried away. This is great news. A lot of people are going to be thrilled. One of them is the boys' sister. She's here right now. I can hardly wait to tell her. We all appreciate your efforts. It's been a long struggle. Thanks so much!"

As soon as the phone was out of his hand, Ken threw an arm around Kim Ang and danced her back to the kitchen.

"Finally, Kim Ang, your brothers are coming to America!"

She was more subdued than he expected.

"You work hard, make that happen. Take long time, but not give up. You do many good thing for me, for my family. What make you do that?"

He hadn't anticipated a question. He thought she'd be unable to contain her excitement. Instead she was pensive, searching for answers.

"Well, I haven't really thought about that, Kim Ang. Of course, Donna and I want you to be happy."

"But not need do so much. I happy. You always want help. You find sponsor for my friends. You help my grandmother, my uncles. You be good friend for Peng Sy and Kim Phang. You help Seng Dao Tong family. You work hard bring Chhun Huoy family here. Why you do that?"

"I guess I really hadn't thought about 'why' before, honey. I'll try to explain. Donna told me once she talked to you about angels.

"Do you remember that?"

"Sure. She say they like wind. They spirit. She say maybe they work inside people at little town, Millbrook, make them want help Cambodians. Maybe that why I come here."

"OK, and I think that's what makes me want to help your people. You see, I wasn't that kind of person before you came to Mendon. I didn't care about helping people. I was only interested in what was best for me, and for Donna. I knew about the trouble the Cambodian people had. But that wasn't important to me. When you came to Mendon, I'm sure angels came and changed me."

"You see angel?"

"No, but I can feel what they've done."

"You hear big wind?"

"Angels don't always come on a big wind. Most often their touch is more like a soft, gentle breeze. They calm me and comfort me. And sometimes they point me in a different direction. They keep me from doing things I shouldn't do, and they help me do things God wants me to do.

"Before you and the angels came, I wouldn't take time for things like finding sponsors for refugees. I just wanted to do my work at the college, go fishing and hiking, be with Donna. Of course, I still like those things. But now I like to help people, too. So I believe I did those things because God sent angels to change me."

"I glad," Kim Ang nodded. "Thank you for help my family. You good father for me, too."

Her words rang a bell. Donna had said something like that. Wasn't it during the blizzard of '77? She was disappointed because he'd bought a new TV with money she hoped they'd use to adopt a child. For the umpteenth time he had refused to go along with the idea and had disappointed her again. She hadn't been bitter, but she let him know she wasn't going to give up her dream. He could remember her words, exactly:

"We can make a difference in some kid's life. I want to be a mother, and I know you'll be a darn good father."

He doubted he'd been particularly good at fatherhood, but he liked it. There had been discouraging days, stress, disappointment.

Nevertheless, being a father to Kim Ang and a friend for her people brought more satisfaction than anything else he'd ever done.

She didn't need to say thanks. But if any reward were needed the expression on her face two weeks later would have been more than enough. That's when her long-lost brothers finally appeared at Gate 19 of Indianapolis International Airport.

Seven years had passed since the Khmer Rouge sent the eleven- and nine-year-old brothers off in one direction to build dams and their thirteen-year-old sister in another to dig canals. And now, half a world from where they'd been separated, they were coming together again.

At first, the young men didn't recognize the woman running toward them across the concourse. When they last saw their sister she was a scrawny child, a little older than they but hardly a woman. It hadn't really registered she'd now be twenty.

Then the woman called out, "Pheng! Heng!"

The sound was familiar. The voice of their sister was inside this mature feminine form. They ran too now, and the three came together in a wild dance of joy.

Ken stood alongside Donna on the far side of the concourse, his arm around her.

"Too bad the rest of them aren't here to be a part of this," he sighed.

That was the day's only disappointment. All the Cambodians except Kim Ang's grandmother and uncles had packed up and left for warmer climes. There hadn't been a snowflake in the air for months, but the memory of Indiana's last winter had taken its toll on Benton County's Cambodian population. One by one the families began moving away.

Seng Dao Tong and his family said good-bye to their Lutheran Church sponsors the first week of July, hoping to find warmer weather and the camaraderie of more of their own people in California.

Then, earlier this month, Peng Sy and Kim Phang called on Ken and Donna and said they were moving to Long Beach. The family of their daughter Chhun Huoy was going at the same time.

And just a few days later Hong Taing told Duane and Shirley Landon he'd be taking his mother and sisters to California. The child who had posed as his son would accompany them as far as Dallas where he'd rejoin his own parents who were now living there.

Those who had been closest to the departing Cambodians were disappointed. But they were understanding. They knew about Indiana winters, and they knew there were warmer places. After all, many of them headed south for at least part of every winter. Besides, the Cambodians had never seen snow until they came to Indiana. They'd been accustomed to temperatures closer to 80 degrees than 8.

Sponsors realized, too, that when their own ancestors came to America they settled in comfortable clusters where the language and culture were familiar. So why shouldn't their friends look for happiness in the Cambodian enclaves of California?

Some in the churches, however, were disgusted. A woman from Ken's own congregation cornered him after last Sunday's service to complain that the Cambodians were ungrateful.

"After all we did for them, they're just up and leaving us."

"I'm sure they appreciate what we've done," Ken replied. "They said that to Duane and Shirley Landon. And Pastor Greenwood told me Hong Taing had tears in his eyes when he said good-bye."

"That's all well and good," the woman whined, "but I gave a chair for them when they came. It was a lovely upholstered one I'd only had for fifteen years. I suppose they're taking it with them."

"Would you like it back?"

"Well, no, but it doesn't seem to me they're at all grateful," the woman persisted. "If they were, they wouldn't go away."

Ken was becoming more than a bit exasperated. The complainer hadn't been involved in the sponsorship anyway—except for the chair. He'd seen it. The fabric was faded and stained.

"When we agreed to sponsor these people, we weren't buying them," he pointed out.

Donna, standing close beside him with her arms folded, nudged him with a finger.

He changed the tone of his voice and continued, "Our sponsorship was a gesture of kindness, an agreement to help the family get a new start. Their moving away isn't a rejection of us. It just shows we've succeeded. We've given the help they needed. Now they can get along on their own."

That had been the only expression of discontent he'd heard. But he suspected there were others. He was sad, too, perhaps more than anyone. He'd be disappointed if any of his best friends moved away. And he had become especially fond of the Cambodians in Mendon and Elm Grove. He'd invested a lot of himself in getting most of them here. He'd be delighted if they'd all stay. But if they felt comfortable moving out on their own, that was OK.

Last night Ken and Donna talked to Bob and Marilyn Gleason about the likelihood of Chen Yi, her three sons, and Kim Ang's brothers moving to the West. Neither the Gleasons nor others at St. Joseph's had any reason to believe they'd go—except for the fact they were the only remaining Cambodian family in the county. It seemed highly unlikely they'd stay.

Then this morning Marilyn called.

"Well, they're going, Donna. Hong told me he promised his mother she wouldn't have to spend another winter in Indiana. I imagine they've just been waiting for Pheng and Heng to get here. They plan to leave a week from tomorrow."

Ken was at the college, and Donna walked into his office five minutes after getting the message from Marilyn. He looked up as she came in.

"They're going. Right?"

"Yes. How did you know?"

"Your face."

"Oh? Yeah, I guess it does show. But it's not them I'm worried about."

She slid a chair across the floor and placed it next to Ken's, then sat down and took his hand.

"What does this mean for Kim Ang? What's going to happen to her, Ken?""

"I don't know. It's been on my mind, too. A grandmother and five young men are going to want a housekeeper. She's probably going with them."

"If she does, Ken, it'll be the end of her education. She won't keep house and go to school, too—especially without us around for support. What can we do?"

He wanted to say something to give Donna hope. Sure, Kim Ang is a woman now. But she's still the child who fulfilled Donna's dreams, the answer to her prayers. If she leaves, Donna will be devastated. He found no uplifting words. He could only say the obvious.

"First, we'll talk to Kim Ang, see what she knows. Then, if necessary, we'll talk to Hong. And we'll do what we've done before when we've faced this kind of situation. We'll pray."

CHAPTER 28

Two Summers

JUNE 10, 1983

"Chen Yi's timing certainly leaves something to be desired," Donna sighed.

The MacKenzies had hoped to get away for a few days of hiking and relaxation at Turkey Run. But a phone call from California a week ago scuttled those plans.

"She definitely has a knack for doing these things when they're sure to louse us up somehow," Ken agreed. "It was the same last summer with her timing of the move to California."

That maneuver had thrown Kim Ang into a dither just when Ken and Donna were trying to put finishing touches on plans for their fall courses. And, of course, when Kim Ang was in turmoil the MacKenzies were caught in the backwash.

"I guess I'm too self-centered," Ken continued. "When Chen Yi's decisions inconvenience us, I let it get to me. Then I realize she's just annoying us, but she's devastating Kim Ang."

"It's so unfair, Ken. After all Kim Ang lived through, she finally escapes to a place where her dreams can come true. Then her closest relatives sabotage her. It may not be intentional, but it's like torture. Her hopes are inflated. Then she comes crashing down. Then it happens all over again."

That's just the way it was last August. Kim Ang knew then, just before the start of the new school year, that if she stayed in Mendon she'd soon be living her dream again. She was just as certain that if she went to California with her grandmother and uncles there'd be no more school.

First, Chen Yi decreed her granddaughter would have to go with her. Then she said Kim Ang couldn't go because she'd disgraced her family and they didn't want her with them. Next she proclaimed the girl had to stay in Mendon until she obtained her green card, and then she'd have to go to California.

Finally, when Kim Ang was nearly an emotional wreck, her grandmother agreed she could stay in Mendon indefinitely. Uncle Hong had persuaded his mother that, for the present at least, more education for the girl would be to the family's advantage. So Chen Yi, her three sons, and Kim Ang's brothers packed up and moved to the West coast, leaving Kim Ang with Donna and Ken.

The week of turmoil preceding her relatives' departure gave Kim Ang another case of itchy red spots. But the rash faded and her state of mind improved, almost as soon as her relatives were out of sight. Nevertheless, the evening they left Donna did find her sitting on the bed in her room, crying.

"Are you sorry you stayed, honey?" She asked.

"No. I want go school. I like be with you. Don't want go California. But I lonesome. No more Cambodian people here. Now I all alone in strange country."

Donna sat on the bed and hugged her.

"I can imagine how it must be. I guess I'd feel the same way. You're not alone, though. Ken and I know we're not your real mother and father, not legally anyway. But we love you as much as if you were our own child. Always remember that, Kim Ang."

"I know. I more happy now than ever was. I never forget."

Kim Ang's loneliness didn't last long, and the months that followed were the happiest she'd ever known. The migration of the other Cambodians had its advantages. There were none left in Mendon who might fuel her self-condemnation about the situation that had triggered Hong Taing's resentment.

She was pleased, too, to finally have her name restored, legally. At the Benton County Courthouse last November, Probate Court Judge Matthew Brigham approved a petition to change her name from Tan Chhun Ly to Kim Ang Savang. She decided as long as the switch was being made she'd put the parts of her name in the same order Americans did, surname last rather than first.

She hoped she'd be able to correct her birth date, too. Donna understood that.

"No woman wants to be legally nine years older than she really is," she commented to the judge.

"I'm sorry. I can change the name. But there's no way I can alter the date of birth unless you have something to substantiate what you say. Right now the girl has an I-94 saying she was born in 1953. Do you have any papers that prove it was 1962?"

"No. Everything lost when Pol Pot people came," Kim Ang explained.

"Then I can't do anything," the judge repeated. "Your year of birth will have to remain 1953."

"Well, Kim Ang, look at the bright side," Ken consoled. "You'll be able to take early retirement. You can get full Social Security benefits at 56 instead of 65."

"What mean?"

"Oh, it's a little complicated, honey. I'll explain later."

That same afternoon Ken attached copies of the court documents to Kim Ang's application for permanent residency and mailed them to the INS office in Chicago. He had mixed feelings. *The green card is a necessary step on the path to citizenship. But when she has the card grandmother may decide it's time for her to move to California. No need to worry about that now though. The INS isn't noted for its speed.*

Meanwhile, at school Kim Ang's progress was amazing. At the end of the first semester, with a 3.5 grade point average, she proudly displayed a letter of congratulations from the high school principal, Robert Cole. With independent study projects last summer and an extra heavy schedule of classes during the past year she was rapidly closing in on her first educational goal. Additional independent study this summer would give her enough credits for senior class status in the fall. One more year and she'd graduate!

But the MacKenzies were disappointed to learn her brothers wouldn't be getting as good an education in California. In a letter to his sister, Heng said that because he's 16 he was placed in the eleventh grade.

"He just start and he graduate same time as me," Kim Ang pointed out at dinner one evening.

"Maybe he'll graduate, but he won't know much of anything," Ken replied. "He can hardly speak any English."

"They have teacher who talk Khmer. Many Cambodians there, so learn in own language."

"Yes, I know, Kim Ang. That's called bilingual education. But the students don't learn much English if they're taught that way. You studied English as a Second Language before you went to high school. Then you worked hard to learn more English and keep up with the other students. Heng doesn't have any pressure to learn English. It will take him much longer. And because of that he won't learn American customs as quickly either."

"I think you right. I worry about Pheng and Heng."

"Is Pheng going to high school, too?" Donna asked.

"No. Pheng too old go high school there. He 18. Maybe he go adult school, something like where you teach. Maybe he just get job, not go school."

"I'm sorry Pheng and Heng aren't getting a good education," Donna consoled. "But at least they are safe in America now, Kim Ang. That's better than being alone in Cambodia—or in a refugee camp."

"Yes, that right. You and Ken very good to me and my family."

"We're all very happy for them, and for you, Kim Ang. At least all your family and your friends have a chance for a better life now."

Kim Ang didn't respond. Her mind seemed to be miles away.

"They are all here now, aren't they, Kim Ang?"

"Yes," Kim Ang answered. But the tone implied she had more to say.

"Are there others?" Donna prodded.

"Just one."

"I didn't think you had any other relatives, Kim Ang."

"Not family. All family here now—or dead. But have one friend. She in Khao I Dang when I come here, but I think maybe she back in Cambodia now."

"Who is she? Tell me about her."

"Her name Ay Leng. I meet her in Phnom Penh, just before Pol Pot time," Kim Ang replied pensively. "Her father and all brothers and sisters killed when Americans drop bombs on house. Her mother die during Pol Pot time."

She told of the meeting amid the debris of the dud rocket and the reunion at the work camp when Ay Leng told her that her parents and sisters had been killed. She described how she and Ay Leng escaped to Vietnam and then Thailand. She recounted their sad parting on the eve of Kim Ang's departure for America.

"I never see her again. I tell her maybe some day she come to America. But she say that not happen because she not have relative in America—or anyplace."

She paused. There was nothing more to say. Donna looked at Ken, her eyes pleading for some words of hope.

"Well, let's don't give up so easily," he said. "I don't know if it's certain she can't be resettled here. Maybe yes, maybe no. Becky Richards should know. I'll give her a call tomorrow."

Ken made the call, but weeks passed before Mrs. Richards had anything to report.

"I've finally been able to get some information on Ay Leng," she said then. "She was at Khao I Dang a month ago. I've had a cable from a friend who's with the Red Cross there."

"You said she was at Khao I Dang," Ken interrupted. "Does that mean she's not there now?"

"I'm afraid so. The Thais, the Americans, and the UN have been putting tremendous pressure on the refugees to go back to Cambodia. My friend says hundreds of written appeals to the American Embassy and others never get out of the camp. She says she's seen dusty plastic bags stuffed full of them in a camp office.

"But that wasn't Ay Leng's problem. Another Red Cross worker, who knew Ay Leng personally, says she applied for resettlement in America and actually had an interview with an immigration official."

"And how did that go?" Ken asked.

"Not well. The interrogators see it as their job to keep people out, not get them in. They're not friendly. They shout. They refuse to believe. They accuse. That's pretty tough for some people to handle, especially kids."

"So what happened?"

"They told her she wasn't a refugee. The official report reads that her story 'lacked overall credibility.' They don't tell the refugees that their relatives or friends in the U. S. can appeal the decision and have the case reviewed. So Ay Leng just gave up. She apparently figured it couldn't be any worse back in Cambodia, so she went back."

"Where is she now?"

"There's no way of knowing. She could be anyplace—in one of the camps controlled by the Khmer Serei, or a Khmer Rouge camp, or she could be anyplace in the country. She could be dead. Life is cheap in those border camps."

"Isn't there something else we can do?"

"I'm afraid not. This has happened to thousands. I know that's no comfort to you. But really there's nothing we can do now."

Kim Ang blamed herself for Ay Leng's plight.

"I should tell you before," she mumbled to Ken. "Then maybe it be possible she come here. But you busy finding sponsors for my family, other families, too. I not want bother you more."

"Don't go taking all the blame again, Kim Ang. Chances of her being able to come here were pretty slim. Ay Leng could have applied for resettlement earlier. It's not your fault that she didn't. The men who ask the questions do everything they can to get the refugees to go back to Cambodia. You're not to blame for that either. You've got to quit doing that to yourself."

That had been a year ago, and things were going better now. Last week, with her final report card for the year, Kim Ang brought home another letter of commendation from the principal and an invitation to join the National Honor Society.

Besides her independent study this summer, she would also start an introductory course on computers at the college next week. Professors in the Mathematics and Computer Science Department would teach the class for exceptional high school students. Ken made sure Kim Ang was among the first to sign up.

Everything had been going so well that Ken and Donna decided Kim Ang would be able to stay home alone for a few days while they were enjoying the trails at Turkey Run. They'd leave the next morning.

It was then that the phone rang. First Hong, and then Chen Yi, talked to Kim Ang. Then Hong asked to speak to Ken.

"We want Kim Ang be with us this summer," he explained. "My mother miss her. Want her be here little while."

"I'm sure Kim Ang would be happy to see you again," Ken said, "but she will be disappointed to miss some special studies for school."

"Yes, I know. She tell me that. But my mother want her come."

Ken knew arguing would accomplish nothing.

"Will she come back to Mendon for school this fall?" he asked.

"Sure. No problem. My mother just want her come this summer. I already send ticket for airplane."

Ken was suspicious. But he knew nothing he said would make a difference.

The next day his suspicions were confirmed when the mail brought an envelope from Hong. Kim Ang ripped it open, and inside was a ticket for an Indianapolis-Los Angeles flight—one-way.

By that time, though, he and Donna already feared the worst. After the phone conversation with Hong, Kim Ang told them the reason for her summer trip. Her eyes brimming with tears, she stared at the floor as she spoke.

"They want me meet man there." The words were scarcely audible. "They want me marry."

"Oh, Kim Ang!" Donna threw her arms around the girl. "Things have been going so well, and you're so close to finishing school. Can't it wait just one more year?"

"Grandmother want me be in California now. Must go."

"Who is the man they want you to meet?" Ken asked with obvious resignation.

"Don't know name."

"What's he like? Your grandmother and uncles must have met him."

"No. They never meet him. But they talk to friends of man's family. He 32 years old. Has business, restaurant I think. Come from

China. Was student in America many years. Graduate from college."

Donna locked her eyes on Kim Ang's.

"You don't have to go, honey. You're in America now, and you're 21 years old. Nobody can make you do anything you don't want to do. Don't you want to finish school?"

"I want finish high school most of all. But must do what family want."

"They can't make you marry someone you don't want to, someone you don't even know."

"That way do it in my country."

"But America is your country now. We don't marry people off that way in America."

"That way my people do. If do not do what grandmother say, then I have no family any more. And all my people not speak to me."

Ken put his hand on Donna's shoulder and spoke softly.

"Don't pressure her now. It won't do any good. She's caught between two cultures. After living with us, she understands American ways better than any of the others. But she can't just instantly abandon everything that's been important to her in the past, the traditions she's grown up with. Even if she could, she'd be an outcast."

The Turkey Run vacation was off. They had just one week before Kim Ang would leave. They might never see her again.

Ken canceled Kim Ang's enrollment in the computer course and then called the principal's office at the high school.

"No, she won't be able to do the independent studies this summer," he told the secretary. "I doubt very much that she'll be back in the fall either."

Rev. Greenwood was the next call on his list. The church was still Kim Ang's official sponsor, and the pastor needed to know what was going on. Besides, he may have some suggestions. Ken told him the disappointing news.

"I'd like to talk to her, Ken," the pastor responded. "And I think our Refugee Family Committee should meet as soon as possible. Could Kim Ang come to my study tomorrow after the worship service?"

"I'm sure she can."

"Then let's plan a committee meeting for Tuesday night. Will you and Donna be able to make that?"

"We'll be there."

At the Tuesday night session, the pastor summarized events of the past several days. Most members of the committee were already aware of what was happening.

"Shortly after Ken phoned me," Rev. Greenwood said, "I had another call, from Mr. Cole, the principal at the high school. He's very upset about the possibility of Kim Ang not coming back to graduate. He asked that we do everything possible to see she returns before September."

"Do you think that's likely?" Duane Landon asked.

"I don't know. I met with Kim Ang on Sunday. On the one hand, she appears to accept her family's decision and their choice of a husband. But she says she's not ready for marriage yet. She wants to complete her education, high school at least, and she hopes she can persuade her grandmother to let her return to Mendon for her senior year. If we go by what Kim Ang's uncle told Ken, she'll be coming back for school. But if we consider his flight arrangements for Kim Ang, we have reason to be skeptical. He sent a one-way ticket."

"Well, for one thing," Duane responded, "I think we need to give her some help in case she decides to return. We should exchange her ticket, get a round-trip one. And I'd suggest we give her some mad money, at least enough to get to the airport."

The others agreed.

"I believe someone else needs to talk to Kim Ang's uncle," Shirley Landon added. "The MacKenzies are in a rather awkward position. Kim Ang's relatives probably think Ken and Donna are biased. Most likely, they see this as some kind of custody struggle, sort of like a dispute between adoptive and biological parents. Of course, Kim Ang is no longer a minor so, legally, she controls her own destiny. But that's not the way her grandmother and uncles see it."

"What do you have in mind?" Ken asked.

"I think Pastor Greenwood should call Hong," she replied. "He's the head of the sponsoring institution. As such he should express our concern about Kim Ang's future."

"I'll be glad to do that," the pastor agreed.

Later that night he called Ken to report his discussion with Kim Ang's uncle.

"I told Hong we know a marriage is being planned for Kim Ang. I said we'd been contacted by school officials who are concerned about her and want to know if she'll be returning to finish high school. During the course of the conversation I asked him three times if she'd be coming back. Each time he assured me Kim Ang is going there just to be with her grandmother, that she'll return before September."

"And what did he say about the marriage?" Ken asked.

"Well, he told me they do plan a meeting with a prospective husband. But he said Kim Ang will have the final say. He assured me she will not be forced into a marriage she doesn't want."

Ken was still skeptical. But he knew they'd done all they could.

This morning the MacKenzies were up before sunrise. Kim Ang needed to be at the airport in Indianapolis by 6:30 for the flight to the West Coast.

What a contrast to the joy when she and the others came, Donna thought to herself as they left Mendon behind and drove eastward toward the highway to Indianapolis. A glow in the sky ahead promised sunshine after dawn. But that didn't dispel the gloom inside the car.

Finally, Donna broke the silence.

"Kim Ang, I understand how difficult this is for you. You can't just give up your family, your only remaining relatives. And you can't just forget your dream of an education. But right now it seems impossible to have both. I don't know what I'd do if I were you. I'm sorry you have to go through this. I wish I could do something."

Kim Ang reached forward and put her hand on Donna's shoulder.

"You do all you could. You help me more than anyone ever do before. I sorry I not stay."

Ken glanced at the two women, then focused again on the road ahead.

"Remember, you have a round-trip ticket now, Kim Ang. And do you have the money in a safe place?"

He didn't wait for her to answer. He was sure she did.

"If your family tries to make you stay in California and you don't want to, we need to be sure you can get back to us."

"Yes, I know. I keep everything safe place."

Donna turned and reached across the back of the seat to take Kim Ang's hand.

"Sometimes I wonder if what we did was right—taking you into our home, I mean. Living with us, you've become more Americanized than the others. You've learned the new ways, and your relatives are still doing things the old way, following the old customs. If you hadn't lived with us, if we hadn't encouraged you to go to school, perhaps what you're facing now wouldn't be as difficult."

"You only try help me. If I not come to live with you, I be married long time ago. You do best thing for me. You give me home, make me your own daughter. You love me. You help me follow my dream, give me hope."

Donna knew they couldn't have done otherwise. She appreciated Kim Ang's affirmation. Kim Ang hesitated, then added with determination, "I not give up my dream. I hope I come back your house end of summer, go school again. If not, I know some day my dream come true. I never give up. And I always love you. You my Mother, Father now."

At the airport, hands of the clock on the concourse wall appeared to race past the numbers. They'd hardly checked in and reached the waiting area, it seemed, when the boarding call echoed through the terminal. Hand in hand, Donna on one side of Kim Ang and Ken on the other, they walked to the gate.

"Bye, Mom."

Forcing a smile, Kim Ang wrapped her arms around Donna.

"I love you, honey. You're my only child. Don't forget that."

Ken moved closer and embraced them both.

"I'm going to miss you this summer. You take care of yourself and hurry back."

He was trying to put up a good front, but he wondered if he'd ever see her again. Tears filled his eyes. Kim Ang didn't notice at first. Their three heads were pressed tightly together.

"Last call for flight 247 to Los Angeles," the PA system intoned.

After a final squeeze, Kim Ang pulled herself away and walked slowly down the long passageway to the plane. She didn't look back. That would have been too painful for all of them. The other passengers had already boarded. The solitary figure moved steadily, but ever so slowly, away. Each step seemed taken with painful deliberation. Donna and Ken thought she might spin around at any moment and come running back, wrap her arms around them again, and tell them she was going to stay.

But she didn't. She turned the corner at the end of the corridor. She was gone. Moments later, jet engines whining, the huge plane carried her away.

CHAPTER 29

Fulfillment

Ken wished summer were over. In autumn he'd be busy preparing lessons, evaluating papers, counseling students. He'd need to give those things his attention. But now, without the pressure of academic responsibilities, he had too much time to think. And his thoughts were always two thousand miles away, in California. He might start out planning one of next fall's courses, but he'd end up wondering how Kim Ang was doing.

He'd berate himself for not having done something to preclude her present torment. He'd ponder whether there was anything he still could do. A week after the trip to the airport he felt guilty, frustrated, depressed.

"Ken, there was nothing else we could do," Donna tried to console. "We've done what we could. Remember, when the rest of the Cambodians left, you told everybody they had to be willing to let go."

"Well, this is different. It's not like we were just friends. We loved her. She loved us. She was our daughter."

"*Is*, Ken. She *is* our daughter. We're not sure she isn't coming back. Maybe the family will let her finish school. If they don't, she may decide to leave them and come back anyway."

"But that's not likely to happen."

"It could. OK, maybe she won't come back. But she's been our child for nearly three years. There's no way we can just forget her. We'll see her again sometime, someplace. This isn't going to be the end. One of the last things Kim Ang said was she's not going to give up her dream. How can we give up on her?"

"Yeah, you're right. I feel so helpless though. She's all alone out there, trying to make a decision that would baffle Solomon."

But two days later Donna, too, was discouraged when Kim Ang called to tell them she would become engaged the next day during a party at her grandmother's house.

"How do you feel about that?" Donna asked, trying not to sound as disappointed as she was.

"Don't know. Not happy. But that what best for me now."

"How are you feeling otherwise, Kim Ang?"

"OK. But have itch, red spots again."

"I'm sure that's because you've been upset, honey. Use the salve I gave you. I think that will help."

Ken listened for a moment at Donna's side in the kitchen, then went to his study to pick up the phone there.

"Did you meet the man yet?" he inquired.

"Yes."

"What's he like?"

"He very nice."

"What's his name?"

"Don't remember."

"Kim Ang, I heard you tell Donna you're not happy about getting engaged. I admit I don't understand the Cambodian way of doing things. I'm sad because you're becoming engaged and are not happy about it. I'll be even more sad if you are married and aren't happy. Are you sure you want to go ahead with this?"

"What I want not important now. Have to do what make family happy. That be best for me, too."

"Don't give up yet, Kim Ang. I know it wouldn't be easy, but you can still leave if you want to and come back here. You have the ticket and the money, don't you?"

"Yes, I have. But I not come back."

"OK, but don't decide that yet. If you want to leave, we will do whatever we can to help you."

When he hung up, Ken was sure he'd said too much.

"I guess I should have been trying to comfort her," he told Donna. "Instead I added to her misery. But I can't just sit back and watch her sacrifice herself for her family again. There's nobody out there advising her to consider any alternative to a forced marriage."

"What you said was all right, Ken. If she had shown any enthusiasm about getting married, it would be different. You didn't create the concerns and questions that caused the distress. You merely pointed out they're still there. We can talk to her again tomorrow and be a little more upbeat."

That's what they did. But when Kim Ang came to the phone, she sounded even more weary than the day before. Donna decided to take a stab at cheering her.

"Have you been doing too much partying, Kim Ang? You sound tired."

"Yes, we already have party."

"Ken and I want to give you our best wishes, honey. We know the past days have been very difficult. We hope the future will bring you much happiness."

"Thank you."

The response was mechanical, without feeling.

"Is your rash gone today?"

"No. Red spots still hurt. But I OK."

Donna groped for a way to lift the girl's spirits.

"Tell me about the party, Kim Ang. Who was there? What dress did you wear? I want to know everything that happened."

As the young woman provided the answers, she seemed to perk up a bit.

"And how about his name?" Ken cut in. "Now that you're engaged, do you know the name of your husband-to-be?"

"His name Sam."

"Oh, he has an American name."

"Yes, but that not real name. That name he use now. Real name is Chong Dy. He say after we married he take trip to Mendon with me, meet my friends."

Realization that Kim Ang might come back, even if only for a visit, encouraged Donna.

"That would be wonderful, honey! Is Sam there now? We'd like to speak to him."

When Kim Ang's fiance came to the phone, Donna offered their congratulations.

"Kim Ang is a special young lady," she told him. "You are a very fortunate man."

"Yes, I know," he replied. "And I will take good care of her. I promise. She told me all about you. You have done many good things for her. She loves you very much. I hope I will meet you soon."

His fluency in English was a byproduct of his several years of study in the United States. But the MacKenzies were more impressed by his soft-spoken sincerity.

"Kim Ang tells us you will come to Mendon with her," Ken remarked.

"Yes, I hope so. At least I will try. But I can't promise. With my business, it's difficult for me to get away. I don't want to make a promise I may not be able to keep. But I want very much to meet you, and I hope that will happen soon."

After the conversation, Ken and Donna felt better. They still weren't happy about Kim Ang being forced into a marriage. But at least her fiance seemed pleasant.

"It's refreshing," Ken noted, "that Sam doesn't make promises if he isn't sure he can keep them. He apparently has sufficient confidence to feel he doesn't have to tell people just what he thinks they want to hear."

They hoped the next time they talked to Kim Ang she'd feel better about the forthcoming marriage, too. But she didn't.

She called a week later to tell them the wedding date had been set.

"It will be July 9," she said.

"Oh, so soon!" Donna gasped without thinking, then tried to smooth things over. "Are you getting excited about it now, Kim Ang?"

"No."

The response was straightforward, matter-of-fact, unemotional.

"Sam seems like a very nice man," Donna offered.

"Yes, he nice."

There was a long pause. Kim Ang didn't say more.

"But you don't like him."

"I like. But not love. I not ready be married."

"Kim Ang, it's not too late to call it off," Ken reminded her again. "You can still decide to come back here."

"No, that not possible. It embarrass family."

The helplessness and frustration Ken and Donna had felt earlier returned. They didn't know what else they could do. No matter what they said, Kim Ang didn't feel good about the prospect of marriage. But she planned to go ahead with the wedding. They hoped Pastor Greenwood might have insights that would help them or Kim Ang. They asked him to call her, and he did. Afterwards he was as frustrated as they.

A week later Kim Ang called again. She sounded the same. Her grandmother and Sam's mother had gone to a Cambodian fortuneteller who prophesied she and Sam would have a happy marriage.

"But the man tell them," Kim Ang said, "this dangerous time for me. He say I must not go outside house, must not talk to people who tell me what to do."

"It sounds to me," Ken said bluntly, "like they're trying to hold you prisoner. Kim Ang, do you still want to go ahead with this wedding?"

"Not want. But must. Cannot make family feel bad."

"That's not a good reason to get married."

"Yes, it good enough."

The conversation ended with the MacKenzies feeling even more hopeless. Neither could think of anything else they could say to help.

"Isn't there anything we can do?" Donna wondered aloud. "Isn't there someone out there who can help her?"

Suddenly a face from the past flashed into Ken's mind.

"I know somebody!"

"Who?"

"Ted Randolph, a friend in college. Last I heard he was pastor of a church someplace in the LA area. Where's my alumni directory?"

He found the book on a shelf in his study. Sure enough. There it was:

Randolph, Rev. Theodore, pastor, Trinity United
Methodist Church, Torrance, California.

Ken put a finger next to the phone number, lifted the handset, and started to dial. After three rings, a familiar "Hello."

"Ted, this is Ken MacKenzie. I hope you remember me."

"Of course. But it's been a long time—25 years, right? Where are you? Nearby, I hope."

"No, I'm in Indiana—teaching at a small liberal arts college here, Mendon College. And I'm calling to ask a favor."

"Ah, you're on the committee to jack up the alumni fund. How much do you want?"

"No, you can put your wallet away, Ted. I need you, not your money."

"Oh oh, sounds serious."

"Yeah, it is. Donna—that's my wife—and I have a problem. We hope you can help. Someone we love very much is going through a tough time. She's in California, not far from you. We're hoping, if she needs to turn to someone for help, you might be willing to fill in for us. We feel so helpless, being thousands of miles away. But I'm getting ahead of myself. Do you have a few minutes so I can fill you in?"

"Of course."

Ken related the whole story, beginning with Kim Ang's horrendous experiences in Southeast Asia and ending with her present dilemma in Long Beach.

"We've talked to her several times in the past few weeks, Ted, most recently just a couple minutes ago. She's out there, all alone, facing a really impossible situation. She's trying to live up to the contradictory aspirations of her grandparents. Her grandfather, dying in her arms, gave her a burning desire for an education. Her living grandmother insists she forget about school and get married. Kim Ang wants desperately to stay in school. But she feels she can't embarrass her grandmother by refusing to marry.

"Donna and I are concerned about her entering into a marriage with feelings of despair rather than joy. We've told her it's not too late to change her mind. She has money enough for a cab to the airport and she has a ticket back to Indiana, though she probably won't use either. We think we've said all we should. And at this distance there's really nothing we can do. We think, though, she'd be glad to know a friend of her friends is close by, that he'd be willing to listen, help her think through her options—give her a hand in case of an emergency.

"I guess it's asking a lot, Ted, but would you mind if we gave her your address and phone number in case she needs it? I think it would be a comfort to Kim Ang. I know it would make Donna and me feel better."

"I'd be pleased to help any way I can," Ken's old friend responded. "But I have another idea. How about me calling her? That would establish the contact right now. I'll assure her I'm here to help if she needs me. I'll give her my number and address. I'll tell her, too, she can contact me any time—now or later, whether she's in trouble or not. I'd like to meet her."

"That would be wonderful, Ted. I can't find the words to say how much that would mean to Donna and me."

"Ah, forget it. What are friends for? If Kim Ang does stay in California, I presume you and Donna will be out here to visit her eventually. I'd like to meet Donna, too. Those must be two special women. They'd have to be to turn the guy I used to know into the compassionate person I've been listening to."

"Glad to see you haven't lost your sense of humor," Ken responded. "You are trying to be funny, aren't you?"

They both laughed.

"But you're right," Ken added. "I have changed. And they are two special women. I want you to meet them. Thanks for your willingness to help, Ted."

A few days later when Ken and Donna called Kim Ang, they learned Ted Randolph had indeed called her. And the change in her state of mind amazed them. She'd be married in two days, and she actually seemed carefree. *Could Ted have worked such a miracle?* Ken wondered.

"We talk long time," Kim Ang said of her phone conversation with Ken's old friend. "He tell me lots about when you go to college."

"Not too much, I hope," Ken cut in. "He didn't say I did anything bad, did he?"

"Little bit." She chuckled. The sound was refreshing.

"Like what did he say?"

"Oh, one thing, he say you teach him how do hot-foot. When somebody sleeping, you put match at bottom of shoe. Light other end. Then it go poof and make man's foot hot. He wake up and be real mad."

"You don't believe I'd do that, do you?"

"Sure. He say, too, sometimes you don't study much. Like to take girls to movies. All time have different girl. More than anybody else."

"I want to hear more about that," Donna chimed in. "What is Ted's telephone number?"

"OK, you two, enough of that," Ken pleaded. "What else did Pastor Randolph say, Kim Ang? Did he say anything about you?"

"Yes, he say if need help I call him. He give me his number and he tell me where he live and where church is."

"Good. Donna and I feel better now that you know there is someone near who will listen if you want to talk, or can help if you decide to come back to Indiana."

"But I not going back now. Maybe some day. Now I going be married, live here, California."

There was no hint of the earlier despair.

"What made you so accepting, Kim Ang?" Donna asked. "I mean, last time we talked you sounded very depressed about getting married. You were only doing it to please your family."

"That still main reason. But Pastor Randolph ask me lot of questions, tell me some things. That help."

"What did he say?"

"He ask me what really most important now, please my family or go school. I say I want go school, but family most important.

"He ask, if I go school now, can I get family back later. I say, 'Don't think so.'

"He ask, if get married now, can I go school later. I tell him, 'Yes, pretty sure I can do that.'

"So I see only one way I can have family and education, too. That is be married now.

"He tell me, no matter what I do, you always love me and be my mother, father. I say, 'I know that.'

"He say somebody else love me, help me."

"Who's that?" Donna asked.

"Jesus. I say you tell me about Jesus. Know about angels, too. Know angels look out for me."

Ted surely has had something to do with this miracle, Ken thought to himself. *And so has Donna. How did I ever happen to remember Ted was out there and might be able to help? Angels?*

"Now I not worry about me any more," Kim Ang continued. "I only sad about Ay Leng. I pray, ask God send somebody help her like you help me. I hope angel go there, too."

"I'm sure there are angels there, Kim Ang," Ken assured. "We'll pray, too. And it's important that we don't forget and don't give up. We'll pray for all the Cambodian people who are still in danger— and especially for Ay Leng. And we'll thank God for bringing you into our lives. You've brought us fulfillment."

"What mean, fulfillment?"

"Well, when we say you've brought us fulfillment we mean you've helped us do something that makes us feel good, something that's really worthwhile. You see, it's mostly because of you that I've had a part in helping some refugees get a new start, have a better life. That's been very fulfilling for me."

"And you're the daughter I always wanted," Donna added. "That's fulfilled my dream. You've made me really happy."

"I think best way have fulfillment, be happy, is help somebody else be happy," Kim Ang observed. "Some day I help somebody. Then I be more happy."

Donna said the obvious.

"Not some day, honey. You've already helped so many. How about Hong Taing and his family? Because of you, they could come to America. How about your grandmother? You're giving up your dream now, just so she'll be happy. And how about Ken and me? You've certainly made us happy. You have more reason to feel fulfilled than any of us. Now it's time for you to start enjoying the happiness."

"Yes, now I be more happy. Now I know I have friend who help me. I not be afraid or worry any more."

The new confidence in her voice was reassuring. They knew she'd be all right now.

"You know what, Ken?"

"No. What, honey?"

"I sit by window now and feel breeze, soft and gentle."

The Real Story
Marriage and Families

In Khmer culture not only is the family of utmost importance but its older members are accorded great respect and are deferred to in consequential decisions. To Cambodians, the welfare of the family is considered to be of greater significance than that of the individual.

Since girls must be above reproach if a favorable marriage for them is to be arranged, their discipline is typically more strict than that of boys and their lives are planned to assure that the best interests of the family are met.

The arrangement of a marriage may involve not only parents of the prospective couple but also relatives and friends, particularly those of the woman. Sometimes a young man suggests a desired spouse to his parents, but in some cases he, too, has little to say in the selection of a life partner. Theoretically, a girl also could veto the selection of a husband by her parents, but to attempt to do so could risk alienation from the family.

Usually a matchmaker approaches the family of the prospective bride to present the possibility of marriage. Investigations by both families then are made to assure its son or daughter is marrying into a good family and that the arrangement will be a beneficial one. Finally, a wedding date is selected with the guidance of an *achar*—a person who is familiar with the Cambodian calendar and who takes into consideration the birth dates of the young man and woman, astrological patterns, and lucky and unlucky days.

During its reign of terror, the Khmer Rouge sought to destroy the family as a meaningful unit. First, few Cambodian families escaped loss of members through murder by the Khmer Rouge or starvation. Also, family names were abolished, and individuals used only one name, usually an abbreviated derivative of their given name. Children were urged to condemn their parents, so adults became cautious about talking in their presence.

After resettlement in the United States, traditional Khmer family roles came under assault, too. Not only was there a conflict of cultures, but the roles of parents and children often were reversed because children were quicker to learn the new language and customs. Typically, in conferences with educational and social agencies and in business dealings, children needed to assume the important roles of linguistic interpreter and consultant on proper procedure.

For more details, see:

John Barron and Anthony Paul, *Murder of a Gentle Land* (New York, Reader's Digest Press, 1977), pages 136-137

Elizabeth Becker, *When the War Was Over* (New York, A Touchstone Book published by Simon & Schuster, Inc., 1986), page 237

Rev. Francis Ponchaud, M. E. P., *Approaches to the Khmer Mentality* (Washington, D. C., National Conference of Catholic Bishops, 1977), pages 9-11

Russell R. Ross, ed., *Cambodia: A Country Study*, Area Handbook Series (Washington, D. C., United States Government as represented by the Secretary of the Army, 1990), pages 88-90, 94-97

Herbert H. Vreeland, *Cambodia: Its People, Its Society, Its Culture* (New Haven, HRAF Press, 1959), pages 77-85

Afterword

And if a stranger sojourns with you in your land, you shall not mistreat him. But the stranger who dwells among you shall be to you as one born among you, and you shall love him as yourself, for you were strangers in the land of Egypt.

LEVITICUS 19:33-34

Few of us in America have had to flee for our lives. But let's pretend. Suppose something happens that makes it necessary for you to run. Suppose that within the next few minutes you'll see your family and friends for the last time—if you have a chance to see them at all. You'll walk out of your home and never return. You'll take with you only what you can carry.

That's what it's like to be a refugee, at the beginning. It gets worse before it gets better—if it gets better. You'll be hungry, and there may be nothing to eat. You'll be weary, and you'll have to keep walking.

If you survive, you may rejoice at the sight of a border and the prospect of safety. But soldiers may stop you and turn you back. Or if you've made your escape in a rickety boat, a Coast Guard ship may pick you up and return you to your oppressors.

If you are more fortunate, you may be permitted to cross the border and stay in a crowded, dirty place that's more like a prison than a camp. Perhaps after months, more likely years, you'll even be able to enter the country as a resident alien, or be resettled in a third country.

Certainly that will be cause for rejoicing. But your initial jubilation will likely give way to depression. You'll be in a strange place with strange customs. You'll be on the bottom rung of the economic ladder. You won't understand the language. And when you're finally able to comprehend a few words, you'll understand you're really not welcome. Your new neighbors will say you're responsible for their problems—you're taking their jobs, you're causing higher taxes, you're increasing the crime rates, you're lowering property values. That's what it's like to be a stranger in another land.

But it can be better—if you happen to be among the minority welcomed by Christians. When we befriend refugees we minister to Christ and continue His work of bringing healing to the world. If you are willing to be involved in this kind of ministry, Exodus World Service will help you. Exodus is a nonprofit agency that has enlisted hundreds of Christian volunteers to serve thousands of refugees. Though most of its activity has been in and near Chicago, Exodus has developed innovative programs and materials that have benefitted refugees and their Christian benefactors throughout the country.

Exodus is working toward the day when every newly arrived refugee family is welcomed and served by a local Christian community. Write or call and ask how you and Exodus can work together to help refugees. The address is Exodus World Service, PO Box 620, Itasca, IL 60143-0620. Phone numbers are 312-R-E-F-U-G-E-E and 630-307-1400. Faxes may be sent to 630-307-1430.

APPENDIX: CHARACTERS

KENNETH MACKENZIE .... PROFESSOR OF ENGLISH AT MENDON COLLEGE, MENDON, INDIANA

DONNA MACKENZIE .... WIFE OF KENNETH AND A PART-TIME TEACHER OF SOCIAL STUDIES IN ADULT EDUCATION CLASSES FOR MENDON PUBLIC SCHOOLS

SAVANG KIM ANG .... A CAMBODIAN GIRL, BORN IN PHNOM PENH IN 1962

SAVANG SIEK .... RICE MERCHANT IN PHNOM PENH; KIM ANG'S FATHER

SIENG SANG .... KIM ANG'S MOTHER

SAVANG PHENG .... KIM ANG'S BROTHERS
SAVANG HENG

SAVANG KIM LANG .... KIM ANG'S SISTERS
SAVANG KIM LEANG

IENG SY .... KIM ANG'S GRANDFATHER; FATHER OF SIENG SANG

CHEN YI .... KIM ANG'S GRANDMOTHER; MOTHER OF SIENG SANG

SIENG HONG .... UNMARRIED SONS OF SIENG SY AND CHEN YI
SIENG TONG
SIENG TENG

SIENG NHENG .... ANOTHER SON OF SIENG SY AND CHEN YI; A DOCTOR AT PREA KET MEALEA HOSPITAL IN PHNOM PENH

THAY CHHUN PHING .... SIENG NHENG'S WIFE

SIENG DAO SIV .... SON OF SIENG NHENG AND THAY CHHUN PHING

SIENG LANG .... DAUGHTER OF SIENG SY AND CHEN YI

PHIM KIM ENG .... SIENG LANG'S HUSBAND; OFFICER IN THE ARMY OF THE KHMER REPUBLIC

PHIM CHHUN PHON .... DAUGHTER OF SIENG LANG AND PHIM KIM ENG

PHIM MENG TY .... SON OF SIENG LANG AND PHIM KIM ENG

HENG VANN .... SERGEANT IN PHIM KIM ENG'S ARMY UNIT

HENG AY LENG .... FRIEND OF KIM ANG; SURVIVOR OF U. S. BOMBING OF NEAK LUONG

NUOM YONG .... COUSIN OF CHEN YI

DAP HONG TAING .... NUOM YONG'S SON

TAN CHHUN LY .... DAP HONG TAING'S WIFE

DAP MENG FOU .... SON OF DAP HONG TAING AND TAN CHHUN LY

DAP CHHUN PING .... DAUGHTERS OF NUOM YONG
  DAP CHHUN SANG
  DAP CHHUN HEANG
CHEA MENG HONG .... DAP CHHUN PING'S SON
CHEA KIM NGIM .... DAP CHHUN PING'S DAUGHTER
SENG MENG .... SON OF A FRIEND OF DAP HONG TAING
NUOM PENG SY .... NUOM YONG'S BROTHER
SENG KIM PHANG .... NUOM PENG SY'S WIFE
NUOM MENG TIENG .... SONS OF NUOM PENG SY AND SENG KIM
                   PHANG
  NUOM MENG PHOK
  NUOM MENG YU
NUOM CHHUN HUOY .... DAUGHTERS OF NUOM PENG SY AND SENG
                   KIM PHANG
  NUOM CHHUN LENG
  NUOM CHHUN NY
SENG DAO TONG .... BROTHER OF SENG KIM PHANG
HAING HOK .... DISTANT COUSIN OF KIM ANG
WILLARD WINSTON .... IMMIGRATION AND NATURALIZATION SERVICE
                   OFFICER
WILLIAM E. SCOTT .... PRESIDENT OF MENDON COLLEGE (1958-1974)
JAMES KIRCHENER .... INTERIM PRESIDENT OF MENDON COLLEGE
                   (1974-1976)
EDGAR M. EDWARDS .... PRESIDENT OF MENDON COLLEGE (1976-1979)
JOHN P. BENNINGTON .... CHAIRMAN, MENDON COLLEGE BOARD OF
                   TRUSTEES
MARY SWENSON .... SECRETARY TO THE PRESIDENT, MENDON
                   COLLEGE
JAMES DUNN .... DEAN OF STUDENTS, MENDON COLLEGE
MARY REYNOLDS .... PRESIDENT OF STUDENT CONGRESS, MENDON
                   COLLEGE
JOSEPH WATERFORD .... VICE PRESIDENT OF BRADLEY & NOLAND,
                   PUBLIC RELATIONS CONSULTING FIRM
SCOTT DELANEY .... PUBLIC RELATIONS CONSULTANT, BRADLEY &
                   NOLAND
DUANE LANDON .... OWNER, DUANE'S TV SALES & SERVICE
SHIRLEY LANDON .... WIFE OF DUANE
REV. JEROME B. GREENWOOD... PASTOR, MENDON UNITED METHODIST
                   CHURCH
JUD HARTMAN .... FINANCE COMMITTEE CHAIRMAN, MENDON
                   UNITED METHODIST CHURCH
BARBARA MOORE .... YOUTH ACTIVITIES DIRECTOR, MENDON
                   UNITED METHODIST CHURCH

DAVID CRANSTON .... MEMBER OF FIRST PRESBYTERIAN CHURCH, LAFAYETTE

KATHY WENGER .... BOARD CHAIRPERSON, MENDON LUTHERAN CHURCH

REV. NELSON STEPHENS .... PASTOR, MENDON LUTHERAN CHURCH

REV. HENRY MCALLISTER .... PASTOR, ELM GROVE BAPTIST CHURCH

BECKY RICHARDS .... CHURCH WORLD SERVICE REPRESENTATIVE IN INDIANAPOLIS

FRANK FOREMAN .... INDIANA CONGRESSMAN

MARILYN AND BOB GLEASON ... FRIENDS OF DONNA AND KENNETH MACKENZIE

MATTHEW BRIGHAM .... PROBATE COURT JUDGE, BENTON COUNTY

BEN DUGAN .... PROPRIETOR, DUGAN'S HARDWARE

CHONG DY (SAM) .... KIM ANG'S FIANCE

REV. THEODORE RANDOLPH ...... COLLEGE CLASSMATE OF KENNETH MACKENZIE; PASTOR OF TRINITY UNITED METHODIST CHURCH, TORRANCE, CALIFORNIA

GLOSSARY

ANGKALOEU—The Khmer words *Angka* (organization) and *Loeu* (higher) translate into English as the Higher Organization, but a better rendition of the meaning probably would be the Organization on High.

CALENDAR—Cambodians use a 12-year-cycle calendar which originated in China. Each year is known by one of 12 animals in combination with a numeral from 0 to 9. After 60 years the number and animal combinations repeat themselves. The names of the animals, in the order used, are: rat, ox, tiger, hare, dragon, snake, horse, goat, monkey, rooster, dog, and pig.

FANK—Forces Armees Nationales Khmeres or Khmer National Armed Forces, the military component of Lon Nol's Khmer Republic.

GALLUP—George Horace Gallup was a public opinion analyst and statistician. Through his polling techniques he accurately predicted the outcome of the 1936 presidential election. His public opinion surveys, Gallup Polls, have been well known ever since.

GREEN CARD—Common name of Form I-151, a card issued by the Immigration and Naturalization Service to permanent resident aliens. Though they were green before 1960, they actually were pink and blue for many years. Refugees are eligible to apply for permanent resident alien status, a first step toward citizenship, after one year of residency in the United States.

IMMIGRATION AND NATURALIZATION SERVICE (INS)—Agency of the U. S. Department of Justice which is empowered to administer laws relating to the admission, exclusion, and deportation of aliens. The INS registers aliens and has the authority to conduct hearings to determine whether aliens are deportable. It also investigates qualifications of applicants for citizenship, and its agents patrol borders to prevent illegal entry.

I-94—The most important document a refugee has when entering the United States, this three-by-five-inch piece of paper is proof of legal entry. It includes the refugee's name, date and place of birth, country of citizenship, address overseas and in the U. S., point of departure, type of entry document and date of issue, alien number, and employment authorization.

KHMER—People who are the ethnic majority in Cambodia. About 80 percent of Cambodia's people are Khmer. Khmer is also the name of the language of these people.

KHMER ROUGE—Communists who gained control of Cambodia in 1975 and were in power until routed to the border region by the Vietnamese who invaded in 1979. Headed by Pol Pot, the Khmer Rouge forced the entire population of the country to work as slaves in rural communes. Between a million and three million of Cambodia's seven million people died as a result of Khmer Rouge oppression.

KHMER SEREI—Free Khmer. An anti-communist force fighting against both the Khmer Rouge and the Vietnamese occupiers of Cambodia.

KRAMA—A checkered cotton cloth used as the traditional Cambodian headdress or scarf. Its many uses include shielding the head from the sun, carrying food such as grain and vegetables, covering the body for modesty while washing in a stream. During the terror of the Khmer Rouge era, some Cambodians used the krama to hang themselves.

LLADRO—Fine porcelain figurines made at a factory near Valencia, Spain.

MEKONG—Khmer Rouge overseer placed in charge of New People in villages established after evacuation of cities.

MIT NEARY—Female Khmer Rouge soldiers.

NEW PEOPLE—Those who were evacuated from the cities by the Khmer Rouge in April of 1975 and forced to become slave laborers in the countryside. They were moved frequently, forced to do the hardest work, and lived in the poorest conditions. They had little or no privacy and received the smallest rice rations. They were subjected to continuing political indoctrination and were subject to execution without trial.

OLD PEOPLE—A middle class of Khmer Rouge society, below the Khmer Rouge themselves but above the New People. The Old People lived in Khmer Rouge areas during the war and contributed to the revolution.

PATHET LAO—Pro-communist forces in Laos.

POL POT—Pseudonym of Saloth Sar, the Parisian-educated head of the Khmer Rouge. Victims of Khmer Rouge oppression usually referred to all members of the Khmer Rouge organization as Pol Pot People.

RIEL—The basic unit of currency in Cambodia.

SAMPOT—A loose-fitting, sarong-like garment which is wrapped around the waist and tucked through the legs. More elegant sampots are made of silk, while those for work are of cotton.

VIET CONG—Vietnamese who supported North Vietnam in the war with South Vietnam.

WATERGATE —Political scandal which began with the 1972 burglary and wiretapping of the Democratic party's campaign headquarters at the Watergate apartment and office complex in Washington, D.C., and culminated in the resignation of Richard M. Nixon as president.

YEAR—See CALENDAR.

YOTEAR—Armed Khmer Rouge soldier.

A Gentle Breeze
from
Gossamer Wings

Gordon Beld
Interviewed by his editor, Anne McKinney

PREP Publishing
Fayetteville, North Carolina

Talking Things Over with Gordon Beld

Q: **Not many authors have their first novel published when they are in their 70s. Was this your first attempt to write professionally?**

GB: This was my first attempt to write fiction. But I first wrote professionally at age 16. It was my good fortune then to meet Ralph Truax, assistant sports editor of *The Grand Rapids Press*, who gave me a chance to write about competition of my school's teams, then provided encouragement and additional opportunities. Within a few months I had experienced the thrill of seeing my first byline, over an account of a Detroit Tiger exhibition game in my home town.

Q: **Did you keep on writing after that early experience?**

GB: Yes. It's always been an important part of my life. I've enjoyed writing, and I've been fortunate to have had a variety of jobs that permitted me to write as well as pursue another major interest, working with young people. For many years I was, simultaneously, a high school teacher and a journalist, teaching during the day for about nine months a year and spending evenings, Saturdays, and summers at *The Press* and *The Grand Rapids Herald*. Then, in 1965, I combined my journalistic and educational interests in a single position as public relations director at Alma College. PR work at a small liberal arts college had been my career goal, and I was at Alma until my retirement in 1989.

Q: **In the first half of your novel you've shifted the action back and forth between Cambodia and the American Midwest, much as Dickens moved between London** and Paris in *A Tale of Two Cities*. Did that story influence the way you handled the plot of *A Gentle Breeze from Gossamer Wings*?

GB: Let me say up front that *A Tale of Two Cities* is my favorite of the classics. However, it had nothing to do with the way I approached *Breeze*. My intent in shifting between locales in Part I of the story was to contrast the lives of average people in Cambodia and the United States. Actually, I hadn't thought of the similarities in approach until you asked the question. Telling what was going on in the lives of Americans in one chapter and then focusing on the difficulties of Cambodians in the next, I believe, clearly demonstrates that the worst of times for most of us in America really haven't been all that bad.

Q: **Interspersed throughout your book are several short segments of factual information headed "The Real Story." Would you comment on that technique?**

GB: Their purpose really is to help interested readers find additional information, in non-fiction books and articles, that will contribute to a more complete understanding of what is happening. Actually, the more significant parts of the "Real Story" segments are the sources listed under "For more details, see:" at the end of each segment. The brief text preceding the lists gives readers an idea of what the sources will reveal. In early drafts of the story considerable background information was included in the text, and I used endnotes to refer readers to sources of further information. When I submitted the manuscript to PREP, the evaluating reader suggested pulling out this material and putting it into mini-chapters. So that's what I did. I'm indebted to her for what I believe is an effective technique.

Q: *A Gentle Breeze from Gossamer Wings* is a historical
novel. Were you always interested in history?

GB: Somewhat, but my interest increased greatly in 1959 when
research for a feature story led me to interesting accounts
of past events in the Grand Rapids area. From them I
developed a weekly series on local history. At the time, *The
Press* had a Sunday magazine and I also wrote other series
on Michigan and regional history for that publication—
the first on action of the War of 1812 in the Midwest, then
on Michigan Indians, Michigan railroads, Michigan
rivers, and forts along the U.S.-Canadian border. Later I
produced two 52-part series that were published by several
newspapers—one on Michigan history and the other on
events of the Revolutionary War in the Old Northwest
(Illinois, Indiana, Michigan, Ohio, and Wisconsin).

Q: What made you decide to try writing fiction?

GB: It wasn't so much a matter of writing fiction as it was
communicating a message. In the late '70s my wife and I
became involved in attempts to resettle refugees from
Southeast Asia. We first tried, with members of several
churches in our town, to resettle a Vietnamese family. The
group was overly cautious about preparations, and
nothing happened. About a year later, our own church
decided to sponsor a Cambodian family. That involvement
acquainted us with the richness of another culture. We met
people whose problems dwarfed our own minor
difficulties. We learned there are millions who don't even
have the option of going home. Since then, I've tried to
find ways to communicate the satisfaction that awaits
persons who help those in need, refugees or others. That's
what I've tried to do in *Breeze*.

Q: **In what other ways have you tried to interest people in refugee issues?**

GB: Before retirement my time was limited. But as my career at Alma College neared its end, I wrote to several agencies to offer assistance. One response was from Episcopal Migration Ministries, asking for help with a project that needed to be done immediately. Retirement was still two years away, but I had unused vacation time. So, after conferring with the EMM staff in New York City, I interviewed Hmong refugees and service providers in Syracuse (N.Y.), La Crosse (Wis.), and Fresno (Calif.) and wrote *The Hmong in a Promised Land*, an account of adaptation of refugees to life in the U. S., which was published in 1987. My letters also led to a relationship with Exodus World Service, an agency that links refugees with Christians in the Chicago area. I've been privileged to work with the Exodus staff as a volunteer for the past 10 years.

Q: **Is there a particular reason why you chose to use a small town rather than a larger city as the American setting in *A Gentle Breeze from Gossamer Wings*?**

GB: Two reasons, really—familiarity and fondness. I've never lived in or near what most would call a large city. For the first 38 years of my life, and a few more later, I lived in suburban Grand Rapids. Most don't consider GR a big city. Of course, I've been in cities like Chicago, New York, Los Angeles, San Francisco, and Detroit briefly for business, professional meetings, and visits with friends. Big cities are exciting places. But there's something special about the relaxed atmosphere and friendliness of smaller communities. For 24 years my home was in a small town (population less than 10,000) in the heart of Michigan farm country. So I know about life in that kind of place, and I like small town people.

Q: Did your experiences at Alma College influence *A Gentle Breeze from Gossamer Wings?*

GB: My years at Alma contributed to my understanding of higher education and campus life. But I've been involved in education nearly all my life, and I also spent many years on the campuses of Hope College, the University of Michigan, and Davenport College. Though events such as the athletic controversy at Mendon College have no basis in fact, one character in the story was inspired by an actual person at Alma. That's William E. Scott, the Mendon College president. He's modeled after Robert D. Swanson, Alma's president for many years and a man for whom I have the greatest admiration.

Q: Do you have a special place where you write?

GB: For the most part, I write in a room I've fixed up as a sort of study. Since 1992, my wife, Martha, and I have lived in a retirement community at the edge of a bayou of the Macatawa River in downtown Holland, Michigan. It's less than a ten-minute walk from the campus of Hope College where Martha and I met in 1948. We have a two-bedroom apartment, and the larger of the two is used as my study. It's in the far corner of the apartment, and I can isolate myself there somewhat so I'm not disturbed. Yet the windows provide a nice view of the bayou and, on the opposite shore, an old windmill that was brought over from the Netherlands and rebuilt there.

Q: How is the room furnished?

GB: The prominent piece of furniture is an old rolltop desk that I bought for $10 in the early '60s. I probably should feel guilty for taking it at that price, but the people who sold it knew the value of furniture. They were owners of a furniture store. It was their old office desk and was built in the early 1900s. Opposite the desk is an L-shaped computer station with the usual shelves and surfaces for printers, scanners, etc. And between the desk and computer equipment is my chair, another $10 item—same vintage as the rolltop desk, wooden with a cane seat that I've redone, twice, myself. In the nearest corner is an old wooden four-drawer file cabinet. Against one wall are glass-fronted bookcases and, on shelves above them, an old electric train and a collection of about a hundred dimestore lead soldiers of the 1930s—remnants of my childhood.

Q: **You said your study is in an area that enables you to be somewhat isolated. Do you find it essential to be undisturbed while writing?**

GB: No, not really. Most of my earlier writing was done in newsrooms. There was no isolation there. Nearly all the editorial staff would be in one big room. Phones were ringing. People were yelling. There were all kinds of things going on. I learned to write in that kind of environment. Though I prefer not to be disturbed when I'm writing, I can pick up where I left off if I am. When I'm writing, Martha tries to protect me from interruption. I have a phone right next to me on the desk though, and when it rings I answer it.

Q: **You mentioned a computer. I trust you used a type-writer earlier. Did you have any adjustment problems?**

GB: Yes, it wasn't easy. I was afraid of computers before I sat down at one. When I revisited *The Press* newsroom after taking the job at Alma, all the old typewriters had disappeared. Computer terminals and keyboards stood where they'd been. *If I ever have to go back to work here,* I thought, *I'll never be able to write.* Words couldn't possibly come unless you sit in front of a faithful old Remington or Underwood. Soon, of course, Alma College also became computerized and I was forced to try to keep up with the rest of the world. Our mainframe system then left much to be desired. At periods of peak usage, words sometimes wouldn't appear on the screen for what seemed an eternity after they'd been typed. I wasn't good at remembering to file either and when the system would go down, as it often did, I'd sometimes lose a whole morning's production. Then, in frustration, I'd pull the plug on the computer and for several weeks go back to my old IBM Selectric. Now, of course, I can't imagine writing without a computer.

Q: **Your work at Alma College and for newspapers also involved photography. Have you used any of your pictures in your decor?**

GB: Most would say I've overused my photography in my study. Nearly half the wall surface, from ceiling to floor, is covered by pictures. Most are photos I've taken since the 1930s. On the wall I face when I'm at my computer are an assortment of mementoes—family pictures including one of my grandfather as a soldier in the Dutch Army; a 1951 certificate that made me one of Michigan's earliest driver education instructors; the wooden sign that hung in front of our weekend retreat, an old one-room schoolhouse; framed press cards issued to me by *The Press* (1944) and the U.S. Constabulary (1946); the first photo of Martha and me together, taken by Bob Schuller in 1949; postcards showing buildings in which I've worked.

Q: **Where did you meet Rev. Schuller?**

GB: He and I lived in the same dormitory when we were students at Hope College. Bob was a couple years ahead of me, but he continued his study at Western Theological

Seminary on the same campus. Since several hundred miles separated him from his family in Iowa and mine was only about 20 miles away, he'd occasionally come home with me on weekends. He seemed to like my mother's cooking better than what we were getting at the college.

Q: **I understand you have made many trips to the Basque Country of northern Spain. Why are you particularly interested in that part of the world?**

GB: The main attractions there are my grandchildren. I have only two. My grandson, Alar, is 21 and my granddaughter, Dee, is 18. They live in a small village on the Bay of Biscay. That came about because of the educational interests of their mother—my first child, Dala. A Spanish and history major at Alma College, she studied in Madrid during the summer of 1972. Afterward, touring with friends, she met a young man, Antxon Basurko, on a train near San Sebastian. Back in Michigan, she corresponded with him. Then she went back to the Basque Country for research on author Pio Baroja. Following graduation from Alma, she knew she wouldn't find work as an attorney in Spain but could teach English. So she declined acceptance to the University of Michigan Law School and switched to linguistics for a master's degree, then went back to Europe and married Antxon. So now, if I want to see my grandchildren, I go to the Basque Country.

Q: **Had you traveled to Europe before going there to visit your daughter's family?**

GB: Just once, courtesy of the U. S. Army. In 1946-47 I was stationed at Degerndof, Germany, with the 66th Constabulary Squadron. The Constabulary was a police force in occupied Germany, and I was a clerk/typist and investigator in the intelligence section.

Q: **Do you have other children?**

GB: Yes. My son, Scott, is an archaeologist. His academic specialty is Near Eastern Studies and he's done some digging in Iraq, the last time just before the Gulf War. But he has as much expertise concerning Native Americans, and most of his archaeological research has been in Michigan. My youngest child is Barbara, and dogs are her passion. She's an excellent trainer and has worked with them nearly all her life.

Q: **Your story evidences a pro-immigration attitude that's not particularly popular today. Is that an accurate statement?**

GB: Yes. I am in favor of a more liberal U.S. immigration policy. And in that respect I'm not in agreement with the majority of Americans. My not-too-distant ancestors came here from Germany, Scotland, and the Netherlands, so I have a hard time justifying closing the door on immigrants. I agree with President John F. Kennedy who, in his book *A Nation of Immigrants*, defined immigration as "a gesture of faith in social mobility" and "the expression in action of a positive belief in the possibility of a better life."

Q: **Why do you think so many Americans want less immigration?**

GB: Probably because of a fear that more immigrants will negatively impact their lifestyle. To be somewhat less diplomatic, we might describe it as selfishness. Though America is often described as a nation of immigrants, anti-immigration sentiment has been with us for a long time. As early as the late 1700s a congressman argued that, while a liberal immigration policy was all right when the country was new and unsettled, now that America was fully populated immigration should stop. Today, many feel that immigrants take jobs away from persons born here. In actuality, many of us who have been here longer wouldn't take the jobs immigrants are willing to do. At the same time, many immigrants have established their own businesses and hired persons born in the U. S.

Q: **How would you go about trying to persuade persons to accept your viewpoint about immigration?**

GB: I'd try to find a way to personally acquaint them with immigrants. Perhaps it's understandable that some dislike the idea of thousands of foreigners swarming into the country to take a share of the pot we think is rightfully ours. But if you get to really know just one newcomer, if you listen to the reasons that prompted surrender of everything familiar to start a new life in a strange place, if you see the determination to succeed, if you realize this is someone very much like you, then I think you'll feel more kindly toward immigrants. And if you study the matter thoroughly, I think you'll agree that immigration enriches America.

Q: **You were born just a couple of years before the beginning of the Great Depression. Were your childhood years difficult ones?**

GB: Not at all. I was very fortunate in several respects. For one thing, my parents showered me with attention and love. Maybe I was a bit spoiled. I was an only child until my sister Peg joined our family through adoption when I was 10. We were especially blessed, too, since our father was continuously employed during those years of trouble for so many. An exceptional man, my dad spent his entire career with one employer, a Grand Rapids appliance manufacturer.

He started out as a part-time floor sweeper; never finished high school but took a few business college courses; became a full-time accountant at age 16; earned a succession of promotions; and became plant manager of the company, then the largest employer in Grand Rapids, before retiring 45 years later.

Q: "Gossamer Wings" implies angels. Do you believe in angels?

GB: Definitely. But I can't say for certain that I've seen one. On the other hand, I have seen things that could only have been done by angels—or by persons influenced by angels. As I've pointed out in the preface to *Breeze*, I think a lot of angels are mistaken for people. And sometimes people are mistaken for angels.

Reading Group Questions and Discussion Topics

1. Are there times when it's OK to lie? How about handling a touchy situation (like the interview seeking a green card in a different name) by just not volunteering information that might cause difficulties?

2. In 1970, as campuses across the country erupt in protest of the U. S. invasion of Cambodia and the killing of Kent State University students by National Guardsmen, Ken MacKenzie is content to let others worry about what should or shouldn't be done in Southeast Asia. "I'm not going to get all worked up over things I know nothing about," he says. How would you have responded to him?

3(a). In 1973 some American B-52 pilots—who had helped to drop more bombs on Cambodia than fell on Japan during all of World War II—described their missions as impersonal and boring. Do you think they would have felt that way if anyone on the ground below had weapons capable of hitting them? Elaborate.

3(b). The American public, too, seemed to have little concern about bombing a neutral country. In 1969, when a New York Times reporter broke the story of the secret bombing of Cambodia, Americans were, for the most part, indifferent. But the following spring, when U. S. ground forces crossed into Cambodia, there were violent protests, mostly on university campuses. Why do you think there was so much more opposition to the ground attacks than the air raids?

4. What are some problems and situations today that are causing people to protest? Are the issues involved of sufficient concern to you to do anything about them? Why or why not? If so, what could you do?

5. William Scott, the college president, says that "there's more to education than preparing for a job—and more to life than accumulating possessions." Do you agree or disagree with each of those opinions? Elaborate on your views.

6. What kinds of experiences/training would condition men and boys to treat their own countrymen the way Pol Pot's soldiers did when they entered Phnom Penh—forcing sick and wounded people out of hospitals and into the streets, shooting parents in front of their children? Were their actions any more or less a crime than those of American soldiers who massacred Vietnamese civilians at My Lai? Than those of American pilots who dropped bombs on Cambodian civilians? Why?

7. When Ken MacKenzie quotes from Browning's *Pippa Passes*, Donna doesn't remember its content. After reading the poetic drama, she says she's pleased that little girls don't have to do hard work in such terrible places anymore. How does her comment relate to what is happening in Cambodia on the same day? Are there still places in the world where children are abused in the workplace? If so, is there anything we should be doing about it?

8. In the exodus from Phnom Penh, Kim Ang carries her grandmother's electric fan—an apparently unimportant, if not useless, item in view of the circumstances, except perhaps as a symbol of hope. If you were forced to flee from your home and could take only the things you yourself could carry, what would they be?

9.   One of the devastating aspects of Pol Pot's New Society for Cambodians was its assault on traditional family relationships and values, virtually eliminating their effectiveness as meaningful units. Do you think there's a danger of that happening in America today, perhaps in a more subtle way? If so, from what causes?

10. One of the precepts that Kim Ang's relatives developed for survival under the Khmer Rouge stated that selfishness is OK. How do you feel about that?

11. Through the years, as church support began to dwindle, many colleges turned increasingly to corporations, foundations, and individuals for funds. Then, to keep the money coming, the institutions changed policies the churches had dictated. In a continuing downward spiral, churches would again cut support and colleges would move further from founding principles. At Mendon, Ken MacKenzie contended, that trend had brought the college to the point that "the only difference between Mendon and a university like Indiana or Purdue is the size of the place." Do you know of church-founded colleges whose concern for Christian principles seems no greater than that of neighboring public institutions? Do you consider that a problem? A disappointment? If so, what should be done about it?

12. How hungry would you have to be to eat lizards, rats, worms, and insects? How desperate would you have to be to seriously desire to be dead? Do you think there are people in your community who have either of those feelings? If so, what could be done to help them?

13. Though much of the evening political education sessions endured by Cambodians under the Khmer Rouge was boring, they also included the dreaded *kosangs*—accusations

which could be leveled at anyone, with or without cause. In what ways are the *kosangs* similar to, and in what ways are they different from, the back-biting that goes on among groups of employees and in organizations of which you may be a part?

14. Responding to Ken MacKenzie's apparent lack of concern about the situation in Cambodia, Donna says, "We ignored Hitler when he was killing millions of Jews. Then thirty years later the Khmer Rouge kill millions of their own people and nobody does anything about that... We can't keep sticking our heads in the sand, Ken." Are there places in the world where innocent people are being killed today? If so, what should we be doing about it?

15. Both the United States and Vietnam assaulted Cambodia during the 1970s. The American attacks contributed to Pol Pot's success and the resultant holocaust. The Vietnamese Invasion freed Cambodians from Pol Pot's reign of terror. Given those circumstances, should the United States have done more than it has for Cambodians? Why?

16. If your alma mater (or a college or university which you admire or support) were involved in a scandal such as the one that infuriated many Mendon College alumni, would you be disturbed? Why? Do you think American colleges and universities put too much emphasis on athletics? If so, what should be done?

17. Twice, when Ken MacKenzie has to make a difficult decision concerning his employment, his wife refuses to help him decide. Is that the right thing for her to do? Why?

18. During the late 1970s more than 500,000 refugees flooded into Thailand from Laos, Vietnam, and Cambodia. Does that justify the Thais' forced repatriation of 40,000

Cambodians during June 1979? Was the United States justified in interdicting Haitians at sea during the 1990s and forcing them back to the country they had fled? Substantiate your opinions.

19. According to United Nations estimates, more than 110 million landmines are buried in 64 countries with another 100 million stockpiled. They can cost less than $3 each to manufacture and up to $1,000 each to clear. While 100,000 are cleared each year, another two to five million are deployed. Each year an estimated 26,000 innocent persons are killed by landmines—one person every 17 minutes. Discuss the significance of these statistics and what should/could be done.

20. In her effort to persuade Ken to agree to adopt a child, Donna MacKenzie says that, if they give of themselves to make a child happy, their own love will grow stronger. Do you think that's likely? Are there factors that could make the opposite effect possible?

21. Do you approve of the Cambodians' use of deceit in their efforts to be resettled in the United States? What would you have done if you had been in their place? If you would not have used deceit under those circumstances, can you think of any that might prompt you to be deceitful to escape danger? Were there any respected persons in the Bible who used deceit to avoid harm or death? Who?

22. David Cranston tells parishioners of Mendon United Methodist Church that angels were responsible for his involvement with refugees. Do you believe his reasoning is credible? Have you experienced angels or events that could have been influenced by angels?

23. The last part of the 25th chapter of the Gospel according to Matthew was the text for Pastor Greenwood's sermon about refugees. What do those verses (31-46) have to do with refugees?

24. Do you think it was right for Ken MacKenzie to volunteer for a minor role in the refugee assistance project so he'd have an excuse not to do more? Did his ploy work? Why?

25. Have you had contact with immigrants who were attempting to learn English? Have you lived, or traveled, in a place where the language was not one you understood? Would you consider moving to a place where you would need to learn a new language? If not, can you imagine any circumstances that might make you change your mind?

26. If you were to introduce a family of immigrants to your community, what would you be sure to show and explain to them during the first few days? Tell why those things would be important, or of interest, to them.

27. Considering what you've learned about Donna MacKenzie, is it surprising that she devotes so much time to helping Hong Taing establish a business? How about Ken MacKenzie's spending so much time with the Cambodians and getting involved to the extent that he does? Have you known persons whose attitudes have changed that much?

28. What things about Chhun Ly (Kim Ang) puzzle Donna? Would they have made you wonder? Would they have made you more suspicious of her than Donna was? Why?

29. Most persons try to find excuses when they're accused of doing something wrong. Chhun Ly, however, seems to go out of her way to blame herself for any problem that arises.

Do you think there really are people like that? Have you known any? Why would a person be that way?

30. Think back to your response to the first question above: "Are there times when it's OK to lie?" How about in a situation such as Donna's when she returns to the church kitchen after the tea break at her home? What would you have said or done?

31. Hong Taing seems to be most responsible for the conflict that develops among the Cambodians, but are there factors that justify his attitude and actions? That make it understandable? If so, what are they?

32. We think of Christmas as a time of joy, but for some persons the season brings on depression. Why is that? What makes the MacKenzies depressed on the day before Christmas? Would their depression have been as great if the situation developed at another time of the year?

33. At the end of the Christmas Eve candlelight service, Kim Ang's comment prompts Ken to reflect on the essence of Christmas and to observe that she has seen something that others have missed. What had she said? Did she really understand the deeper significance of her words?

34. During the days of Pol Pot's oppressive regime, sleep often brought relief from the terror. Then, after refugees reached safety, sleep invariably triggered nightmares that rekindled the horror. Do you think you might be reluctant to go to bed if you believed sleep would transport you back to days of despair? If so, what impact might that have on other aspects of your life?

35. Limitations in understanding and communicating because of unfamiliarity with a new language, obviously, complicate learning for immigrant children. Had you thought about the difficulties they face because they don't share their classmates' knowledge of nursery rhymes, childhood games, holidays, and basic historical facts? In what other ways might they be at a disadvantage?

36. When Ken MacKenzie tries to use humor in his conversation with Peng Sy's family, he finds himself more involved in refugee resettlement efforts than he intended. Have you ever had the experience of joking with persons, only to find they were taking you seriously? Did it cause difficulty or embarrassment for you? If so, tell about it.

37. In explaining his change in attitude about refugees, Ken says, "When they were on one side of the ocean and I was on the other, it was one thing. But now we've met. I realize they're people just like you and me." If you are opposed to liberal immigration policy, do you think your views might be changed if you spent a few hours a week with an immigrant family? Why?

38. When Kim Ang picks up and carries three big bags of groceries, leaving Ken empty-handed, he's embarrassed. What factors contribute to her insistence on carrying everything? Does cultural disparity have anything to do with it?

39. Does the pickup driver have a point when he complains, "Blasted foreigners are takin' all the jobs an' us white folks are goin' hungry"? Is there merit in Ken's contention that the man is on thin ice because, except for Native Americans, all of us or our ancestors at one time or another were foreigners?

40. How does Pastor McAllister use the parable of the Good Samaritan to make the point that doctrine isn't significant until it's applied? Do you agree with him? Why?

41. How is it that her grandmother's effort to arrange a marriage puts Kim Ang in a can't-win situation? Obviously, Kim Ang's method of dealing with it is not a good solution. Can you understand why she took the step she did? Explain.

42. When Kim Ang is upset about the grades on her report card, does Ken give her the right advice when he suggests she not be too hard on herself? Is that the kind of advice most parents would give their children? If not, what would they say?

43. When refugee families begin to move away, one woman complains they are being ungrateful. Ken's response is that "when we agreed to sponsor them, we weren't buying them." Can you understand why the woman feels as she does? Do you agree with her or with Ken?

44. In recent years there has been considerable controversy concerning the merits of bilingual education for students with limited ability in English. How do bilingual education and English-as-a-Second-Language instruction differ? Which do you believe is the best approach?

45. What accomplishments or activities have been most fulfilling for you? Kim Ang observes that perhaps the best way to have fulfillment is to help somebody else be happy. Do you think that's really true? If so, how come more of us aren't trying to do that?

46.   At the end of the story, Kim Ang says she is sad only about Ay Leng. Are you, too, disappointed in the lack of a better outcome for Kim Ang's friend? Why do you think the author left her fate uncertain, but bleak at best? Could she be a symbol of the many refugees throughout the world who are in that situation?

About The Author

A native of Grand Rapids, Michigan, Gordon Beld began writing professionally at age 16 for *The Grand Rapids Press*. For several years he worked simultaneously as a newsman with Grand Rapids newspapers and as a teacher of English and history. He served two years as an academic advisor at Davenport College and 24 as director of news services and publications at Alma College. His articles and photographs, mostly on historical topics, have appeared in *Sports Illustrated, Chicago Tribune, Miami Herald, Detroit News, Christian Science Monitor,* and many other publications. Involved with refugees for the past 20 years, he presently provides editorial assistance to Exodus World Service, an agency which links refugees and Christians in greater Chicago, and tutors immigrants learning English in Holland, Michigan, Community Education classes. In 1994 he received Exodus's first Open Arms Service Award for efforts in behalf of refugees. He frequently travels to Spain's Basque Country, home of his only grandchildren, spending time en route in London. He has also visited France, Scotland, Wales, the Netherlands, and Germany where he served with the U.S. Army's Constabulary in 1946-47. He has a B.A. degree from Hope College and an M.A. from the University of Michigan. He and his wife of 48 years, Martha, now live in Holland, Michigan, two blocks from the Hope campus where they met.

ALSO BY PREP PUBLISHING

BACK IN TIME
Patty Sleem

SECOND TIME AROUND
Patty Sleem

WHAT THE BIBLE SAYS ABOUT ...
WORDS THAT CAN LEAD TO SUCCESS AND HAPPINESS
Patty Sleem

BIBLE STORIES FROM THE OLD TESTAMENT
Katherine Whaley

COVER LETTERS THAT BLOW DOORS OPEN
Anne McKinney

RESUMES AND COVER LETTERS THAT HAVE WORKED
Anne McKinney

RESUMES AND COVER LETTERS THAT HAVE WORKED FOR
MILITARY PROFESSIONALS
Anne McKinney

LETTERS FOR SPECIAL SITUATIONS
Anne McKinney

GOVERNMENT JOB APPLICATIONS AND FEDERAL RESUMES
Anne McKinney

RESUMES AND COVER LETTERS FOR MANAGERS
Anne McKinney

PREP Publishing Order Form

You can order any of our titles through your favorite bookseller! Or send a check or money order or your credit card number for the total amount*, plus $3.20 postage, to PREP, Box 66, Fayetteville, NC 28302. If you have a question about our titles, e-mail us at preppub@aol.com and visit our website at http://www.prep-pub.com

Name: _____

Phone #: _____

Address: _____

E-mail address: _____

Payment Type: ☐ Check/Money Order ☐ Visa ☐ MasterCard

Credit Card Number: _____ Expiration Date: _____

Check items you are ordering:

☐ $25.00—RESUMES AND COVER LETTERS THAT HAVE WORKED. Anne McKinney, Editor

☐ $25.00—RESUMES AND COVER LETTERS THAT HAVE WORKED FOR MILITARY PROFESSIONALS. Anne McKinney, Editor

☐ $25.00—RESUMES AND COVER LETTERS FOR MANAGERS. Anne McKinney, Editor

☐ $25.00—GOVERNMENT JOB APPLICATIONS AND FEDERAL RESUMES: Federal Resumes, KSAs, Forms 171 and 612, and Postal Applications. Anne McKinney, Editor

☐ $25.00—COVER LETTERS THAT BLOW DOORS OPEN. Anne McKinney, Editor

☐ $25.00—LETTERS FOR SPECIAL SITUATIONS. Anne McKinney, Editor

☐ $16.00—BACK IN TIME. Patty Sleem

☐ $17.00—(trade paperback) SECOND TIME AROUND. Patty Sleem

☐ $25.00—(hardcover) SECOND TIME AROUND. Patty Sleem

☐ $18.00—A GENTLE BREEZE FROM GOSSAMER WINGS. Gordon Beld

☐ $18.00—BIBLE STORIES FROM THE OLD TESTAMENT. Katherine Whaley

☐ $20.00—(hardcover) WHAT THE BIBLE SAYS ABOUT... *Words that can lead to success and happiness.* Patty Sleem

_____ **TOTAL ORDERED (add $3.20 for postage)**

* PREP offers volume discounts on large orders. Call us at (910) 483-6611 for more information.